laboratory investigations in CHEMISTRY

Second Edition

Dennis C. Condon
Douglas S. Cody

Nassau Community College

Pearson
Custom
Publishing

PEARSON CUSTOM PUBLISHING
75 Arlington Street, Suite 300, Boston, MA 02116
A Pearson Education Company

CONTENTS

To the Student

The *Laboratory Investigations in Chemistry Laboratory Manual* has been written expressly to meet the needs of a science majors' first year chemistry laboratory program.

Organization

The experiments in this laboratory manual are arranged in a sequence that the authors believe would be most helpful in reinforcing topics normally taught in chemistry. We have included appendices and tables required for use in calculation of experimental data. Additionally, Laboratory Safety Rules and Policies on Personal Protective Equipment are included.

Objectives

1. To provide a complete, coherently structured, easy to use laboratory manual for the first year curriculum in chemistry.

2. To develop laboratory techniques and to reinforce lecture-related concepts.

3. To increase awareness of essential safety and environmental concerns related to the use of chemical substances.

Notice to the Users

Any chemical may present some degree of danger if treated in an unsafe manner. Therefore it is of utmost importance that they be handled properly and with respect. The editors have made every reasonable attempt to provide appropriate directions, instructions, and safety suggestions for each of the experiments that are included. However, the ultimate responsibility for safety remains with the student and his or her instructor.

Acknowledgments

Books are the result of a collaborative effort of many talented and dedicated people. We thank our colleagues Edward Gerardi, George Smit and Doris Trevas for their contributions to our series of department-authored experiments. We also want to thank our colleagues in the chemistry department at Nassau Community College for their valuable suggestions, guidance, help and support. We are especially grateful to Andrea Cody for her proofreading of the manuscript and for her assistance in bringing this manual to completion. Finally, we thank our families for their encouragement and support during preparation of this manual.

We hope you enjoy this manual and will continue to submit corrections and suggestions for improvements to the editors.

Dennis C. Condon
Douglas S. Cody

COMMON LABORATORY GLASSWARE

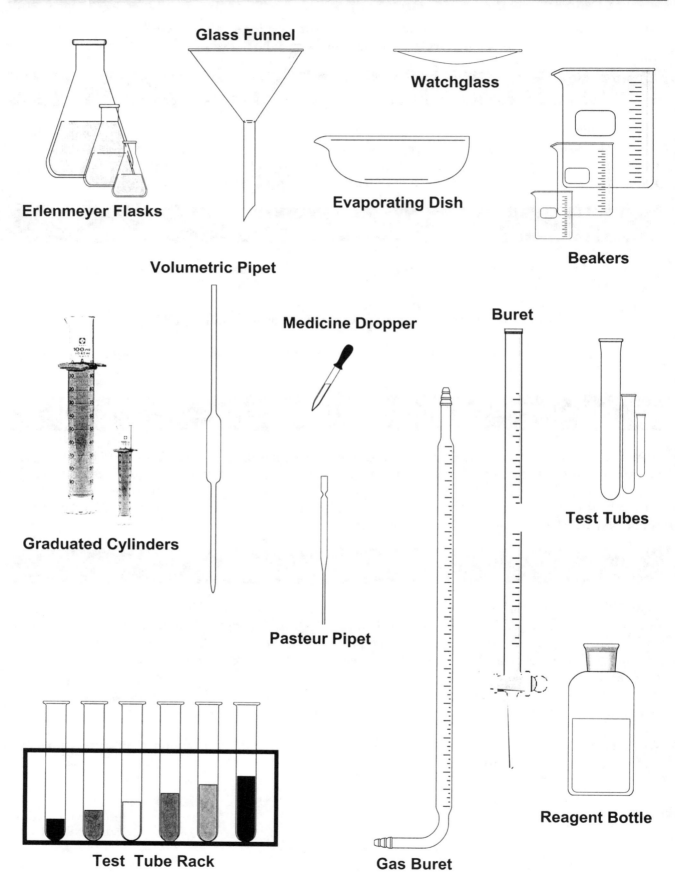

Glass Funnel

Watchglass

Erlenmeyer Flasks

Evaporating Dish

Beakers

Volumetric Pipet

Medicine Dropper

Buret

Graduated Cylinders

Test Tubes

Pasteur Pipet

Test Tube Rack

Gas Buret

Reagent Bottle

COMMON LABORATORY EQUIPMENT

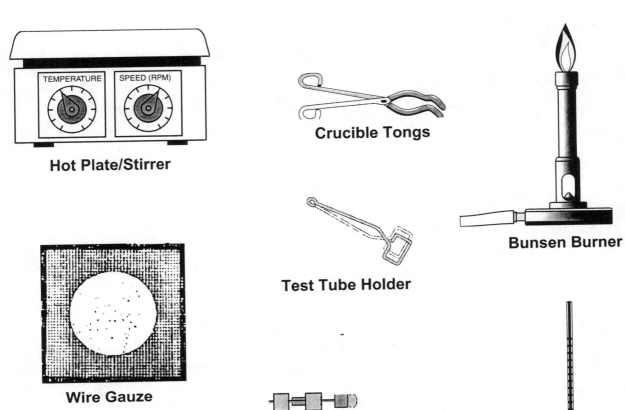

Hot Plate/Stirrer

Crucible Tongs

Bunsen Burner

Test Tube Holder

Wire Gauze

Thermometer

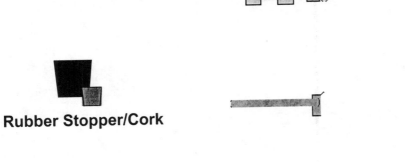

Rubber Stopper/Cork

Ringstand/Clamps

Balance

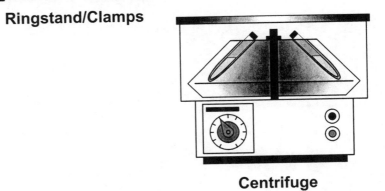

Centrifuge

SAFETY IN THE LABORATORY

To the Student

The chemistry laboratory is the place where you are able to conduct approved experiments that demonstrate the chemical principles you learn in the lecture portion of the course. The experiments you will be performing are carefully written with an emphasis on personal safety and environmental protection.

Safety in the laboratory is an extremely important element of any chemistry program. Failure to follow safe practices can cause laboratory accidents which may result in the loss of time, damage to clothing and other property, and most importantly personal injury. By following suitable precautions, you can anticipate and prevent situations that would lead to accidents.

Safety Equipment in the Laboratory

All students, faculty and staff are required to use the following protective equipment when working in the chemistry laboratory:

CHEMICAL SPLASH SAFETY GOGGLES

Individuals who do not wear prescription glasses must wear chemical splash goggles that include:

1. An optically clear lens that has anti-fog coating and meets ANSI Z87.1 impact requirements.

2. INDIRECT AIR VENTS designed to restrict the entry of particles and liquids.

3. Size clearances sufficient to accommodate prescription glasses (if you wear them).

Individuals who normally wear prescription glasses must:

1. Wear the splash goggle described above over their prescription glasses.

OR

2. Wear prescription glasses equipped with frames having SIDE, TOP and BOTTOM splash protection.

Lenses must meet ANSI Z87.1 impact requirements.

PROTECTIVE CLOTHING

Individuals working in a laboratory environment are required to wear one of the following:

1. A laboratory coat (with front closure) that is long enough to provide approximately knee length protection.

OR

2. A laboratory apron large enough to protect the front of the body, including chest, abdomen, and legs to approximately knee length.

3. Outerwear such as coats, jackets, sweatshirts, or sweaters **DO NOT** meet this requirement.

4. Shorts and/or sandals are **NOT** permitted.

> **BE ADVISED:** There is some evidence that protective clothing made of 65% Dacron polyester/35% cotton may increase the severity of burn injury if the garment should catch fire. We therefore strongly recommend the use of cloth protective garments made of 100% cotton rather than a polyester/cotton mix.

Management of Laboratory Waste

DISPOSAL: Place all wastes in their proper receptacles. If you are uncertain about waste disposal please consult your instructor for additional instructions.

1. Every laboratory experiment which requires the use of chemicals is a source of laboratory wastes. It is the individual instructor's responsibility to manage the generation and collection of waste in an environmentally correct manner. It is the student's responsibility to use and dispose of chemical substances in accordance with the procedures specified by the instructor and/or provided in this manual.

2. All laboratories are equipped with gray-colored plastic garbage cans for laboratory glass disposal. These bins are strictly for glass disposal only.

3. Trash baskets are provided beneath sinks for regular trash and disposal containers are provided in the laboratory for chemical waste. Waste materials MUST be placed in the appropriate container.

Laboratory Safety Rules and Practices

You are required to read, understand and implement the safety precautions delineated in this laboratory manual and summarized below. Your signature indicates your willingness to abide by these precautions while you are in the laboratory.

Personal Protection

1. You may work in the laboratory only if the instructor is present. You must work only on authorized experiments.

2. You must wear proper eye protection and either a lab apron or lab coat in the laboratory whenever any laboratory work is in progress.

3. You must not wear contact lenses in the laboratory. (Vapors can dissolve and be concentrated in the fluid behind the lenses, and can even permeate "soft" lenses and be released into the eyes over time.)

4. You must wear shoes which do not have open spaces; sandals and open-toe shoes are not acceptable.

5. You may not eat, drink or smoke in the laboratory. You must not even bring food or drink into the laboratory.

6. You must confine long hair and neckties. You must cover frilly or flared clothing with a lab apron or lab coat. (Loose jewelry may also be a hazard.)

7. You must not engage in acts of carelessness while in the laboratory.

8. You must work carefully with a full awareness of what you are doing in order to avoid breaking equipment or spilling chemicals.

Proper Laboratory Practices

1. Carefully read the label on a bottle twice before using its contents.

2. Take only the quantity of reagent needed. Never return an unused reagent to its container.

3. Mix reagents only when specifically directed to do so.

4. Never place chemicals directly on the balance pan. Weigh reagents using a beaker, flask or other chemically inert container.

5. If instructed to observe the odor of a chemical, do so by fanning air over the container toward your nose. Do not smell the substance directly.

6. Never taste reagents. Furthermore, ice from the ice machine in the stockroom may be contaminated and should never be eaten.

7. Avoid handling chemicals directly with your hands unless directed to do so. If contact occurs, immediately flush the area with cool water.

8. Lubricate the end of glass tubing or thermometers with glycerin before inserting them into rubber stoppers. Protect your hands with a towel or gloves and hold the glass close to the stopper. Slowly insert the tube with a twisting motion.

9. Use a suction bulb or a pipetting device to draw liquids into a pipette. Never pipette by mouth.

10. When diluting strong acids or strong bases, the acid or base should be added to the water, not vice versa.

11. Before igniting a Bunsen burner, make sure no flammable liquids or vapors are in the area.

12. Do not heat test tubes with a direct Bunsen flame unless the experimental procedure instructs you to do so. Solutions in test tubes are always heated in a water bath.

13. Stay clear of an open vessel in which water is boiling or a process is occurring that could produce spattering.

14. Keep reagents and equipment well back from the edge of the lab bench.

15. Do not use cracked glassware as it may break when under stress.

Accidents and Injuries

Report all accidents and injuries to the instructor as soon as possible. You may also have to complete an Incident Report.

First Aid kits with some supplies and gloves are available to the laboratory. Band-Aids are available at the stockroom. Wear gloves when helping with an open wound. In the event of an injury, some basic first aid procedures to be followed immediately include:

1. Skin burns: Place the affected area immediately under cold running tap water for 5 - 10 minutes to remove the heat or irritant.

2. Chemicals in Eyes: Flush your eyes with water at the eyewash for at least 15 minutes.

3. Hair or Clothing Fires: Use the safety shower to extinguish flames.

Fires

1. Instructors or other trained personnel are responsible for extinguishing small fires.

2. If a burner started the fire, first turn off the burner.

3. If the fire is contained in a beaker, try to smother it with a watch glass or wet paper towel placed over the beaker.

4. In the event of a large or uncontrollable fire, instructors, according to the following evacuation procedure, must direct students to immediately evacuate the room:

   a. Direct students to leave the building.
   b. Shut down all equipment in the laboratory, and contain the fire to its room of origin. Closing the door serves to prevent the spread of the fire and smoke.
   c. Activate the building alarm system by going to the nearest alarm pull box and activating it.
   d. Report the fire by dialing the Emergency Number and telling the person who answers: the location of the fire, any injuries, and answer any other questions they may have. DO NOT HANG UP UNTIL TOLD TO DO SO!

Chemical Wastes

Special instructions and containers for wastes are given each week in the pre-laboratory lecture. Students should carefully read waste container labels and put wastes in the proper container. Never pour organic solvents or toxic wastes, such as solutions containing chromium, mercury or lead, into the drain.

Cleaning Responsibilities

Students are responsible for (1) cleaning any equipment used in the experiment (2) cleaning their immediate work area, and (3) returning equipment to the proper places. Additional responsibilities for cleaning designated areas of the laboratory will be assigned by the instructor. Students should follow the practices listed below:

1. Clean all glassware before storing it. Soap solution is provided at the sinks.

2. Use tap water to wash and rinse glassware.

3. Clean any special equipment and return it to the designated areas.

4. Sponges are available for cleaning the bench tops and wiping spills.

5. Dustpans, brooms and brushes are available at the stock room for sweeping broken glass from the benches and floor. Place broken glass in the special containers provided.

6. Remove any paper, broken glass or other debris from the sinks.

Name _____ Semester _____

Course Number/Section _____ Date _____ Laboratory Room Number _____

Lab Instructor Name _____ Locker Number _____

I have read carefully and understand all of the safety rules contained herein. I also agree to read all rules for specific exercises contained in this laboratory manual or supplementary handout required for this course. I recognize that it is my responsibility to obey them faithfully.

I realize that all chemicals may be potentially dangerous; therefore I will exercise care in handling them. If I am unsure of the potential hazards of any chemical, I will discuss this with my instructor prior to using the chemical in question.

I understand that I am required to wear safety goggles at all times when directed to do so in the laboratory. I also understand that there are dangers involved in wearing all types of contact lenses in laboratory situations where reactive chemical agents or volatile organics are in use. I am aware that even when safety goggles are worn, the Chemistry Department strongly discourages wearing of contact lenses in these situations. If I do elect to wear contact lenses in the laboratory, I will inform my instructor.

I FURTHER UNDERSTAND THAT I AM PERMITTED TO WORK IN THE LABORATORY ONLY WHEN IT IS UNDER THE SUPERVISION OF A LABORATORY INSTRUCTOR.

Any student behaving in an unsafe manner in the laboratory is subject to immediate expulsion from the laboratory. Unsafe behavior includes, but is not limited to, failure to wear proper goggles, proper lab coat/apron, and proper clothing/shoes. Any student expelled in this manner will receive NO credit for that experiment.

Sign all copies of this form. Retain this copy in your laboratory notebook. Your laboratory instructor will collect and retain the other signed copies.

Name _____ Signature _____

Name _____ Semester _____

Course Number/Section _____ Date _____ Laboratory Room Number _____

Lab Instructor Name _____ Locker Number _____

I have read carefully and understand all of the safety rules contained herein. I also agree to read all rules for specific exercises contained in this laboratory manual or supplementary handout required for this course. I recognize that it is my responsibility to obey them faithfully.

I realize that all chemicals may be potentially dangerous; therefore I will exercise care in handling them. If I am unsure of the potential hazards of any chemical, I will discuss this with my instructor prior to using the chemical in question.

I understand that I am required to wear safety goggles at all times when directed to do so in the laboratory. I also understand that there are dangers involved in wearing all types of contact lenses in laboratory situations where reactive chemical agents or volatile organics are in use. I am aware that even when safety goggles are worn, the Chemistry Department strongly discourages wearing of contact lenses in these situations. If I do elect to wear contact lenses in the laboratory, I will inform my instructor.

I FURTHER UNDERSTAND THAT I AM PERMITTED TO WORK IN THE LABORATORY ONLY WHEN IT IS UNDER THE SUPERVISION OF A LABORATORY INSTRUCTOR.

Any student behaving in an unsafe manner in the laboratory is subject to immediate expulsion from the laboratory. Unsafe behavior includes, but is not limited to, failure to wear proper goggles, proper lab coat/apron, and proper clothing/shoes. Any student expelled in this manner will receive NO credit for that experiment.

Sign all copies of this form. Retain this copy in your laboratory notebook. Your laboratory instructor will collect and retain the other signed copies.

Name _____ Signature _____

Labels are the primary initial source of warning when handling chemical substances. Federal and State regulations mandate that all labels on original/stock containers of hazardous chemicals include the name of the hazardous chemical, appropriate hazard warning(s), and the name and address of the manufacturer, importer, or other responsible party. When chemicals are transferred from the manufacturer's original container to a secondary container, that new container is labeled as to chemical identity and hazard warning(s).

Hazard warnings found on the labels of chemical containers may be composed of pictures, symbols, and words, or any combination thereof that convey the hazard(s) of the chemical. Picture hazard warnings help to identify the properties and classes of hazardous compounds. Examples include the flaming letter "O" (oxidizer), hand/bar of steel (corrosive) and skull-and-crossbones (poison). Symbol hazard warnings provide basic information in determining what precautionary measures to use when handling chemical substances and/or dealing with a fire. Word hazard warnings contain a word or words intended to capture the user's immediate attention (e.g. flammable, poison, fatal if swallowed). These word labels should be in English, but other languages may be used where needed.

The NFPA's Hazard Rating Diamond

The National Fire Protection Association has developed a rating system to identify and rank hazards of a material. You may have seen the colorful labels used to communicate these hazards. The label is diamond-shaped and made up of four smaller diamonds: one each blue, red, yellow, and white. A number or special symbol is placed on the four diamonds.

So what do those colors mean? The blue diamond, appearing on the left side of the label, conveys Health Hazard information for persons exposed to the material. A number from 0 to 4 is written in the blue diamond. The higher the number the higher the hazard, as follows:

0 = Normal Material
1 = Slight Hazard
2 = Moderately Hazardous
3 = Extremely Hazardous
4 = Deadly

The red diamond, appearing at the top of the label, conveys Flammability Hazard information. Again, the numbers 0 to 4 are used to rate the flammability hazard, as follows:

0 = Will not burn
1 = Above 200 degrees Fahrenheit
2 = Between 100-200 degrees Fahrenheit
3 = Below 100 degrees Fahrenheit
4 = Flash point below 73 degrees Fahrenheit

The yellow diamond, appearing at the right side of the label, conveys Reactivity (or Stability) information. The numbers 0 to 4 are also used to rank reactivity hazards, as follows:

0 = Stable
1 = Unstable if heated
2 = Violent chemical change
3 = Shock or heat may detonate
4 = Rapidly capable of detonation or explosion

The white diamond, appearing at the bottom of the label, conveys Special Hazard information. This information is conveyed by use of symbols which represent the special hazard. A few of the common symbols are shown here:

ACID-acid
ALK-alkali
COR-corrosive
OX-oxidizer
P-polymerization
(W with a line through it) – Use no water

Some facilities use the white diamond to convey personal protective equipment requirements when using the material. You may see a picture of gloves, safety glasses, or a respirator in the white diamond.

To determine the NFPA Hazard Ratings for a material which does not have the label affixed, check the Material Safety Data Sheet. NFPA Hazard Ratings are commonly displayed there.

Taking a quick glance at the NFPA label provides a wealth of information. This information is useful to learn the hazards of a particular material and what you should do to use it safely. Follow the warnings on the NFPA label or any label affixed to a container of material. A careful reading of the Material Data Safety Sheet (MSDS), always a prudent action for any substance, is particularly important if the NFPA hazard rating number is 2 or higher. Remember, when you're working with hazardous materials, your safety depends on you.

Material Safety Data Sheets

The OSHA Hazard Communications Standard requires that Material Safety Data Sheets (MSDS) be provided to users of chemicals by their manufacturers and distributors. Employers are required to obtain an MSDS for each chemical used in the work place. Employees must have access to MSDS for the chemicals used in their work areas.

Material Safety Data Sheets are a primary source of information when determining the risks associated with any substance used in the workplace. MSDS include useful information on toxicity, reactivity and physical properties of the substance.

The regulation does not specify in what particular form or arrangement the information must be provided nor does it limit the information contained in a completed MSDS. The following information is intended to serve as a general guide to the data that is typically available in a MSDS and the general arrangement or location of the data.

Section I. PRODUCT IDENTIFICATION

This section should provide the manufacturer's name, address, and regular and emergency telephone numbers (including area code). The trade name should be the product designation or common name that is associated with the material. The synonyms are those commonly used for the product, especially formal chemical nomenclature.

Section II. HAZARDOUS INGREDIENTS

This section lists the chemical components by percent, purity, and Chemical Abstracts Service (CAS) number. The items listed in this section should be those component substance(s) in a product which individually meet any criteria as a defined hazardous substance. Thus one component of a multi component product might be listed because of its toxicity, another component because of its flammability, while a third could be included both for its toxicity and for its reactivity.

Chemical substances should be listed according to their complete name as derived from a recognized system of nomenclature.

The percentages of hazardous ingredients in a product are often given but are not required by the present regulation.

Toxic hazard data should be stated in terms of concentration, mode of exposure or test, and animal used. Concentrations are often written in parts per million (ppm) or mg/m^3. Additional information as to dosage and concentration should be provided [e.g. Lethal Concentration (LC) and Lethal Dose (LD).] Toxic Hazard Data must be from published sources such as the Threshold Limit Value (TLV) list by the American Conference of Governmental Industrial Hygienists (ACGIH).

Flammable or reactive data should be included to indicate flash point, shock sensitivity, or other brief data indicating nature of the hazard.

Section III. PHYSICAL DATA

The data in this section should be for the total mixture or product. The boiling point and melting point at sea level should be indicated in degrees Fahrenheit or Centigrade (or both) and be clearly designated; specific gravity of the product (compared to water being equal to 1); vapor density of a gas or vapor (compared to air equal to 1); solubility in water in parts per hundred by weight; percent volatile by weight or volume at room temperature (usually 70°F or 15.5°°C); evaporation rate for liquids or solids; appearance and odor. Boiling point, vapor density, percent volatile, vapor pressure and evaporation rate are all used in designing proper ventilation systems for control of toxic vapors.

This information is also useful for design and deployment of adequate fire and spill containment equipment. The appearance and odor may facilitate identification of substances if a label is missing or the material is spilled.

Section IV. FIRE AND EXPLOSION DATA

This section should contain the appropriate fire and explosion data for the product, including flash point and auto ignition temperature in degrees Fahrenheit or Centigrade, or both; flammable limit in percent by volume in air; suitable extinguishing media or materials; special fire fighting procedures; and unusual fire and explosion information. If the product presents no fire hazard, a statement to that effect should be included in this section.

Section V. HEALTH HAZARD INFORMATION

The "Health Hazard Data" should be a combined estimate of the hazard of the total product. This can be expressed as a time-weighted average concentration, permissible exposure, or by some other indication of acceptable standard. Other data such as LD 50 may be used.

Under "Principal Routes of Absorption," comments in each category should reflect the potential hazard from absorption of the product. Comments should indicate the severity of the effect and basis for the finding whenever appropriate. The basis might be animal studies, analogy with similar products, or human exposure. Typical comments might be:

- Skin contact, single short contact - No adverse effects likely.

- Prolonged or repeated contact - Mild irritation and possibly some blistering.

- Eye contact - Some pain and mild transient irritation. No corneal scarring.

Effects of overexposure should indicate relevant signs, symptoms and disease entities that could arise from acute and chronic exposure to the hazardous substance.

The Emergency and First Aid Procedures should be primarily first aid treatment information that could be used by paramedical personnel and individuals trained in first aid. Information in the Notes to Physicians section should include any special medical information, which would be of assistance to an attending physician, including diagnostic procedures, and medical management of overexposed individuals.

Section VI. REACTIVITY DATA

This section relates to safe storage and handling of hazardous unstable substances. Important aspects include the instability or incompatibility of the product to common substances or circumstances such as water, direct sunlight, metals used in piping or containers, and corrosives.

"Hazardous Decomposition Products" include those products released under fire conditions. It also should include dangerous products created by aging, such as peroxides in the case of some ethers. The product's shelf life should also be indicated under this section when applicable.

Section VII. SPILL OR LEAK PROCEDURES

This section should include detailed procedures for clean up and disposal of the substance with emphasis on precautions to be taken to protect individuals who are involved in spill clean up.

Disposal methods should also be explicit, including proper labeling and handling of containers holding clean-up residue.

Section VIII. SPECIAL PROTECTION INFORMATION

Specific information should be provided in this section as to the preferred methods of hazard control for each listed substance. When required, respirators should be specified as to their type and class. Protective clothing and equipment should be specified as to type and material of construction when appropriate.

Section IX. SPECIAL PRECAUTIONS

This section may include label statements selected for use on containers or placards. Additional information on any aspects of safety or health not covered in other sections should be found here.

The lower block may contain reference to published guides or procedures for more specific information for identification, handling or storage of the product. It may also contain other information such as Department of Transportation markings and classifications and other freight, handling, or storage requirements and environmental control procedures.

Finally, the name and address of the responsible person who completed the MSDS and the date the information was compiled should be entered here. This information is necessary to facilitate correction of errors and to identify a source for additional information.

Safety in the Laboratory
General Safety Quiz

Name_____ Section_____ Date_____

READ THE DISCUSSION FIRST!

1. List at least three essential safe laboratory practices.

2. What specific personal protective safety equipment is required to be worn in the laboratory? Include clothing and other items that are not recommended.

3. What are the recommendations concerning the wearing of contact lens in the laboratory?

4. Name three categories of waste discussed under "Management of Laboratory Waste" and specify their method of disposal.

5. Explain the first aid procedure for:

   a. Skin burns:

   b. Chemicals in Eyes:

6. What should you do if a fire breaks out in the laboratory?

7. Describe your responsibilities concerning clean up while operating in the laboratory.

8. What resources could you use to determine the potential hazards of a chemical?

Safety in the Laboratory
Material Safety Data Sheet (MSDS) Exercise & Quiz

Name_____ Section_____ Date_____

READ THE DISCUSSION FIRST!

Part A – Understanding MSDS Sheets

1. MSDS are the primary source of determing <u>what</u> about the substance?

2. Name three pieces of useful information that a MSDS provides about a substance.

3. Do the written regulations specify a particular form or arrangement for the information that must be provided? Please explain?

4. Give a brief explanation of what is contained in the following sections of a MSDS sheet.
   a. Product Identification

   b. Hazardous Ingredients

c. Physical Data

d. Fire and Explosion Data

e. Health Hazard Information

f. Reactivity Data

g. Spill and/or Leak Procedures

h. Special Protection Information

i. Special Precautions

Safety in the Laboratory
Material Safety Data Sheet (MSDS) Exercise & Quiz

Name_____ Section_____ Date_____

Part B – Finding Information from a MSDS Sheet

Your instructor will provide you with a copy of an actual MSDS sheet.
Use this document to answer the questions below.

1. What is the chemical name, trade name (if applicable), synonyms and manufacturer's name?

2. What is the boiling point and melting point of the substance(s) found on the MSDS sheet?.

3. Determine the "Principle Routes of Absorption" and explain the effects of exposure?

4. List applicable first aid measures for exposures to this substance.

5. Discuss the storage requirements for this substance. Include information about the substance's stability, compatibility and special circumstances for handling and storage.

6. Explain the specific procedure(s) to use if a spill or leak occurs for this substance.

7. Explain the preferred methods for hazard control. Include which personal protective equipment (PPE) is required when handling this substance.

8. List any special precautions that may be helpful in handling this substance. If available list the NFPA classification for storage and handling.

SIGNIFICANT FIGURES — MASS VOLUME EXERCISE

The science of chemistry has been largely developed through the careful observation and measurement of matter behavior in a laboratory setting. Accordingly, your study of chemistry will include laboratory experiments designed to demonstrate or clarify principles discussed in the lecture classroom. However, if these experiments are to provide useful information, accurate, precise measurement and careful observation will be required.

The purpose of this, our first experiment, is to help us define the concepts of ACCURACY and PRECISION and to demonstrate the importance of SIGNIFICANT DIGITS (meaningful numbers) as they relate to our experimental conclusions. The exercise will also provide a little practice with scientific notation, metric conversion, and DENSITY relationships ... all topics to be presented early in the lecture sequence.

This experiment contains definitions of accuracy and precision, a summary of the concepts and rules of significant digits, and problem examples relating to their application. Use these as reference when completing the advance problem assignment and the lab report for this experiment, and for ALL FUTURE EXPERIMENTS.

Accuracy, Precision, and Significant Numbers

Accuracy is a comparison against a true or accepted value: A student experimentally determines a flask volume to be 10.6 mL. If the true volume is 10.0 mL, the relative error is about six percent. Note that the evaluation of accuracy requires knowledge of a true or accepted value.

ABSOLUTE ERROR = Difference between the experimental result and the true value.

RELATIVE ERROR = The absolute error divided by the true value and then multiplied by 100 (percent), or 1000 (parts per thousand), etc.

Precision in multi-trial analysis refers to the agreement among what should be identical results. For instance, five volume determinations on the same flask should yield the same volume. If one compares the differences between these results, one can evaluate the reliability of the average volume.

DEVIATION: Subtract the average value from the experimental value.

AVERAGE DEVIATION: Add the deviations without regard to sign and then divide the sum by the number of trials.

STANDARD DEVIATION: Square the deviations, add them, divide by one less than the number of trials, and take the square root of the answer.

1

Precision also identifies the limits on our knowledge of a quantity. The volume of the flask above is known to the tenth of a milliliter. A mass of 2.847 grams measured on our laboratory balance is known to the thousandth of a gram. The mass is therefore more precise because the uncertainty in its value is smaller than the uncertainty in the flask volume. The precision of a number is identified by the location of its LAST (farthest right) SIGNIFICANT DIGIT, and the uncertainty is assumed to be ± 1 in that place unless specified or known to be otherwise (see examples below). The last (farthest right) significant digit is, therefore, the number that <u>contains the uncertainty.</u>

Significant Numbers [Significant Figures or Digits]

1. Numbers that one obtains from a measuring device (balance, graduated cylinder, etc.) are significant numbers.

2. Non-zero numbers are significant:

$$276 = 3 \text{ sig. figs.} \quad \pm 1.$$
$$0.55 = 2 \text{ sig. figs.} \quad \pm .01$$

3. Zeros between significant digits are significant:

$$403 = 3 \text{ sig. figs.} \quad \pm 1.$$
$$70.2 = 3 \text{ sig. figs.} \quad \pm .1$$

4. Zeros used to indicate PRECISION are significant:

$$15.00 = 4 \text{ sig. figs.} \quad \pm .01$$
$$0.880 = 3 \text{ sig. figs.} \quad \pm .001$$

5. Zeros used to indicate MAGNITUDE (often termed "place holder" zeros) are <u>NOT</u> significant:

$$1500 = 2 \text{ sig. figs.} \quad \pm 100.$$
$$0.005 = 1 \text{ sig. figs.} \quad \pm .001$$
$$2.61 \times 10^4 = 3 \text{ sig. figs.} \quad \pm .01 \times 10^4$$

6. Numbers that are EXACT, either by nature or by definition, have UNLIMITED significant digits (and unlimited precision.) For instance:

100 centimeters per one meter is exact by DEFINITION. Both 100 cm. and 1 m. have unlimited significant figures.

The number of experimental trials or a number of drops collected is exact by NATURE. Five trials or 25 drops both have unlimited significant digits.

Significant Numbers in Calculated Values

The first NON-SIGNIFICANT digit is written as a subscript

1. <u>**Multiplication/Division (Powers & Roots):**</u> The number of SIGNIFICANT DIGITS in the answer must be the same as the number of digits in the LEAST significant digit value used in the calculation. (The precision of the numbers used has no bearing on the answer.) EXACT numbers do not affect the answer.

   Note that 0.0267 and 26.7 have three sig. figs., 3.1 has two sig. figs., the first *non-significant* number is written as a subscript in calculated numbers.

   $(0.0267) \times (3.1) = 0.082_7$ two sig. figs., precision to the thousandths place

   $(26.7) \times (3.1) = 82._7$ two sig. figs., precision to the units place

   $(3.1) / (0.0267) = 11_6.$ two sig. figs., precision to the tens place

2

2. **Addition/Subtraction:** The PRECISION of the answer must be the same as the LEAST precise number used in the calculation. (The number of sig. figs. in the values used has no bearing on the answer) NOTE: Exponential notation (scientific notation) numbers should not be added or subtracted unless the exponents are identical. EXACT numbers do not affect the answer.

Tenth place:

$$26.7$$
$$+ 3.1$$
$$29.8_0 \text{ (3 sig. figs.)}$$

Units place:

$$26.7$$
$$+ 31.$$
$$57._7 \text{ (2 sig. figs.)}$$

Thousandth place:

$$0.664$$
$$- 0.662$$
$$0.002_0 \text{ (1 sig. fig.)}$$

3. **Note:** that calculation cannot improve the *precision* of a measured value. For instance, volume determinations of 36.2, 36.7, and 36.4 mL on the same flask would yield an average volume of 36.43 ± 0.01 mL (according to the above rules). This value is more precise (hundredth place) than the least precise volume (tenth place) used in its calculation. Reporting the average volume beyond the tenth of a mL is therefore NOT valid. The average is reported as 36.4_3 mL even though the above rules indicate otherwise.

$36.2 + 36.7 + 36.4 = 109.3$ PRECISION to the tenth place (4 sig. figs.)

$109.3 / 3 \text{ trials} = 36.43_3$ Four SIG. FIGS. (precision to the hundredth place)

The answer is more precise than the values used to calculate it – NOT VALID.
The average can only be reported to the tenth place: 36.4_3

4. In **Sequential Calculations:** the first non-significant digit is used rather than a rounded off number. This digit is written as a subscript (see above examples) to indicate that it is not a significant number. The final answer may be rounded off if desired or left in subscript notation.

$[26.56 + 19.7] / 3.0$ is: $26.56 + 19.7 = 46.2_6$ then $46.2_6 / 3.0 = 15._4$

Accuracy, Precision, and Significant Numbers – Examples

The first NON-SIGNIFICANT digit is written as a subscript.

The exact volume of a 25 mL graduated cylinder was determined by measuring the mass of water it contained and dividing by the density of water at the temperature of the experiment. The experiment was performed five times on the same graduated cylinder when the density of water was 0.99720 g/mL.

i.e.:   Density = Mass / Volume   therefore   Volume = Mass / Density

For trial one:

Mass of cylinder and water	34.751 g
Mass of empty cylinder	– 9.211 g
Mass of water in the cylinder	25.540_0 g

$$\text{Volume of water in the cylinder} = \frac{25.540_0 \text{ g}}{0.99720 \text{ g} / \text{mL}}$$

$$= 25.611_9 = 25.612 \text{ mL}$$

3

All five trials are summarized as follows:

TRIAL	VOLUME	AVERAGE	DEVIATION	(DEVIATION)^2	(DEVIATION)^2
1	25.612 mL		+0.010$_0$	1.0$_0$ x 10^{-4}	10.$_0$ x 10^{-5}
2	25.598		−0.004$_0$	1.$_6$ x 10^{-5}	1.$_6$ x 10^{-5}
3	25.603	25.602$_0$	+0.001$_0$	1.$_0$ x 10^{-6}	0.1$_0$ x 10^{-5}
4	25.604		+0.002$_0$	4.$_0$ x 10^{-6}	0.4$_0$ x 10^{-5}
5	25.593		−0.009$_0$	8.$_1$ x 10^{-5}	8.$_1$ x 10^{-5}
	128.010$_0$		0.026$_0$		20.$_2$ x 10^{-5}

AVERAGE (MEAN) = 128.010$_0$ / 5 trials = 25.6020 = 25.602$_0$

AVERAGE DEVIATION = 0.026$_0$ / 5 trials = 0.0052 = 0.005$_2$,

$$\text{\textbf{VOLUME}} = 25.602_0 \pm 0.005_2 \text{ mL}$$

$$\text{\textbf{STANDARD DEVIATION}} = \sqrt[2]{\left(20._2 \times 10^{-5}\right)\Big/(5-1 \text{ trials})} = 0.0071 = 0.007_1$$

$$\text{\textbf{VOLUME}} = 25.602_0 \pm 0.007_1 \text{ mL}$$

Note that the average volume, average deviation, and standard deviation would be precise to the ten thousandth place according to the significant number calculation rules. These are more precise than the volumes or the deviations (both precise only to the thousandth place) used to calculate them. The rules are therefore not valid in this case, and the values must all be reported only to the thousandth place.

If the theoretical (true) volume of the cylinder is assumed to be 25.000 mL, then:

Absolute Error = 25.602$_0$ - 25.000 = 0.602$_0$ mL
Relative Error = (0.602$_0$ / 25.000) x 100 = 2.40$_8$ percent

__Range__ is defined as the difference between the largest and the smallest trial (theoretically, Range should be zero!) It is most often utilized in populations of less than five trials because Standard Deviation is not valid for small populations.

RANGE = 25.612 - 25.593 = 0.019$_0$

4

Mass and Volume Measurement

The Electronic Balance

The electronic balance available to you in the laboratory is sensitive to one milligram ($\pm$ 0.001 gram) and is therefore a very delicate (and expensive!) instrument. Please keep the following guidelines in mind when weighing objects or preparing samples. They will prevent damage to the balance AND insure the accuracy of your work.

① GENTLY open and close the glass draft shields, and place objects on the balance pan with care. Sudden "jolts" can damage the mass sensing system or break the glass.

② Be certain the objects you put on the balance pan are DRY on the outside. Check the pan to be certain the person before you did the same!

③ Never load chemicals into a container while the container is within the balance draft shield, and don't use "weighing paper" to support chemicals within the draft shield.

Balance surfaces and the mass sensing mechanism are permanently damaged by chemical exposure.

④ Close the draft shield before you ZERO the balance or RECORD the mass of a weighed object.

Additional information concerning WEIGHED SAMPLES and ELECTRONIC BALANCES is presented in the **Appendix** of this laboratory manual.

Volume Measurement

Your instructor will demonstrate the correct use of the pipet, pipettor and other calibrated glassware. Also refer to the *Appendix: Use of a Volumetric Pipet.*

5

Significant Figures – Mass Volume Exercise
Advanced Problem Assignment

Name_____ Date_____

READ THE EXPERIMENT FIRST!

Show calculation "set-ups."

PART IB: Measurement Using a <u>1.00 cm Ruler</u>:

Use Scientific Notation/Correct Significant Figures

Length   **56.75** cm = _____ cm   = _____ mm   = _____ m

Width   **21.45** cm = _____ cm   = _____ mm   = _____ m

Height   **26.20** cm = _____ cm   = _____ mm   = _____ m

VOLUME= _____ cm^3 = _____ mm^3 = _____ m^3

SHOW CALCULATION "SET-UPS"

PART IIB: Volume of a <u>10 mL Pipet</u>:

USE CORRECT SIGNIFICANT FIGURES

Mass Beaker and Water   ____**86.714** g   **SHOW CALCULATION SET-UP**

Mass Beaker   ____**76.684** g

Mass Water   _____ g

Density of Water   ____**0.9970** g/mL

Volume of Water   _____ mL

Theoretical Volume   ____**10.000** mL

Relative Error   _____ %

7

PART III: Average <u>Volume of the 10 mL Pipet</u>:

USE CORRECT SIGNIFICANT FIGURES
Use Scientific Notation Where Appropriate

Trial	Mass Beaker & Water	Mass Beaker	Mass Water	Volume of Water	Deviation	(Deviation)^2 *
1	__86.714__ g	__76.684__ g	_____ g	_____ mL	_____	_____
2				10.08$_7$___ mL	_____	_____
3				10.01$_2$___ mL	_____	_____
4				9.98$_7$___ mL	_____	_____
5				9.95$_1$___ mL	_____	_____

Average Volume _____ mL

Water Density **0.9970 g/mL**

Average Deviation _____

RANGE of Volumes _____   Sum of (Deviation)^2 *   _____

Standard Deviation _____

Theoretical Volume **10.000** mL   Relative Error_____Percent

SHOW CALCULATION "SET-UPS"

8

WEAR YOUR SAFETY GLASSES!

Experimental Procedure

PART I: Experimental Determination of Volume in Cubic Length Units

The right side of this page contains a metric ruler calibrated in centimeters.
Use this ruler to measure the length, width, and height of your lab locker.
RECORD your measurements in centimeters **to the nearest** 0.1 cm.

REPEAT these measurements using a <u>METER STICK</u> calibrated in millimeters (0.1cm).
RECORD your measurements in centimeters **to the nearest** 0.05 cm.

1. EXPRESS each measurement in SCIENTIFIC NOTATION. CALCULATE the volume of the locker in cubic <u>centimeters</u>. REPORT the volume in scientific notation AND correct significant digits.

2. CONVERT each measurement to millimeters (scientific notation) and then calculate the volume in cubic <u>millimeters</u> (scientific notation/significant digits).

3. CONVERT each measurement to meters (scientific notation) and then calculate the volume in cubic <u>meters</u> (scientific notation/significant digits).

4. Are the volumes determined using the METER STICK more or less precise? WHY?

PART II: Experimental Calibration of Volumetric Measuring Devices

1. Weigh a DRY 50-mL beaker, recording its mass to the nearest milligram.

2. Fill your 10 mL GRADUATED CYLINDER to the 10.0 mL mark. Use a dropper to adjust the level so that the bottom of the meniscus just touches the 10.0 mL mark.

3. Transfer the water into your pre-weighed 50 mL beaker, and weigh to the nearest milligram on the SAME BALANCE.

4. CALCULATE the mass of water and the VOLUME of water transferred from the cylinder. Also calculate the RELATIVE ERROR between this value and the theoretical volume of 10.000 mL. [CORRECT Significant Digits!]

5. Dry and REWEIGH your 50 mL beaker. Use a 10 mL PIPET to transfer exactly 10.0 mL into the beaker and weigh again. CALCULATE the mass and volume transferred and the relative error as before. <u>Also</u> record this data as Trial one of **PART III** below.

6. COMPARE the accuracy of the pipet with that of the cylinder. Which is more accurate?

PART III. Calibration of the 10.0 Milliliter Pipet

1. REPEAT experiment five of PART II above FOUR more times. Be sure to use the same pipet and dry and reweigh the beaker each time.
RECORD this data as <u>trials</u> <u>two</u> through <u>five</u> on PART III of the data summary.

2. CALCULATE the Average Volume, the Range of Volumes, the Deviation, Average Deviation, and the Standard Deviation. Assuming a theoretical volume of 10.000 mL, what is the Relative Error of the average volume?

9

0.0

5.0

10.0

15.0

20.0

25.0

Significant Figures – Mass Volume Exercise
Experimental Data & Calculations

Name_____   Date_____

PART IA: Measurement Using a 1.0 cm Ruler:

Use Scientific Notation and Correct Significant Figures   (Estimate to ± 0.1 cm)

Length _____ cm = _____ cm = _____ mm = _____ m

Width _____ cm = _____ cm = _____ mm = _____ m

Height _____ cm = _____ cm = _____ mm = _____ m

VOLUME= _____ cm^3 = _____ mm^3 = _____ m^3

SHOW CALCULATION "SET-UPS"

PART IB Measurement Using a 1.00 cm Ruler:

Use Scientific Notation and Correct Significant Figures   (Meter stick — Estimate to ± 0.05 cm)

Length _____ cm = _____ cm = _____ mm = _____ m

Width _____ cm = _____ cm = _____ mm = _____ m

Height _____ cm = _____ cm = _____ mm = _____ m

VOLUME= _____ cm^3 = _____ mm^3 = _____ m^3

Which measurement exercise above is more PRECISE?   _____

SHOW CALCULATION "SET-UPS"

PART II   **A. Volume of a 10 mL CYLINDER:**   **B. Volume of a 10 mL PIPET:**

Mass Beaker and Water   _____ g   _____ g

Mass Beaker   _____ g   _____ g

Mass Water   _____ g   _____ g

Density of Water   _____ g/mL   _____ g/mL

Volume of Water   _____ mL   _____ mL

Theoretical Volume   _ 10.000____ mL   __10.000____ mL

Relative Error   _____ %   _____ %

Which of the above volume devices is more ACCURATE?   _____

SHOW CALCULATION "SET-UPS"

PART III: Average Volume of the 10 mL Pipet:

Use Correct Significant Figures

Use Scientific Notation Where Appropriate

Trial	Mass Beaker & Water	Mass Beaker	Mass Water	Volume of Water	Deviation	(Deviation)^2 *
1	_____ g	_____ g	_____ g	_____ mL	_____	_____
2	_____ g	_____ g	_____ g	_____ mL	_____	_____
3	_____ g	_____ g	_____ g	_____ mL	_____	_____
4	_____ g	_____ g	_____ g	_____ mL	_____	_____
5	_____ g	_____ g	_____ g	_____ mL	_____	_____

Average Volume _____ mL

Water Density _____ g/mL

Average Deviation _____

Sum of (Deviation)^2 * _____

Range of Volumes _____ mL   Standard Deviation _____

Theoretical Volume **10.000** mL   Relative Error _____ Percent

12

EXPERIMENTAL DETERMINATION OF DENSITY

The DENSITY of a sample of matter is defined as the MASS of that substance contained in a specific volume of sample. For liquids and solids density is usually expressed as GRAMS per CUBIC CENTIMETER (g/cm^3) or GRAMS per MILLITER (g/mL), while for gas materials density is mass per LITER (g/L).

The metric unit of mass, the GRAM, was defined as the mass contained in one cubic centimeter of water at its temperature of maximum density (4°C). The density of water has therefore been DEFINED as exactly one gram per exactly one cubic centimeter (at 4°C) and is the standard against which other densities are measured. (Water density is slightly less than $1.000 \ g/cm^3$ above and below 4°C and has been determined throughout its liquid range – see the *APPENDIX: Properties of Water – Table 1.*)

Densities are experimentally determined quantities obtained by accurately measuring the mass and the volume of a sample and then dividing **MASS/VOLUME = DENSITY**. In fact, experimental measurement of any two of the three terms in the density definition allows one to calculate the third. For instance, once a liquid density has been determined it can be used to calculate the volume of a known mass of the liquid or the mass of a known volume.

MASS is determined by weighing the sample; this is ideally performed on a balance that is sensitive to one milligram. Of course, one usually weighs the empty container, then the container with the sample, and then subtracts to obtain the sample weight.

Liquid and gas VOLUME must be determined using volumetric containers such as graduated cylinders, burets or containers having accurately known and reproducible volumes (termed PYCNOMETERS).

The volume of solids having a regular shape can be measured directly (by measuring length, width, height, and calculating volume, for example). However, most solid samples consist of many, irregular shaped pieces that do not permit accurate measurement of their dimensions. The volume of these solids must therefore be determined by an indirect method. For instance, one first partially fills a graduated cylinder with water and records the volume reading. The solid sample is then added to the cylinder, and the new volume in the cylinder is recorded. The differences in the volume readings represent the metal volume. Note, however, that it is NOT the METAL VOLUME that is measured. The volume of WATER DISPLACED BY THE METAL was measured under conditions where the water displaced is identical to the metal volume – an indirect volume determination.

Unfortunately, volume measurements are often of limited precision. A 50-mL graduated cylinder, for example, can be read to only ±0.2 mL. If these are in opposite directions for the two readings needed to obtain displaced volume, the uncertainty is 0.4 mL. A laboratory balance, however, is sensitive to ±0.001 grams. If one determines the MASS of water displaced, the volume can be calculated from the density expression and the water density at the experimental temperature (**APPENDIX**). By using a more precise instrument (the balance), we can obtain a more precise value for the displaced water volume. Accordingly, we will use this technique to determine the volume of our metal sample in this experiment.

A container of known and reproducible volume (a pycnometer) is also required. Our experiment uses a 25 mL flask with a ground glass stopper. The ground stopper will insure that the interior volume of the flask is always the same when the stopper is inserted. We will measure the mass of water that occupies the flask at known temperature and calculate its' volume using the density expression. If we are careful to ensure the water completely fills the flask, the water volume will also be the flask volume.

Once the pycnometer has been calibrated in this manner, it can be used to determine the density of an unknown liquid as well as the density of an unknown solid.

WEAR YOUR SAFETY GOGGLES/LAB COAT!

WASH YOUR HANDS WHEN FINISHED!

Experimental Procedure

READ THE INSTRUCTIONS TWICE BEFORE YOU BEGIN!

A. Obtain a dry 25 mL Erlenmeyer flask with ground glass stopper (a pycnometer) and a sample of dry metal (in a large test tube) from the laboratory cart. RECORD the identification number of this metal sample on your data page.

B. Obtain experimental weights in the following order. Please note that the sequence in which you take the weights is NOT the order in which they are to be used in calculation. Use the SAME analytical balance for all weights, and record each mass to three decimal places.

    1.   **Mass of DRY Flask/Stopper**   _____ **g**

    2.   **Mass of DRY Flask/Stopper and DRY Metal**   _____ **g**

Add 10 to 15 mL of water to the flask, and GENTLY agitate the metal/water mixture to eliminate air bubbles trapped between pieces of metal. Then add water until the pycnometer is completely FULL. Insert the stopper, check to be certain there are no air bubbles inside, and DRY the outside. Then determine:

    3.   **Mass of Flask/Stopper, Metal, and Water**   _____ **g**

Open the flask and pour off the water. Transfer the metal onto paper towels to dry. Again, FILL the pycnometer with water. Insert the stopper, ensure there are no air bubbles inside, and DRY the outside. Then determine:

    4.   **Mass of Flask/Stopper and Water**   _____ **g**

14

Your instructor will assign an unknown liquid for you to use. RECORD the identification number of this liquid sample on your data page.

Empty the water from the pycnometer. Add approximately 5 mL of this unknown liquid, insert the stopper, and rotate the pycnometer to coat the interior surface with the liquid. Discard this "rinse" into the WASTE CONTAINER in the hood. Completely fill the pycnometer with the unknown liquid. Insert the stopper, ensure there are no bubbles inside, and dry the outside. Then determine:

5. **Mass of Flask/Stopper and Unknown Liquid** _____ **g**

DISPOSAL: Put the unknown liquid into the container labeled "Used Density Solvent" provided by your instructor.

C. Put your unknown metal sample back into its test tube, and return it to the laboratory cart. Return the flask and stopper to the laboratory cart. **DO NOT INSERT THE STOPPER INTO THE FLASK!** Leave the flask open so it will be dry for the next class.

D. TRANSFER your mass data to the Data Summary/Calculation page. NOTE that the sequence in which the mass data was obtained is NOT the same sequence as that which will be used in calculation. Be sure to record your weighings in the proper locations.

CALCULATE the pycnometer volume, the unknown liquid density, the volume of the unknown metal, and the unknown metal density. Your answers are to be consistent with the appropriate significant figures and precision rules.

Determination of Density
Advanced Problem Assignment

Name_____   Section_____   Date_____

READ THE EXPERIMENTAL DISCUSSION FIRST!

Complete the data table below using correct significant digits.

Show your problem "set up" and calculations on the next page.

A.		Pycnometer Calibration		
	1.	Water Density at Temperature of the Experiment	0.9973	g/mL
	2.	Mass of Empty Flask/Stopper	32.634	g
	3.	Mass of Flask/Stopper Full of Water	59.479	g
	4.	Mass of Water Occupying the Flask When Metal is Not Present	_____	g
	5.	Volume of Water Occupying the Flask (i.e. VOLUME of the PYCNOMETER)	_____	mL
B.		**Density of an Unknown Liquid**		
	1.	Mass of Flask/Stopper Full of Liquid	50.376	g
	2.	Mass of Liquid Occupying the Flask	_____	g
	3.	**Density of the Liquid**	_____	g/mL
C.		**Density of an Unknown Metal**		
	1.	Mass of Flask/Stopper plus Metal	152.047	g
	2.	Mass of Metal	_____	g
	3.	Mass of Flask/Stopper, Metal, and Water	165.541	g
	4.	Mass of Water in the Flask When Metal is Present	_____	g
	5.	Mass of Water DISPLACED by the Metal	_____	g
		Volume of Water DISPLACED by the Metal (i.e. VOLUME of the METAL)	_____	mL
		Density of the Metal	_____	g/mL
D.		**WHY is the value determined for the metal density likely to have a larger RELATIVE ERROR than the value determined for the liquid density?**		

17

Determination of Density
Experimental Data & Calculations

Name_____ Section_____ Date_____

A.	Pycnometer Calibration		
	1. Water Density at Temperature of the Experiment (See *APPENDIX: Properties of Water*)	_____	g/mL
	2. Mass of Empty Flask/Stopper	_____	g
	3. Mass of Flask/Stopper Full of Water (Only Water in the flask)	_____	g
	4. Mass of Water Occupying the Flask When Metal is Not Present	_____	g
	5. Volume of Water Occupying the Flask (i.e. VOLUME of the PYCNOMETER)	_____	mL

B.	**Density of an Unknown Liquid**	Unknown Number	
	1. Mass of Flask/Stopper Full of Liquid	_____	g
	2. Mass of Liquid Occupying the Flask	_____	g
	3. **Density of the Liquid**	_____	g/mL

C.	**Density of an Unknown Metal**	Unknown Number	
	1. Mass of Flask/Stopper plus Metal	_____	g
	2. Mass of Metal	_____	g
	3. Mass of Flask/Stopper, Metal, and Water	_____	g
	4. Mass of Water in the Flask When Metal is Also Present	_____	g
	5. Mass of Water DISPLACED by the Metal	_____	g
	Volume of Water DISPLACED by the Metal (i.e. VOLUME of the METAL)	_____	mL
	Density of the Metal	_____	g/mL

D.	**WHY is the value determined for the metal density likely to have a larger RELATIVE ERROR than the value determined for the liquid density?**

19

WATER OF HYDRATION
Determination of Composition and Formula for a Hydrate

Most solids will contain some water if they have been exposed to the atmosphere for any length of time. In most cases the water is adsorbed on the surface of the solid particles or crystals and is therefore present in very small amounts. However, a number of compounds formed from solution as crystalline solids have a definite proportion of water. These solids are termed **HYDRATES** and generally consist of an ionic compound with water molecules trapped within the crystal structure in a definite mole ratio of compound to water.

An example is ordinary plaster, the material often used to cover the interior walls of buildings. Plaster consists of the ionic compound calcium sulfate $CaSO_4$. When water is not present, it is termed ANHYDROUS (without water) calcium sulfate and will absorb water from liquids and gases by forming HYDRATED calcium sulfate. One hydrated form, plaster of Paris, contains one half mole of water for each mole of calcium sulfate and is used to make plaster. Addition of water to plaster of Paris produces another form, calcium sulfate dihydrate $CaSO_4 \cdot 2H_2O$ (gypsum, the hardened ingredient in plaster). Hydrate formulas are written as above, rather than as CaH_4SO_6, to clearly show that the substance actually consists of two different compounds (an ionic salt and molecular water) in a definite mole ratio.

Water in a hydrate can often be easily removed by heating the hydrate a little above the boiling temperature of water. This results in the formation of a different hydrate or production of the anhydrous form of the ionic salt. For instance, heating the hydrate cobalt(II)chloride hexahydrate (red) produces cobalt(II)chloride dihydrate (violet). Continued heating produces anhydrous cobalt (II)chloride (blue):

$$CoCl_2 \cdot 6H_2O \quad \Rightarrow \quad CoCl_2 \cdot 2H_2O \quad \Rightarrow \quad CoCl_2$$

$$(RED) \qquad\qquad (VIOLET) \qquad\qquad (BLUE)$$

Since the water is part of the crystal structure of a hydrate, its removal results in changes in color and consistency of the solid. Generally compounds of small, highly charged ions such as Cu^{+2} or Ca^{+2} form hydrates while compounds of larger, singly charged ions such as Na^{+1} or K^{+1} do not. Hydrates are often highly colored if the positive ion is a transition metal ion.

Some hydrates spontaneously lose water without heating: a process called **EFFLORESCENCE**. The amount of water lost depends on the amount of moisture in the atmosphere (relative humidity). As shown in the example above, hydrated cobalt(II) chloride is red in moist air, becomes blue in dry air, and is violet at intermediate humidities.

By the same token, some anhydrous (dry) ionic compounds can spontaneously absorb water from the air to form hydrates. These are called **DESSICANTS** and are said to be **HYGROSCOPIC** (water absorbing). A few absorb so much water that they actually form a solution rather than a hydrate. This process is termed **DELIQUESCENCE**.

True hydrates generally undergo reversible dehydration. Adding moisture to the anhydrous cobalt(II)chloride, produced by heating the di (violet) or hexa (red) hydrates, restores the original hydrates. All ionic hydrate compounds dissolve in water and are usually prepared by crystallization from aqueous solution. The amount of water bound in the hydrate often depends on the way it was prepared. However, the number of moles of water for each one mole of anhydrous salt MUST be a whole number multiple of one-half. Formulas are written to specify the number of moles of water for each ONE mole of anhydrous salt, as in:

Copper(II)sulfate heptahydrate $CuSO_4 \cdot 7H_2O$

and

Barium chloride dihydrate $BaCl_2 \cdot 2H_2O$

SPECIAL TERMS — HEATING PROCESS

GENTLE HEATING — Heat the bottom of the crucible in the outer Bunsen flame for a one or two "count," pull the flame away for a five or six "count" and repeat.

STRONG HEATING — Heat the bottom of the crucible in the outer Bunsen flame for a five to seven "count," pull the flame away for a one or two "count" and repeat.

CRUCIBLE SLIGHTLY OPEN — The edge of the crucible cover is resting on the edge of the crucible. There is *NO VISIBLE OPENING* between the cover and crucible.

WEAR YOUR SAFETY GOGGLES/LAB COAT!

WASH YOUR HANDS WHEN FINISHED!

Experimental Procedure

For the General Reaction:

$MX \cdot YH_2O$	→	MX	+	$Y\,H_2O$
(Hydrate)	(heat)	(Anhydrous Residue)		(Water)

Thoroughly clean a porcelain crucible and cover with tap water. Check to be certain there are no hairline cracks in the crucible and that the cover loosely fits the crucible. Use an iron ring and ring stand to suspend a clay triangle approximately four inches above the top of a Bunsen burner. Adjust the clay triangle opening so that about two thirds of the crucible rests inside the triangle, and adjust the cover on the crucible to leave a small opening between the edge of the cover and the top of the crucible.

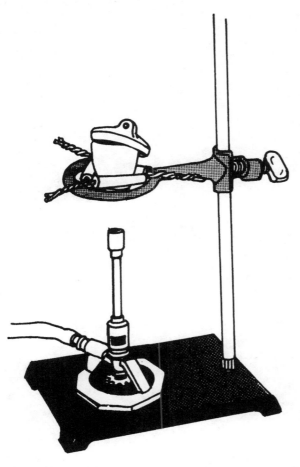

Adjust the Bunsen burner so the flame consists of a large outer cone and a small inner cone. Gently heat the crucible/cover/triangle in the outer cone of the flame for about two minutes to dry the crucible and cover. Your instructor will demonstrate the correct technique for handling hot objects with crucible tongs.

Wait for the crucible and cover to cool and then weigh to the nearest 0.001 g. Record this mass as the empty crucible/cover weight. Obtain a sample of an unknown hydrate and record its identification number. Ask your instructor for the sample size range appropriate for your unknown. Transfer the recommended sample into the crucible. (Ask your instructor how to visually estimate this quantity or refer to the APPENDIX: *Preparation of Weighed Samples*.) Weigh the crucible, cover, and contents to the nearest 0.001 g, and record this mass as the weight of the crucible/cover and hydrate.

Put the crucible back in the triangle, and adjust the cover to slightly open. GENTLY Heat the crucible/cover/triangle in the outer cone of the flame for about five minutes. GRADUALLY increase the intensity of heating over the next five or six minutes. Ideally, you want to achieve STRONG heating of the crucible by the end of this time period and not before.

Then, continue to heat the crucible at STRONG heat (not constant heat) for another ten minutes. Wait for the crucible to cool (a MINIMUM of FIVE MINUTES), and weigh to the nearest 0.001 g. Record this as the weight of the crucible/cover/anhydrous residue.

HEATING TO CONSTANT WEIGHT: Return the crucible to the triangle as before, and heat at strong heat for four to five minutes. Allow the crucible to cool and weigh again. If this mass is within 0.005g of the last weighing then you have proved that the hydrate was indeed dry. If not, you must continue to heat at STRONG heat for successive five-minute intervals until two successive weights do agree. The final weighing is the mass of the crucible/cover/residue used in your lab report calculations.

DISPOSAL of product: Rinse the anhydrous residue into the sink with flowing tap water. Clean the crucible and cover in preparation for the next experiment.

Obtain the formula and formula mass of the anhydrous residue in your unknown. Then calculate the percent of water in your sample and the formula (moles of water per ONE mole of anhydrous residue) of the unknown. What is the IUPAC name of this compound?

Water of Hydration
Advanced Study Assignment

Name_____ Date_____

Examine this data and complete the CALCUALTIONS section below.	
Mass of crucible + cover	21.244 g
Mass of crucible + cover + hydrate	22.326g
Mass of crucible, cover, + anhydrous residue, final heating	21.840 g

Calculations

Mass of Hydrate _____ g

Mass of Anhydrous Residue _____ g

Mass of Water Lost _____ g

Percent Water in the Hydrate _____ %

Percent Residue in the Hydrate _____ %

Formula and Formula Mass of Anhydrous Residue $NiSO_4$ _____ **g/mol**

Grams of Water per 100 g of Hydrate _____ g

Moles of Water per 100 g of Hydrate _____ mole

Grams of Residue per 100 g of Hydrate _____ g

Moles of Residue per 100 g of Hydrate _____ mole

Formula of Hydrate
(Moles of water per one mole of residue)   _____

IUPAC name for this hydrate   _____

NOTE: A Table of Gram Atomic Weights is available in the Appendix.

Water of Hydration
Experimental Data & Calculations

Name_____ Date_____

Show the calculations on the next page.

UNKNOWN #_____

Experimental Measurements

Mass of crucible + cover _____ g

Mass of crucible + cover + hydrate _____ g

Mass of crucible, cover, + anhydrous residue, final heating _____ g

Calculations

Mass of Hydrate _____ g

Mass of Anhydrous Residue _____ g

Mass of Water Lost _____ g

Percent Water in the Hydrate _____ %

Percent Residue in the Hydrate _____ %

Formula and Formula Mass of Anhydrous Residue _____ _____ **g/mol**

Grams of Water per 100 g of Hydrate _____ g

Moles of Water per 100 g of Hydrate _____ mole

Grams of Residue per 100 g of Hydrate _____ g

Moles of Residue per 100 g of Hydrate _____ mole

Formula of Hydrate
(Moles of water per one mole of residue) _____

IUPAC name for this hydrate _____

NOTE: A Table of Gram Atomic Weights is available in the Appendix.

PERCENT COMPOSITION OF A COMPOUND: The Empirical Formula of Magnesium Oxide

In this experiment an accurately known mass of magnesium will be converted to magnesium oxide by heating in air. The mass of oxygen that reacts with the magnesium sample will be used to compute the empirical formula and the percent of magnesium for the magnesium oxide formed in the reaction.

Heating the metal in air, however, forms magnesium nitride as well as magnesium oxide. The nitride must be converted to magnesium hydroxide by reaction with water and then heated to form the oxide. The reactions are as follows:

$$2\,Mg \;+\; O_2 \;\rightarrow\; 2\,MgO \tag{1}$$

$$3\,Mg \;+\; N_2 \;\rightarrow\; Mg_3N_2 \tag{2}$$

$$Mg_3N_2 \;+\; 6\,H_2O \;\rightarrow\; 3\,Mg(OH)_2 \;+\; 2\,NH_3 \tag{3}$$

$$Mg(OH)_2 \;+\; heat \;\rightarrow\; MgO \;+\; H_2O \tag{4}$$

SPECIAL TERMS

<u>CRUCIBLE CLOSED</u> — The interior surface of the crucible cover is in full contact with the top edge of the crucible. The cover should move freely on the crucible.

<u>CRUCIBLE SLIGHTLY OPEN</u> — The edge of the crucible cover is resting on the edge of the crucible. There is *NO VISIBLE OPENING* between the cover and the crucible.

<u>CRUCIBLE OPEN</u> — The crucible cover is resting on top of the crucible with an opening between the cover and the crucible that exposes the interior contents. (Approximately one quarter to one half open.)

<u>GENTLE HEATING</u> — Heat the bottom of the crucible in the outer Bunsen flame for a one or two "count". Pull the flame away for a five or six "count" and repeat.

<u>STRONG HEATING</u> — Heat the bottom of the crucible in the outer Bunsen flame for a five to seven "count". Pull the flame away for a one or two "count" and repeat.

<u>CONTINUOUS HEATING</u> — Heat the bottom of the crucible in the outer Bunsen flame continuously. The bottom of the crucible will develop a red "glow". (Continuous heating is sometimes termed "red heat" for this reason.)

WEAR YOUR SAFETY GOGGLES/LAB COAT!

WASH YOUR HANDS WHEN FINISHED!

Experimental Procedure

1. Clean a crucible and cover with tap water. Carefully examine the crucible to ensure there are no hairline cracks and that the cover fits without binding.

2. Support the crucible and cover SLIGHTLY OPEN in a clay triangle on a ring/ring stand assembly. Apply STRONG HEAT for about two minutes to dry the container. COOL, weigh and record the mass of the crucible and cover to 0.001 g precision.

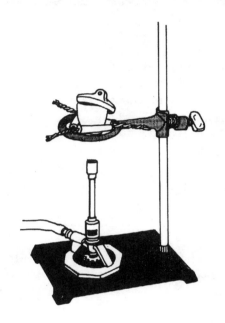

3. From the laboratory cart, obtain a loosely wrapped magnesium ribbon ball small enough to fit into the crucible. The sample should be 0.17 to 0.27 grams. Weigh and record the mass of the crucible, cover, and magnesium to 0.001 g precision. Return the crucible, cover and contents to the clay triangle on the ring/ring stand assembly.

4. With the crucible cover SLIGHTLY OPEN, heat the crucible/magnesium metal CONTINUOUSLY (Red Heat). If "smoke" escapes, close the cover and continue for three or four minutes. Then adjust the cover to SLIGHTLY OPEN again and continue at Red Heat. If smoke again escapes, close the cover. Repeat this process until you can heat SLIGHTLY OPEN at Red Heat with no escaping smoke. Then increase the cover opening to allow more air into the crucible. If smoke escapes, close the cover, heat for a few minutes, and try again to open the cover. The goal is to heat the crucible at Red Heat with the cover OPEN for about two minutes without seeing any sign of reaction (smoke/sparks) inside the crucible.

5. COOL the crucible and contents to room temperature (a MINIMUM of five minutes). Use a stirring rod to crush the contents exposing any unreacted metal. The rod should be set aside in a manner that will prevent loss of any solids clinging to the rod. Adjust the cover to OPEN and heat at Red Heat until there is no sign of reaction within the crucible. Then cool to room temperature.

6. Use a medicine dropper to add water until the solid has been moistened. Use a few drops to rinse the solids on the stirring rod into the crucible, and rinse the inside of the cover as well. USE AS LITTLE WATER AS POSSIBLE. DO NOT ALLOW THE STIRRING ROD TO CONTACT THE MOISTENED SOLIDS.

7. Adjust the cover to SLIGHTLY OPEN, and heat GENTLY for about five minutes. Gradually increase to STRONG HEAT, and then heat CONTINUOUSLY for about five minutes. COOL to room temperature.

8. Weigh the crucible, cover, and contents. Heat the crucible CONTINUOUSLY for another three to five minutes, COOL, and weigh again to verify constant weight. (Two successive weighings must agree within 0.005 grams.) Record this mass as the final weighing, and use it in your lab report calculations.

 DISPOSAL of product: Wash the Magnesium oxide residue into the sink drain with flowing tap water. Clean both the crucible and the cover with tap water in preparation for a later experiment.

9. Determine the mass of magnesium, mass of oxygen, and the mass of magnesium oxide compound in your sample. Calculate the EMPIRICAL FORMULA and, based on this formula, the theoretical percent magnesium in the compound. Then calculate the experimental percent magnesium in your sample, and the relative error in the experiment.

If your relative error is significantly larger than two percent, check for calculation errors. For a discussion of RELATIVE ERROR, please refer to the SIGNIFICANT FIGURES – MASS VOLUME experiment.

The Empirical Formula of Magnesium Oxide
Advanced Study Assignment

Name_____ Date_____

Show the calculations in the spaces provided.

Mass of crucible + cover + metal	20.714 g
Mass of crucible + cover	20.213 g
Mass of crucible + cover + metal oxide	
Final heating	20.917 g
Mass of metal	_____ g
Mass of oxygen	_____ g
Mass of metal oxide	_____ g
Number of moles of metal	_____ moles E
Number of moles of oxygen	_____ moles O
Empirical Formula of metal oxide	_____
Experimental % metal in the oxide	_____ %
Theoretical % metal in the oxide	_____ %
Relative Error	_____ %

Calculations

Gram Atomic Mass: Metal E = 39.785, O = 15.999

The Empirical Formula of Magnesium Oxide
Experimental Data & Calculations

Name_____ Date_____

Show the calculations in the spaces provided.

Mass of crucible + cover + magnesium	_____	g
Mass of crucible + cover	_____	g
Mass of crucible + cover + magnesium oxide		
Final heating	_____	g
Mass of magnesium	_____	g
Mass of oxygen	_____	g
Mass of magnesium oxide	_____	g
Number of moles of magnesium	_____ moles Mg	
Number of moles of oxygen	_____ moles O	
Empirical Formula of magnesium oxide	_____	
Experimental % magnesium in the oxide	_____ %	
Theoretical % magnesium in the oxide	_____ %	
Relative Error	_____ %	

Calculations
Gram Atomic Mass: Metal Mg = 24.305, O = 15.999

REACTION STOICHIOMETRY
Mass Relationships in Balanced Chemical Equations

According to the principle of conservation of mass, the total mass of each element in the product of a chemical reaction must be identical to the total mass of each element in the reactant. For this reason chemical equations, our descriptions of chemical change, must be balanced utilizing appropriate numerical coefficients. The balanced equation specifies the relationships between moles/mass of reactants consumed and moles/mass of products formed. These relationships are referred to as "reaction stoichiometry" and are used to predict amounts of reactant consumed and/or product formed. In some situations the stoichiometry can also help identify a particular reactant or product.

For instance, iron forms two different chloride compounds, $FeCl_2$ and $FeCl_3$. Both of these react in aqueous solution with magnesium metal, forming elemental iron and magnesium chloride:

$$1. \quad FeCl_{2(aq)} \quad + \quad Mg_{(s)} \quad \rightarrow \quad MgCl_{2(aq)} \quad + \quad Fe_{(s)}$$

$$2. \quad 2\,FeCl_{3(aq)} \quad + \quad 3\,Mg_{(s)} \quad \rightarrow \quad 3\,MgCl_{2(aq)} \quad + \quad 2\,Fe_{(s)}$$

Note that one mole of iron(III)chloride produces one and a half times the amount of magnesium chloride that would be produced by one mole of iron(II)chloride. If one experimentally measures the amount of magnesium chloride produced by a specific mass of iron chloride, the identity of the iron compound can be determined by comparison with the stoichiometric mass of magnesium chloride that is predicted by each reaction. A 1.00 gram sample of iron(II)chloride ($FeCl_2$) will theoretically produce 0.751 grams of $MgCl_2$:

$$(1.00\ g\ FeCl_2)[1\ mol\ /126.75\ g]\,[1\ mol\ MgCl_2\ /1\ mol\ FeCl_2]\,[95.218\ g\ /1\ mol\ MgCl_2] = \mathbf{0.751_2\ g}$$

However, 1.00 gram of iron(III)chloride ($FeCl_3$) will produce 0.881 grams of $MgCl_2$:

$$(1.00\ g\ FeCl_3)[1\ mol/162.206g]\,[3\ mole\ MgCl_2/\,2\ mol\ FeCl_3]\,[\,95.218\ g\,/\,1\ mol\ MgCl_2] = \mathbf{0.880_5\ g}$$

If the experimentally measured mass of magnesium chloride actually produced was 0.868 grams, we can conclude that the reacting compound was iron(III)chloride. On the other hand, if the actual mass of $MgCl_2$ were close to 0.751 grams, iron(II)chloride would be identified as the reacting compound.

Many reactions occur between solutes in solution phase. One often knows what the solute is, but not its concentration (molarity). The stoichiometry of the reaction can be utilized to determine concentration if the formula, and thus the equation is known. For example, experimental measurement of the mass of magnesium chloride produced by an aqueous solution sample of $FeCl_3$ according to reaction 2 allows one to calculate the moles of $FeCl_3$ solute present in the sample (2 mol $FeCl_3$ for every 3 mole of $MgCl_2$ produced). Concentration of the reactant in moles per liter can then be determined from the calculated moles of $FeCl_3$ solute and the volume of the $FeCl_3$ solution sample used in the reaction:

If, for example, a 10.00 mL sample of a $FeCl_3$ solution produced 0.440 g of $MgCl_2$ upon reaction with magnesium, the molarity of that solution is determined to be 0.344 M via equation **2**:

$$\textbf{(0.440 g)}[\text{ 1 mol MgCl}_2 \text{ / 95.218 g}][\text{2 mol FeCl}_3 \text{ / 3 mol MgCl}_2] = \textbf{3.44}_4 \textbf{ x 10}^{-3} \textbf{ mol FeCl}_3$$

$$\text{Molarity} = 3.44_4 \text{ x } 10^{-3} \text{ moles FeCl}_3 \text{ / 0.01000 liters of solution } = \textbf{0.344}_4 \textbf{ M}$$

The reactions of **sodium carbonate** and **sodium hydrogen carbonate** with hydrochloric acid both produce carbon dioxide gas, sodium chloride, and water. Water vapor and the gas are easily removed by heating, allowing the yield of sodium chloride to be readily determined by mass measurement. The balanced equations are:

$$\textbf{3.} \quad NaHCO_{3(s)} \quad + \quad HCl_{(aq)} \quad \rightarrow \quad CO_{2(g)} \quad + \quad H_2O_{(l)} \quad + \quad NaCl_{(s)}$$

$$\textbf{4.} \quad Na_2CO_{3(s)} \quad + \quad 2\,HCl_{(aq)} \quad \rightarrow \quad CO_{2(g)} \quad + \quad H_2O_{(l)} \quad + \quad 2\,NaCl_{(s)}$$

Note that only one mole of NaCl is produced per mole of $NaHCO_3$, but two moles of NaCl are produced per mole of Na_2CO_3. Therefore, if one knows the mass but not the formula of the compound reacting with HCl, and one can determine the mass of NaCl produced as a result (the *Experimental Yield* of NaCl), the reactant can be identified based on the equation stoichiometry in a manner similar to the iron chloride examples (reactions **1** and **2**) discussed above.

This experiment will employ reactions **3** and **4** above to demonstrate the concepts described for the iron chloride reactions because the product is easily purified by evaporation. The mass of sodium chloride produced is related to the nature of the reacting compound by the stoichiometry of reactions **3** and **4** in the same manner as the mass of magnesium chloride produced in reactions **1** and **2** was related to the nature of the iron chloride compounds.

TERMS & PROCEDURES RELATED TO THIS EXPERIMENT

The unknown solution container is fitted with a penny head stopper. Grip the stopper between the first and second fingers of your hand with your palm facing up. Withdraw the stopper, turn your hand so the stopper is pointing away from you, and grasp the bottle with the *SAME* hand using the little finger to support the bottom of the bottle.

Hold the *receiving container* in your other hand and pour the required volume of solution into the receiving container. The desired volume is APPROXIMATE. Do not be concerned if your actual volume is a little more or less than the amount specified in the laboratory procedure.

Catch the drip from the bottle with the edge of the receiving container, put the bottle down on the bench, and insert the stopper.

Put the container down and RINSE THE CLOSED BOTTLE under the tap water in preparation for the next student. **NOTE** that the stopper is *NEVER* allowed to contact the laboratory bench.

Ask your instructor to demonstrate this technique for you if you are uncertain about these instructions.

WEAR YOUR SAFETY GOGGLES/LAB COAT!
WASH YOUR HANDS WHEN FINISHED!

Experimental Procedure

PART A: Preparation

In this experiment, two clean and dry 50 mL beakers will be used as reaction vessels. The white "marking area" should be clean to permit identification of each reaction. Set up two small test tubes with Pasteur pipet droppers in a test tube rack. Put about 50 drops (2.5 mL – about 2 cm or ¾ inch depth in a small test tube) of distilled water in one and 50 drops of 6 M hydrochloric acid HCl in the other. LABEL both test tubes. Electric hot plates (heat setting #2.5), for use in the evaporation step, are set up for you in the laboratory hood area.

PART B: Molarity Determination via Solution Stoichiometry

Please review *"Appendix: Use of a Volumetric Pipet"* before you begin the experiment.
Do NOT pipet by mouth suction.
Wear safety goggles and lab coat and/or apron.

Use a pencil to mark one 50 mL beaker with your initials and the letter "M" (for MOLARITY determination); weigh and record the mass to the nearest milligram.

Obtain a pipet pump and a 5.00 mL volumetric pipet from the laboratory cart.

Use your 10 mL graduated cylinder to measure about 7 to 9 mL of the unknown sodium carbonate solution assigned by your instructor. Then use the volumetric pipet to extract 5.00 mL of this solution from the cylinder and deliver it into the weighed beaker. Record the unknown solution number. **Set the excess unknown solution aside for later use in PART D.**

Add 6 M HCl drop wise (**Eye Protection!**) until effervescence (bubbles) ceases. Add five drops at a time and then GENTLY swirl the container. As the gaseous product, carbon dioxide, escapes, effervescence is observed. Continue adding HCl in five-drop increments, mixing in between, until there is no sign of reaction (this usually requires 20 to 30 drops of acid). Then put the beaker on a hot plate in the hood and allow the liquid to evaporate.

Go on to PART C while the evaporation takes place.

Occasionally check the evaporation process while working on PART C.

When the beaker has been heated 4 to 5 minutes after the contents appear dry, place the beaker on the bench top next to the hot plate and allow it to cool. Weigh the beaker/contents and record the mass to the nearest milligram. Heat the container again for 4 to 5 minutes, cool, and weigh again. Continue until two successive weights agree within 0.005 grams (constant weight has been achieved.) The last weighing will be used in the calculation.

Determine the mass of the sodium chloride produced in this reaction. Use this mass and balanced equation **4** to calculate the <u>moles</u> of sodium carbonate originally present in the 5.00 mL sample.

Calculate the molarity of your unknown sodium carbonate solution.

PART C: Reaction Stoichiometry

Review Appendix: "Preparation of Weighed Samples" before you begin the experiment.
Wear safety goggles and lab coat/apron.

Use a pencil to mark the second beaker with <u>your</u> <u>initials</u> and the letter "S" (for reacting SOLID). Weigh the beaker and record its mass to the nearest milligram. Your instructor will assign an unknown solid (some are sodium carbonate and others are sodium hydrogen carbonate.) Put 0.25 to 0.35 grams (a sample equal in volume to a pencil eraser) of this solid in your beaker, and weigh/record the mass of the beaker and contents. Record the unknown solid number.

Remember to occasionally check/return to PART B when necessary.

Add about 20 drops of distilled water to the beaker, rinsing the solid that clings to the sides into the bottom of the container. Then add 6 M HCl (**Eye Protection!**) drop wise until effervescence (bubbles) ceases. Add five drops at a time and then GENTLY swirl the container. Effervescence is observed as the gaseous product, carbon dioxide, escapes. Continue adding HCl in five-drop increments, mixing in between, until there is no sign of reaction (this usually requires 20 to 40 drops of acid.) Then put the beaker on the hot plate and allow the liquid to evaporate. **The excess HCl solution is set aside for later use in PART D.**

<u>After</u> the contents <u>appears</u> dry, heat the beaker for 4 to 5 minutes. Place the beaker on the bench top next to the hot plate and allow it to cool. Weigh the beaker/contents and record the mass to the nearest milligram. Heat the beaker again for 4 to 5 minutes, cool, and weigh again. Continue until two successive weights agree within 0.005 grams precision (constant weight has been achieved). The last weighing is used in the calculation.

Determine the mass of your <u>unknown</u> <u>solid</u> sample before its reaction with HCl. Determine the mass of the <u>sodium</u> <u>chloride</u> <u>produced</u> in this reaction (the experimental yield of sodium chloride).

<u>Assuming</u> the unknown solid was **sodium carbonate**, calculate the theoretical yield of sodium chloride that should have been produced by your sample.

<u>Assuming</u> the unknown solid was **sodium hydrogen carbonate**, calculate the theoretical yield of sodium chloride that should have been produced by your sample.

Compare these theoretical values with your experimental yield of NaCl. Which solid was your unknown, $NaHCO_3$ or Na_2CO_3?

Once you have identified the solid, calculate PERCENT YIELD for your reaction.

PART D: Clean Up

Eye Protection!

The solid in the beakers is sodium chloride (table salt.) Add approximately 20 mL of tap water to each beaker, stir, **combine the solutions** and place the beaker in a sink. You also have 10 or 20 drops of hydrochloric acid and $2 - 3$ mL of Na_2CO_3 solution left over. Pour both of these into the beaker, rinse their containers, and add the rinse to the same beaker. (You should observe some effervescence as the sodium carbonate neutralizes the excess hydrochloric acid.)

- Add 4–6 drops of **phenolphthalein indicator** to the mixture in the beaker.

- **If** the **mixture remains clear** (water white) in color when phenolphthalein is introduced, add **6.0 M NaOH** <u>one drop at a time</u>, with stirring, until **one drop** causes the solution to turn pink.
  - o Then add **1.0 M HCl** <u>one drop at a time</u>, with **stirring**, until **one drop** causes the pink color to fade clear (water white). **CAUTION:** Do not add excess HCl.

- **If** the **mixture turns pink** in color, add **6.0 M HCl** <u>one drop at a time</u>, with stirring, until **one drop** causes the pink color to fade clear (water white).
  - o Then add <u>one drop</u> of **6.0 M NaOH** — the solution should again turn pink indicating the solution is now one drop basic.
  - o Then add **1.0 M HCl** <u>one drop at a time</u>, with stirring, until **one drop** causes the pink color to fade clear (water white). **CAUTION:** Do not add excess HCl.

- **Rinse** the neutralized solution into the sink drain with flowing tap water.

Rinse the pipet with tap water and return the pipet and pipet pump to the laboratory cart.

Rinse the HCl from the Pasteur pipet dropper with tap water and discard the pipet into the GLASS WASTE container provided in the laboratory.

Reaction Stoichiometry
Advanced Problem Assignment

Name_____ Section_____ Date_____

Complete the calculation summary below.
READ THE EXPERIMENTAL DISCUSSION FIRST!
REPORT ALL ANSWERS TO THE CORRECT SIGNIFICANT FIGUES.
SHOW CALCULATION SET-UP on the next page.

PART B: Molarity Determination via Solution Stoichiometry

Mass of Empty 50 mL Beaker	7.625	g
Mass of Beaker and NaCl (final heating)	7.976	g
Mass of NaCl Produced (*Experimental Yield* of NaCl)	_____	g
Moles of Na_2CO_3 Consumed	_____	moles
Volume of Na_2CO_3 Solution	0.00500	Liter
Molarity of Na_2CO_3 Solution	_____	mole/Liter

PART C: Reaction Stoichiometry

Mass of Empty 50 mL Beaker	8.125	g
Mass of Beaker and Unknown Solid	8.387	g
Mass of Unknown Solid	_____	g
Mass of Beaker and NaCl (final heating)	8.405	g
Mass of NaCl Produced (*Experimental Yield* of NaCl)	_____	g
Theoretical Yield of NaCl if Unknown Solid is Na_2CO_3	_____	grams NaCl
Theoretical Yield of NaCl if Unknown Solid is $NaHCO_3$	_____	grams NaCl
Formula of the Unknown Solid	_____	
Percent Yield	_____	%

43

Calculation Set-Ups: Advance Problem Assignment

FORMULA MASS: $NaCl = 58.441$ $NaHCO_3 = 84.005$ $Na_2CO_3 = 105.986$

Reaction Stoichiometry
Experimental Data & Calculations

Name_____ Section_____ Date_____

REPORT ALL ANSWERS TO THE CORRECT SIGNIFICANT FIGUES.
SHOW CALCULATION SET-UP on the next page.

PART B: Molarity Determination via Solution Stoichiometry   Unknown Solution # _____

Mass of Empty 50 mL Beaker	_____ g
Mass of Beaker and NaCl (final heating)	_____ g
Mass of NaCl Produced (*Experimental Yield* of NaCl)	_____ g
Moles of Na_2CO_3 Consumed	_____ moles
Volume of Na_2CO_3 Solution	_____ Liter
Molarity of Na_2CO_3 Solution	_____ mole/Liter

PART C: Reaction Stoichiometry   Unknown Solid # _____

Mass of Empty 50 mL Beaker	_____ g
Mass of Beaker and Unknown Solid	_____ g
Mass of Unknown Solid	_____ g
Mass of Beaker and NaCl (final heating)	_____ g
Mass of NaCl Produced (*Experimental Yield* of NaCl)	_____ g
Theoretical Yield of NaCl if Unknown Solid is Na_2CO_3	_____ grams NaCl
Theoretical Yield of NaCl if Unknown Solid is $NaHCO_3$	_____ grams NaCl
Formula of the Unknown Solid	_____
Percent Yield	_____ %

Calculation Set-Ups: Data Summary Calculation Report

GRAVIMETRIC ANALYSIS:
Determination of the Empirical Formula of Magnesium Chloride

Prerequisite: Percent Composition
Background: Empirical and Molecular Formula

A pure chemical <u>COMPOUND</u> is defined as a substance composed of two or more <u>ELEMENTS</u> combined in a fixed mass ratio. According to the atomic theory of matter, individual atoms of each element must be combined through some chemical bonding force in order to establish this fixed mass ratio. This also means, of course, that the compound must contain a fixed <u>mole</u> ratio of elements as well. The mole ratio is expressed as the chemical <u>formula</u> of the substance.

The identification and characterization of a chemical compound therefore requires one to experimentally identify what elements combined to form it and then to determine the mass of each element present in a known mass of compound. The mass ratio and the mole ratio (formula) can then be established. Whenever a chemical analysis utilizes mass measurement to identify composition, the process is termed GRAVIMETRIC ANALYSIS.

In this experiment a magnesium-chlorine compound of unknown formula (Mg_xCl_y) will be formed from a sample of pure metal. We will measure the mass of the compound and the mass of each element within the compound. These measured mass relationships will allow the calculation of the smallest <u>whole number mole ratio</u> of elements (EMPIRICAL formula) in the compound.

Chemically, a known mass of magnesium metal (**Mg**) will be converted into soluble magnesium chloride by reaction with hydrochloric acid (**HCl**). The other product, hydrogen (**H₂**), escapes the solution as a gas. Excess hydrochloric acid and water are removed by evaporation, leaving pure magnesium chloride.

$$Mg_{(s)} \; + \; HCl_{(aq)} \; \rightarrow \; Mg_xCl_{y(aq)}$$

$$Mg_xCl_{y(aq)} \; + \; heat \; \rightarrow \; Mg_xCl_{y(s)}$$

The increase in mass of the sample represents the mass of chlorine that combined with the magnesium. The magnesium-chlorine mass ratio thus identified allows us to calculate the empirical formula of the compound.

WEAR YOUR SAFETY GOGGLES/LAB COAT!

WASH YOUR HANDS WHEN FINISHED!

Experimental Procedure

READ the entire procedure BEFORE you begin the experiment.

1. A clean and dry 150 mL beaker will be used as a reaction vessel. The white "marking area" should be clean to permit identification of your experiment. Paper labels MUST BE REMOVED. Electric hot plates (heat setting #2.5) are set up for your use in the laboratory hood area.

   Clean the beaker and dry it with a paper towel. Use a pencil to mark it with your initials. Warm the beaker on a hot plate for two or three minutes. Then, place the beaker on the bench top next to the hotplate and allow it to cool. Weigh the beaker, recording its mass to 0.001 gram.

2. Obtain a sample of magnesium metal (as a 10 cm piece of ribbon or as small metal turnings) from the laboratory cart. Break the ribbon into four or five pieces, and transfer it into the dry, weighed beaker. Weigh the beaker/contents, and record the mass to 0.001 g. <u>Verify</u> that the magnesium sample is approximately **0.10** to **0.15** grams. Consult your instructor if it is not.

3. Add approximately 10 mL of distilled water (use your 10 mL graduated cylinder), and then add approximately 30 drops of 6.0 M hydrochloric acid (HCl). Effervescence (bubbles) will be observed as the gaseous hydrogen escapes the solution. GENTLY swirl the container to mix the contents.

   IF effervescence (bubbling) stops and magnesium metal is still present, add another 10 or 12 drops of 6.0 M HCl.

   IF a WHITE CRYSTALLINE SOLID is observed in the beaker, the magnesium chloride solution is saturated, and excess solid has come out of solution. Add an additional four or five mL of distilled water to dissolve the solid.

   Continue to gently mix the contents until effervescence (bubbles) ceases.

   The dissolving process is complete when the solution is clear and no solids are observed in the bottom of the beaker.

4. Put the beaker on a hot plate (heat setting 2.5) in the hood (escaping HCl gas is irritating) and allow the liquid to evaporate. DO NOT permit the solution to boil vigorously; solids will be lost.

5. When the beaker has been heated for 4 to 5 minutes <u>after</u> the contents <u>appear</u> dry, move the beaker (caution, HOT!) to the bench top next to the hot plate and allow it to cool. Weigh the beaker and its' contents, and record the mass to the nearest milligram.

6. Heat the container/contents again for three or four minutes, allow to cool, and weigh again. Continue this heating-cooling-weighing process until two successive weights agree within 0.005 grams (constant weight has been achieved.) The last weight is the value used in calculation.

DISPOSAL of product: Wash the Magnesium chloride residue into the sink drain with flowing tap water.

7. After you have recorded the final weighing, dissolve the magnesium chloride in tap water. The resulting solution is then rinsed down the laboratory sink with flowing tap water.

8. **Calculation:** Determine the mass of magnesium, mass of chlorine, and mass of magnesium chloride compound in your sample. Calculate the empirical formula and, based on this formula, the theoretical percent magnesium in your compound. Then use your experimental mass of magnesium and experimental mass of magnesium chloride to calculate the experimental percent magnesium in your sample. Calculate the relative error in your experiment.

If your relative error is significantly larger than two percent check for calculation errors. For a discussion of RELATIVE ERROR please refer to the experiment *SIGNIFICANT FIGURES – MASS VOLUME EXERCISE.*

Empirical Formula of Bismuth Sulfide
Advanced Study Assignment

Name_____   Date_____

Produced by the reaction of bismuth metal with $H_2S_{(aq)}$

Experimental Measurements		
Mass of 150 mL Beaker	56.900	g
Mass of Beaker and bismuth metal	57.735	g
Mass of Beaker and bismuth sulfide Final Heating	57.931	g

Calculation Summary		
Mass of bismuth sulfide (Final Heating)	_____	g
Mass of bismuth in the compound	_____	g
Mass of sulfur in the compound	_____	g
Number of moles of bismuth in the compound	_____	moles Bi
Number of moles of sulfur in the compound	_____	moles S
Empirical Formula of bismuth sulfide	_____	
Empirical Formula Mass of bismuth sulfide	_____	
Experimental % bismuth in the compound	_____	%
Theoretical % bismuth in the formula	_____	%
Relative Error	_____	%

Continued on the reverse

Calculations

GRAM ATOMIC MASSES
Bismuth (**Bi**) 208.98 g/mol
Sulfur (**S**) 32.066 g/mol

1. Sulfur has a charge of negative two (-2) in bismuth compounds. Write a balanced NET IONIC equation describing the formation of your bismuth sulfide compound from bismuth ions and sulfur ions.

2. Determine the charge on bismuth in your compound. Is this charge possible or reasonable?

Empirical Formula of Magnesium Chloride
Experimental Data & Calculations

Name_____ Date_____

Section _____ Partner _____

Experimental Measurements

Mass of 150 mL Beaker _____ g

Mass of Beaker and magnesium metal _____ g

Mass of Beaker and magnesium chloride
    Final Heating _____ g

Calculation Summary

Mass of magnesium chloride (Final Heating) _____ g

Mass of magnesium in the compound _____ g

Mass of chlorine in the compound _____ g

Number of moles of magnesium in the compound _____ moles Mg

Number of moles of chlorine in the compound _____ moles Cl

Empirical Formula of magnesium chloride _____

Experimental % magnesium in the compound _____ %

Theoretical % magnesium in the formula _____ %

Relative Error _____ %

Continued on the reverse

53

Calculations

GRAM ATOMIC MASSES
Magnesium (**Mg**)   24.305 g/mol
Chlorine (**Cl**)   35.454 g/mol

1. Chlorine has a charge of negative one (-1) in binary compounds. Write a balanced NET IONIC equation describing the formation of YOUR magnesium chloride compound from magnesium ions and chloride ions.

2. Determine the charge on magnesium in your compound. Is this charge possible or reasonable?

ATOMIC EMISSION SPECTROSCOPY
The Line Spectrum of Hydrogen

Matter that has absorbed energy from some external source often returns the energy as electromagnetic radiation as the excited atoms return to lower energy states. White light is produced, for instance, by electrical heating of the tungsten filament in a bulb while electric discharge through neon gas produces the colored light we observe in signs. Atomic Emission Spectroscopy measures the energies and wavelengths of this radiation and attempts to relate them to transitions occurring within the emitting atoms.

The device one uses to identify the emitted wavelengths is a *spectroscope* (thus the term "emission spectroscopy".) A spectroscope uses a thin slit at the light source to produce a narrow beam from the observed light, a diffraction grating to divide this beam into its component wavelengths, and a view port with an optical scale to precisely determine the wavelengths being emitted by an energized sample. The device is limited to identifying wavelengths in only the VISIBLE region of the spectrum, approximately 400 nm (violet) to 700 nm (red), because the eye is the detector. The ultraviolet (shorter than 400 nm) region and the infrared (longer than 750 nm) regions are not observable.

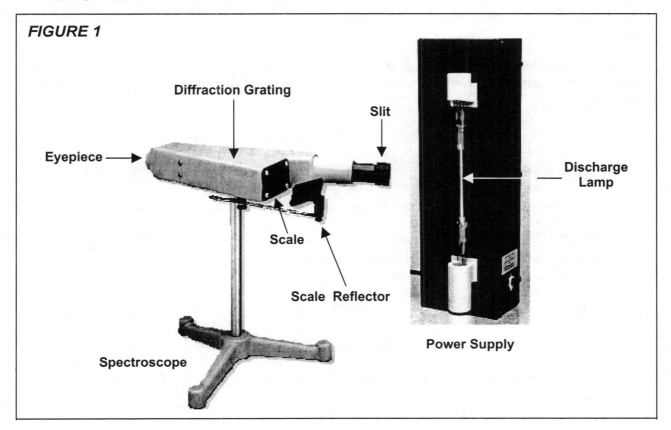

FIGURE 1

Radiation from an excited atom source, such as a tungsten or neon lamp, is formed into a narrow beam of light as it enters the slit. The prism separates the light beam into its component wavelengths, and each is viewed against an illuminated scale.

If a source of white light is viewed through the spectroscope, all the colors of the visible spectrum are observed, the same rainbow one sees as sunlight passes through water vapor. However, when the emissions of a pure element are measured only a few, very specific, wavelengths are seen in the spectroscope. They appear as a thin "line" of color at specific wavelengths. A mercury vapor lamp, for instance, produces only four "lines": violet (405 nm,) blue (436 nm,) green (546 nm,) and yellow (579 nm.) The wavelength patterns observed for elements are termed *line spectra* and are different for each different element. The spectrum of the single electron element hydrogen has only four lines in the visible region, and was important experimental evidence in support of the "orbit theory" of atomic electron structure proposed by Niels Bohr in 1913.

Bohr postulated that an electron could have only <u>specific</u> values of energy in an atom, its **energy levels**. He proposed that each allowed energy would be defined by the relationship **E = –(constant)/n²**, where **n** is an integer number (n = 1,2,3,..∞.) An electron can change energy only by moving from one allowed energy level to another allowed energy level.

The wavelengths observed in the hydrogen emission spectrum would therefore correspond to electrons moving from a higher allowed energy level to a lower allowed level. The constant in Bohr's theory is termed the Rydberg constant, has the value 2.179×10^{-21} kilojoules, and is given the symbol R_H. The energy of each allowed level in the hydrogen atom is therefore:

<u>EQUATION</u> 1 $\quad\quad E_n = -R_H / n^2 = -(2.179 \times 10^{-18} \text{ J}) / n^2 \quad\quad$ **where n = 1,2,3,4...∞**

Energy values are negative, representing a lowering of potential energy relative to a value of zero potential energy assigned to an electron when it is no longer under the influence of the nucleus.

Any energy emitted by hydrogen would correspond to the DIFFERENCE between two of these energy levels (level **n=3** to **n=2**, for instance.) This energy difference can be calculated from the above relationship:

$$\text{For } \mathbf{n = 3}, \quad \mathbf{E_3} = -R_H / 3^2 = -(2.179 \times 10^{-18} \text{ j}) / 9 = -2.421 \times 10^{-19} \text{ joules}$$

$$\text{For } \mathbf{n = 2}, \quad \mathbf{E_2} = -R_H / 2^2 = -(2.179 \times 10^{-18} \text{ j}) / 4 = -5.448 \times 10^{-19} \text{ joules}$$

The energy <u>difference</u> (ΔE) for a level **3** → level **2** transition is 3.027×10^{-19} joules

The WAVELENGTH that corresponds to this transition is found from the energy-frequency relationship $E = h\nu = hc/\lambda$, where Planck's constant $\mathbf{h} = 6.626 \times 10^{-37}$ kJ•s, the speed of light $\mathbf{c} = 3.00 \times 10^{17}$ nm/s, and λ is the wavelength in nanometers.

<u>EQUATION</u> 2 $\quad\quad \lambda = hc / \Delta E = (6.626 \times 10^{-34} \text{ J•s})(2.998 \times 10^{17} \text{ nm•s}^{-1}) / \Delta E$

The wavelength of the level **3** → level **2** example transition above is thus 656.2 nm:

$$\lambda = (6.626 \times 10^{-34} \text{ J•s})(2.998 \times 10^{17} \text{ nm•s}^{-1}) / 3.027 \times 10^{-19} \text{ J} = 656.2 \text{ nm}$$

Bohr's postulates allowed calculation of wavelengths that matched all wavelengths observed in the visible region of the hydrogen line spectrum. (Several other wavelengths were also predicted at ultraviolet or infrared wavelengths. These predictions were later verified after spectroscopes useable in the ultraviolet and infrared regions were developed.) Once the wavelength of a line in the hydrogen spectrum is measured in the spectroscope, comparison with the wavelengths calculated via the above technique allows one to identify what energy levels were involved in the transition that produced that spectral line.

Part of this exercise will calculate energy values for the levels allowed in the hydrogen atom. The possible energy level DIFFERENCES (ΔE's) and their corresponding wavelengths can then be calculated (*Advanced Problem Assignment*). We will also observe the hydrogen line spectrum with a spectroscope and measure each wavelength. We will then attempt to identify the energy level transitions that produced each line in the observed spectrum by comparison of the measured wavelengths with the calculated wavelengths.

The spectroscope has an illuminated scale on which an emission spectrum is superimposed. The divisions on this scale provide only a convenient reference identifying the position of a spectral line, not a direct wavelength measure in nanometers. For this reason, the spectroscope scale must be calibrated against an emission spectrum of accurately known wavelengths before it is used to measure the spectrum of an unknown element. The helium discharge lamp emits several wavelengths in the visible region and thus provides a convenient reference spectrum that one can use to calibrate a spectroscope:

Table I: The Helium Emission Spectrum		
Color	*Wavelength*	*Relative Intensity*
Red	706.5 nm	Moderate
Red	667.8 nm	Moderate
Yellow	587.6 nm	Very Bright
Yellow-green	501.6 nm	Moderate
Green	492.0 nm	Dim
Blue-green	471.3 nm	Dim
Blue	447.1 nm	Moderate
Violet	402.6 nm	Moderate
Violet	389.0 nm	Bright

Our calibrated spectroscope will then be used to determine wavelength values for each line in the hydrogen emission spectrum. The emission spectrum of several other elements may be observed as well.

WEAR YOUR SAFETY GLASSES!

Experimental Procedure

Equipment

1. A laboratory workstation area that is equipped with a spectroscope, and high voltage power packs / lamp holders with Helium and hydrogen discharge lamps.

2. Discharge lamps containing other unknown elements/substances may also be provided.

> **Two students share a spectroscope/discharge lamp set-up, working in pairs. One individual observes the spectrum while the other records scale readings. Then the other individual observes the spectrum while the first observer records scale readings. Each student must observe spectra and then prepare and submit his or her own advance problem and laboratory report.**

3. Small, hand-held spectroscopes are also provided in the laboratory. While you are waiting your turn at the spectroscope/discharge lamp station, use the hand-held spectroscopes to observe the spectra of the different element/substance discharge lamps provided at the workstations. When measuring a spectrum, the spectroscope slit should be aligned with the tube. Record the color and approximate spectroscope scale value of the brightest lines on separate paper. If you also observe the spectrum of a fluorescent lamp, you may be able to identify some of the mercury lines summarized earlier in our discussion.

Safety Precautions

The power supply is very high voltage. **DO NOT TOUCH** the lamp holder, power supply, or electrical leads. **DO NOT attempt to change discharge lamps** or adjust the position of the power supply/lamp holder; ask your instructor.

Discharge lamps emit ultraviolet wavelengths, which are damaging to the eyes, as well as visible wavelengths. However, safety glasses absorb most of the ultraviolet radiation. **WEAR SAFETY GOGGLES at all times**, even when you are not using the spectroscope. Avoid looking at discharge lamps for extended periods of time.

NOTE: The Advanced Problem Assignment MUST be completed before the laboratory begins. The answers are required for PART B of this procedure.

REMEMBER: DO NOT ATTEMPT TO change discharge lamps. Consult your instructor if you suspect a problem with the power supply or discharge lamp.

WEAR SAFETY GOGGLES at all times.

Part A: Calibration of the Spectroscope

Look through the spectroscope eyepiece to make sure the scale is illuminated.

Turn on the power supply to the discharge lamp.

Move the spectroscope so that the slit is directly in front of the Helium discharge tube and look through the eyepiece. Move the spectroscope to obtain the brightest set of lines. If necessary, adjust the scale illumination reflector so that the scale is easily read but is not bright enough to block the spectral lines.

Record the *color* and *scale reading* for each observed spectral line. Also record the *relative intensity* (very bright, moderate, or dim) for each line if possible. You should observe at least four, and possibly more, spectral lines.

Each individual student is to observe and record the Helium spectrum. Therefore, change places at the spectroscope and allow your partner to observe the Helium spectrum while you record his or her observations.

Turn off the discharge lamp power when finished.

Part B: Observation of the Hydrogen Emission Spectrum

Look through the spectroscope eyepiece to make sure the scale is illuminated.

Turn on the power supply to the discharge lamp.

Move the spectroscope so that the slit is directly in front of the Hydrogen discharge tube and look through the eyepiece. Move the spectroscope to obtain the brightest set of lines. If necessary, adjust the scale illumination reflector so that the scale is easily read but is not bright enough to block the spectral lines.

Record the *color* and *scale reading* for each observed spectral line. Also record the *relative intensity* (very bright, moderate, or dim) for each line if possible. You should see at least three lines (red, green and blue/violet) and, hopefully, a fourth (violet).

Each individual student is to observe and record the Hydrogen spectrum. Therefore, change places at the spectroscope and allow your partner to observe the Hydrogen spectrum while you record his or her observations.

Turn off the discharge lamp power when finished.

Part C: Observations of the Emission Spectra of Other Elements

Look through the spectroscope eyepiece to make sure the scale is illuminated as before.

Turn on the power supply to the discharge lamp.

Move the spectroscope so that the slit is directly in front of the Unknown Element/Substance discharge tube. Look through the eyepiece and record the *color* and *spectroscope scale reading* for each observed spectral line. Also record the *unknown identification number*.

Change places at the spectroscope and allow your partner to observe the Unknown Element/Substance spectrum while you record his or her observations.

Turn off the discharge lamp power when finished.

Calculations/Laboratory Report

A. Use the information in **Table I** to assign a wavelength (nanometers) to each line that you observed in the Helium emission spectrum. You may not have observed all the lines listed in **Table I**. The longest wavelength, shortest wavelength, and least intense lines are often difficult to see. You should, however, see four lines at least.

Prepare a graph of the scale reading on the X–axis against wavelength on the Y–axis. The calibration line should be linear, or curve smoothly from upper right to lower left. If your calibration line is not smooth, your wavelength assignment may need to be changed. Remember that the longest and shortest wavelengths and those of "dim" intensity may be missing.

B. Use your calibration graph and the scale readings of the Hydrogen spectrum to assign wavelengths to each line you observed in the Hydrogen spectrum. (If you saw only three lines, you may have missed a fourth line at approximately 410 nm.) Compare these wavelength values with the wavelengths calculated from the Bohr model of the hydrogen atom (*Advanced Problem Assignment*). Identify which of the calculated values match the observed wavelengths. Specify the energy level transition (**n higher → n lower**) that is responsible for each observed wavelength on Part B data page. Also answer the three questions that appear on the same page (See Advance Problem 4.)

Optional

C. You may also be asked to observe emission spectra of one (or more) lamps containing an unknown element/substance. Record the *unknown identification number*, and the *color* and *spectroscope scale reading* of each observed line in the spectrum. Use your spectroscope calibration graph (Part A) to determine a wavelength value (in nanometers) for each observed line and record these next to the scale readings.

The prominent line spectra of several elements are summarized below. Use this information to identify the element in your <u>Unknown</u> discharge tube. List the element name in the Observations Summary next to your emission spectrum diagram.

Several graphical scales of the visible wavelength region (400 nm to 700 nm) are provided in the Observations Summary. Identification of your unknown may be easier if you diagram the emission line spectrum of the unknown discharge lamp on one of these scales. If available, you may use colored pencils to identify each observed line.

NITROGEN: Strong spectrum with many lines violet to red

COLOR	WAVELENGTH
VIOLET	425 nm
VIOLET	445 nm
BLUE	500 nm
BLUE	520 nm
GREEN	550 nm
GREEN	566 nm
YELLOW	580 nm
RED	650 nm
RED	660 nm

NEON: Strong spectrum in green, yellow, orange and red

COLOR	WAVELENGTH
BLUE	490 nm
GREEN	525 nm
GREEN	570 nm
YELLOW	580 nm
ORANGE	605 nm
RED	620 nm
RED	660 nm
RED	670 nm
RED	685 nm

KRYPTON: Strong lines in violet, green, orange and red

COLOR	WAVELENGTH
VIOLET	450 nm
BLUE	490 nm
GREEN	560 nm
GREEN	570 nm
ORANGE	590 nm
RED	630 nm
RED	650 nm

ARGON: Weak multiple lines, most intense in violet

COLOR	WAVELENGTH
VIOLET	440 nm
VIOLET	460 nm
GREEN	520 nm
GREEN	570 nm
YELLOW	590 nm
RED	630 nm
RED	650 nm

CARBON DIOXIDE: Strong lines in violet, green and red

COLOR	WAVELENGTH
VIOLET	425 nm
VIOLET	455 nm
GREEN	510 nm
GREEN	530 nm
GREEN	565 nm
ORANGE	610 nm
RED	620 nm
RED	660 nm

MERCURY: Strong spectrum with five prominent lines

COLOR	WAVELENGTH
VIOLET	405 nm
BLUE	436 nm
GREEN	546 nm
YELLOW	580 nm
ORANGE	610 nm

61

Atomic Emission Spectroscopy
Advanced Study Assignment

Name_____ Date_____

This assignment MUST be completed before the laboratory period begins.
Wavelength values for the hydrogen emission spectrum are required for the experiment.

A few answers have been provided for you.
You may wish to verify some of these to ensure that your calculation methods and significant digits are correct.

1. Calculate energy values for the first SIX hydrogen energy levels using:

$$E_n = - R_H / n^2 = -(2.179 \times 10^{-18} \text{ J}) / n^2 \quad \text{where } n = 1,2,3,4...6$$

Express your answers in 10^{-20} exponential form as a convenience for later calculations.

$E_1 = \underline{\ -217.9_0\ } \times 10^{-20}$ J $E_4 = \underline{\ -13.61_8\ } \times 10^{-20}$ J

$E_2 = \underline{\hspace{2cm}} \times 10^{-20}$ J $E_5 = \underline{\hspace{2cm}} \times 10^{-20}$ J

$E_3 = \underline{\hspace{2cm}} \times 10^{-20}$ J $E_6 = \underline{\ -6.052_7\ } \times 10^{-20}$ J

2. <u>Calculate</u> all possible energy level DIFFERENCES between:
   a. Level **1** and levels **2** through **6**
   b. Level **2** and levels **3** through **6**   SUMMARIZE the ΔE values in the table below
   c. Level **3** and levels **4** through **6**

3. <u>Calculate</u> the corresponding wavelength for each possible ΔE value using:

$$\lambda = hc/\Delta E = (6.626 \times 10^{-34} \text{ J}\bullet\text{s})(2.998 \times 10^{17} \text{ nm}\bullet\text{s}^{-1})/\Delta E$$

SUMMARIZE the wavelengths on the table below underneath their corresponding ΔE.

n higher	6	5	4	3	2
n lower					
1	$211.8_4 \times 10^{-20}$J	$\times 10^{-20}$ J	$204.2_9 \times 10^{-20}$J	$\times 10^{-20}$ J	$\times 10^{-20}$ J
	nm	nm	97.24_1 nm	nm	121.5_5 nm
2	$48.42_2 \times 10^{-20}$J	$\times 10^{-20}$ J	$\times 10^{-20}$ J	$30.26_4 \times 10^{-20}$J	
	410.2_3 nm	434.1_1 nm	nm	656.3_8 nm	
3	$18.15_8 \times 10^{-20}$J	$18.15_8 \times 10^{-20}$J	$10.59_2 \times 10^{-20}$J		
	$1093._9$ nm	nm	nm		

4. <u>**Diagram**</u> each energy level (E_1 thru E_6) on the reverse. <u>**Diagram**</u> all possible transitions between levels. <u>**Label each transition**</u> with its wavelength. <u>**Identify**</u> the ultra-violet, the visible and the infrared wavelengths.

Hydrogen Spectrum -- Energy Level Diagram

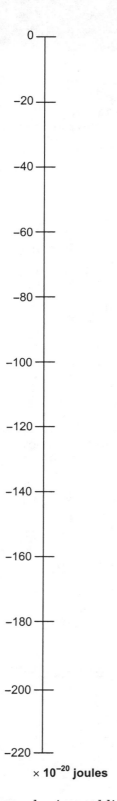

$\times\ 10^{-20}$ **joules**

__Draw__ a horizontal line for each energy level **1** through **6**.

__Draw__ a vertical line to represent each possible transition (**n higher** to **n lower**.)

__Write__ the wavelength that corresponds to the transition next to the vertical line.

__Identify__ which transitions will produce infrared wavelengths, which will produce visible wavelengths, and which will produce wavelengths in the ultra-violet region.

Atomic Emission Spectroscopy Observations Summary

Name_____ Date_____

Partner_____ Course/ Section_____

PART A: Spectroscope Calibration – Emission Spectrum of Helium

Color of Spectral Line	Color Intensity	Spectroscope Scale Value	Wavelength Assigned from Table I (nm)
			nm
			nm
			nm
			nm
			nm
			nm
			nm
			nm
			nm

Prepare a calibration graph (Scale Value on the **X**-axis vs. Assigned Wavelength on the **Y**-axis) for your spectroscope. Attach this graph to your report.

PART B: Emission Spectrum of Hydrogen

Color of Spectral Line	Spectroscope Scale Value	Wavelength from Calibration Graph	Energy Level Transition
		nm	
		nm	
		nm	
		nm	
		nm	

Use the wavelength values calculated in your Advance Problem Assignment to identify the energy level transition for each wavelength you observed in the Hydrogen spectrum. Specify the transition (**n higher** to **n lower**) for each wavelength in the table above.

Calculate the relative error between the observed wavelength and the calculated wavelength (Advance Problem) for the transition from energy level **four** to energy level **two** ($4 \rightarrow 2$.) Refer to the experiment: *Mass-Volume Exercise* for a discussion of relative error.

Did you observe a wavelength that corresponds to the transition from energy level **four** to energy level **one** ($4 \rightarrow 1$)? If YES, what was the color?
If NO, suggest a reason or reasons to explain why it was not visible?

Did you observe a wavelength that corresponds to the transition from energy level **four** to energy level **three** ($4 \rightarrow 3$)? If YES, what was the color?
If NO, suggest a reason or reasons to explain why it was not visible?

Name_____ Date_____

Partner_____ Course/ Section_____

PART C: Emission Spectra of Selected Elements

Element Name	Color of Spectral Line	Spectroscope Scale Value	Wavelength from Calibration Graph
Identification Number of Unknown Discharge Lamp _____ **Element Name** _____			nm
			nm
			nm
			nm
			nm
			nm
			nm
			nm
Identification Number of Unknown Discharge Lamp _____ **Element Name** _____			nm
			nm
			nm
			nm
			nm
			nm
			nm
			nm

Report the result of your element identification on the **Report Summary**, previous page.

Emission Spectra of Selected Elements

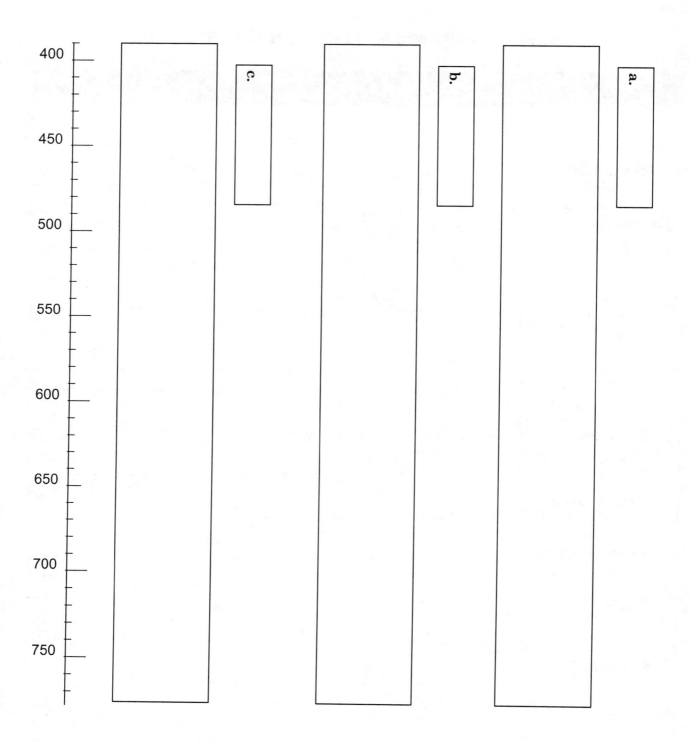

Diagram the emission spectrum of each additional element observed. Identify each element. You may use colored pen/pencil to enhance the diagrams if they are available.

MOLECULAR STRUCTURE AND GEOMETRY

In the early 1900's the American chemist G.N. Lewis introduced a method to predict the structural formulas of molecular chemical compounds based on the concept that bonds are established through sharing of electron pairs. The electrons shared, and the orbitals they occupy, are those in the highest energy level, the <u>valence</u> level. Electrons that constitute the inert gas core of an atom's configuration are energetically stable and do not participate in bonding.

For <u>Representative</u> <u>Elements</u>, the valence level consists of the highest quantum level **s** and **p** atomic orbitals (the **1 s** orbital for hydrogen). These elements form bonds through electron pair sharing in an attempt to achieve the completely filled **s** and **p** orbital configuration (eight electrons, two for hydrogen) characteristic of the very stable inert gas configurations. Atoms therefore share electrons and orbitals in whatever manner is necessary to achieve an inert gas configuration; the "octet rule" for elements other than hydrogen. In some cases this requires MULTIPLE BONDING (more than one bond between the same two atoms). It is also possible for an atom to share a pair of its electrons with the empty orbital of another atom (CO-ORDINATE COVALENT bonding) to help both achieve an inert gas electron configuration.

As the number of atoms in the compound increases, the number of possible legitimate structural arrangements also increases. Different, but perfectly legal, Lewis structures are therefore possible. Compounds having identical chemical formulas but different structures are termed ISOMERS and are not unusual. There are several examples of isomeric compounds in this exercise, but it may not be possible to verify isomerism unless one can view the molecule in three dimensions.

The Lewis principles allow one to predict the most likely structural arrangement of atoms in a compound and eliminate those that probably will not exist. However, the method is limited to arrangements in only two dimensions. One can predict which atoms are bonded to which but not how they are arranged in three-dimensional space. As a result, the Lewis structure of a compound may not allow one to predict its properties.

This exercise will employ molecular models (wooden balls representing atoms and sticks/springs representing electron pairs) to convert two-dimensional Lewis molecular diagrams into the real three-dimensional molecular geometry. However, one must first obtain the correct Lewis structure and then assemble the molecular model based on that structure. One, though certainly not the only, process for determining a Lewis diagram is outlined below in **Tables 1, 2, and 3**. This particular method is not effective for all possible compounds but does work for the compounds selected for this exercise.

Principles and Procedures for Preparing Lewis Diagrams

Table 1. THE REPRESENTATIVE ELEMENTS

A summary of the number of electrons in the valence level and the usual maximum number of bonds they form (maximum valence).

Elements	Alkali Metals **Group I A**	Alkaline Earth **Group II A**	Boron Group **Group III A**	Carbon Group **Group IVA**
Number of Valence Electrons	One	Two	Three	Four
Usual Maximum Valence	One	Two	Three	Four

Elements	Nitrogen **Group VA**	Oxygen **Group VI A**	Halogens **Group VII A**	Inert Gas **Group VIII A**
Number of Valence Electrons	Five	Six	Seven	Eight Two for Helium
Usual Maximum Valence	Three	Two	One	Zero

Table 2. GUIDELINES FOR CONSTRUCTING LEWIS DIAGRAMS COVALENT COMPOUNDS

A. SYMMETRY rule – A symmetric arrangement of atoms in space is usually preferred.

B. VALENCE rule – If possible, do not exceed the usual maximum valence of an atom.

C. OCTET rule – If possible, do not assign more than eight electrons to each atom. (A maximum of two electrons for hydrogen.)

D. ELECTRON COUNT – The total number of electrons assigned to the diagram MUST EQUAL the sum of the valence electrons in the diagram (adjusted for any charge).

E. EXCEPTIONS to **A**, **B**, and **C** can and do occur. The symmetry rule has lower priority while the octet rule takes higher priority. One must justify a valence or octet rule exception via co-ordinate covalent bonding, resonance, or use of "d" orbitals ("expanded octet"). There are no exceptions to the ELECTRON COUNT rule.

70

Table 3. PROCEDURE FOR CONSTRUCTING LEWIS DIAGRAMS COVALENT COMPOUNDS

1. ARRANGE the atoms symmetrically in space, and attach them using the <u>minimum</u> possible number of bonds. If possible, try not to exceed the VALENCE or OCTET rules for any atom. It is usually best to put atoms having the largest possible valence in the center and those with the least outside.

2. ADD ELECTRONS as <u>non</u>-<u>bonding pairs</u> until each atom has eight (two for hydrogen).

3. COMPARE the total <u>diagram</u> electron count with the total <u>valence</u> electron count:
   a. If they AGREE, the diagram is a valid Lewis structure.
   b. If the DIAGRAM count EXCEEDS the VALENCE count, <u>adjust</u> as follows:
      For <u>each</u> <u>excess</u> <u>pair</u> of diagram electrons remove two non-bonding pairs and <u>replace</u> them with one bond. (The pairs must be removed from different atoms.) This will generate any multiple bonding that may exist in the diagram.
   c. If the VALENCE count EXCEEDS the DIAGRAM count, missing electrons must be added to the diagram <u>as</u> <u>non</u>-<u>bonding</u> <u>pairs</u>. This usually generates an octet rule violation using "d" orbitals ("expanded octet").

4. CHECK for RESONANCE: Resonance is occurring when:
   a. The diagram contains multiple bonding, <u>AND</u>
   b. Equivalent diagrams exist, <u>AND</u>
   c. The equivalent diagrams can be interchanged by moving electron pairs (NOT atoms).
   d. If present, draw ALL equivalent diagrams and join with double-ended arrows.

5. JUSTIFY any exceptions to the VALENCE and/or OCTET rules:
   a. A valence rule exception can occur via COORDINATE COVALENT bonding. An atom having a non-bonding pair and an atom having an empty orbital (a Group I, or II, or III element or a positive ion) is usually required.
   b. A valence rule exception can occur via RESONANCE because this implies that an orbital is making more than one bond, a situation not envisioned in the original Lewis concept.
   c. A valence rule and/or an octet rule exception can occur if **d** atomic orbitals in the valence level are utilized (the "expanded octet"). Only atoms in the third or higher periods of the periodic table have **d** orbitals in their valence levels.

6. If the exceptions cannot be explained, a different arrangement of atoms should be attempted.

Molecular Geometry

With the Lewis Diagram as a guide, a three dimensional model of the molecule is constructed using a molecular model kit. The geometry of the molecule in three dimensions can then be identified with a brief verbal description or, for more complex geometries, a drawing. The convention for drawing uses a solid line to represent bonds in the plane of the paper, a broken line to represent bonds below the plane, and a triangle to represent bonds above the plane of the paper. Non-bonding electrons can be identified with a pair of dots. For simple molecules, the following verbal descriptions will suffice:

TWO ATOM Molecules are LINEAR. (The term PLANAR is not relevant): ●———●

THREE ATOM molecules are LINEAR or NON LINEAR (The term PLANAR is not relevant):

eg: H_2S is   Linear   ●——○——●   OR   Non Linear

FOUR ATOM (trigonal) molecules are PLANAR or NON-PLANAR   (LINEAR is not relevant)

eg: NH_3 is Trigonal Planar   OR   Trigonal Non-Planar

FIVE ATOM molecules are SQUARE PLANAR or TETRAHEDRAL (Square non-planar)

eg: CH_4 is   Square Planar   OR   Tetrahedral

DOUBLE or **TRIPLE BONDS** are represented by solid, straight lines   ○≡○

72

Molecular Polarity

Molecules that have their center of positive charge separated from their center of negative charge (an asymmetric distribution of charge) are polar and have a greater interaction with their neighbors (higher boiling points, for instance) than non-polar molecules. In some cases, molecular polarity can be predicted from the two-dimensional Lewis diagram while others require knowledge of the atom arrangement in three dimensions.

A bond between two different atoms is polar because the charge distribution is asymmetric. However, if the bond polarities in a molecule can balance each other, the molecule itself will be non-polar. If these forces do not oppose each other the molecule, as well as the bonds, will be polar. In the compound CH_3F there are three polar C-H bonds and a C-F bond of different polarity. Since there is only one C-F bond, its polarity cannot be balanced no matter how the atoms are arranged in three dimensions. We can therefore conclude the molecule is polar without converting the Lewis diagram into three dimensions. On the other hand, if the H_2S molecule (with two H-S polar bonds) is linear, the polarities will oppose each other and the molecule will be non-polar. But, if it is non-linear, the bond polarities cannot cancel each other and the molecule will be polar. One is therefore required to determine the correct three-dimensional geometry of H_2S before its polarity can be determined.

Molecular Isomerism

As discussed earlier, it is often possible for compounds to have the same molecular formula but different molecular structures. The different structures are said to be ISOMERS of each other and are relatively common in molecules having six or more atoms. The compound $C_2H_4Cl_2$, for instance, can have both chlorine atoms attached to the same carbon or one chlorine atom attached each to a different carbon. Since the structures are different, it is possible that — one is polar and the other is not, both are polar, or both are non-polar. Because of this $C_2H_4Cl_2$ is really two distinctly different compounds, having different physical and chemical properties even though the molecular formulas are identical. As is the case with molecular polarity, one can sometimes identify isomers from the two dimensional Lewis diagrams, but often it is necessary to view the structure in three dimensions in order to confirm that the structures are really different.

Experimental Procedure

This exercise does not require Safety Goggles or a Lab Coat.

Part I

1. Draw Lewis diagrams for the molecules and molecule ions below as explained in the ADVANCE PROBLEM ASSIGNMENT:

$$CH_4 \quad H_2O \quad NH_3 \quad C_2H_6 \quad C_3H_4 \quad H_2O_2 \quad CH_4O$$
$$C\,H_2F_2 \quad H_3O^+ \quad C_2H_4 \quad C_2H_4F_2 \quad CO_2 \quad SO_3$$
$$HF \quad N_2 \quad C_2H_2 \quad C_2H_2F_2 \quad SO_2 \quad SO_4^{-2}$$

2. Obtain a molecular model kit from the laboratory cart, and use it to construct a model of each compound (and isomer) based on the Lewis structure. For best results, any atom that has <u>more</u> <u>than one</u> <u>bond</u> MUST be represented using a wooden ball that has FOUR holes drilled in a TETRAHEDRAL orientation. In the kit, the BLACK ball, and in a very few cases the blue ball, meet this requirement. (Temporarily insert four sticks into a black ball to see what is meant by "tetrahedral" orientation. Do the same for any blue ball in your kit and compare it with the black to see if the blue is also tetrahedral). A yellow ball usually represents hydrogen, while green, orange, or violet balls represent the halogens.

   Use straight wooden sticks to represent single bonds attaching two atoms. Use two or three bent springs to represent double or triple bonds. (Double and triple bonds do not actually look like bent springs, but the resulting arrangement of atoms in space will be correct). If there are non-bonding electron pairs on the atom, it is usually best to let their locations be represented by the empty holes in the black or blue ball. Remember that the geometry of a molecule is determined by viewing its atom arrangement, not its electrons.

3. Compare the models of any isomers you may have identified to verify that they are really <u>different</u> structures. If you can simply rotate one model in space and have it match another, or rotate around a single bond and obtain a match, there is no isomerism. If you must break and then reform bonds to convert one model into another the structures are truly isomers.

4. Describe or draw the three dimensional molecular geometry (including any valid isomers). Remember that there is free rotation about a single bond and that atoms will assume a minimum repulsion (farthest apart) configuration as a result.

5. Is the molecule POLAR or NON-POLAR? Recall that any bond between different atoms is polar, but if these forces balance each other, the molecule will be non-polar. If there are isomers, identify the polarity of each isomer.

Part II (Optional)

1. Draw the Lewis diagram and construct the molecular model for NH_4^+. Compare with NH_3 above. Compare the **Water** (H_2O) – **Hydronium ion** (H_3O^+) system above with the **Ammonia** (NH_3) – **Ammonium ion** (NH_4^+) system. Identify and describe any similarities.

2. Draw Lewis diagrams and construct molecular models for the ions NO_3^{-1} and CO_3^{-2}. Compare these with SO_3. Identify and describe any similarities that exist between all three.

3. Draw Lewis diagrams for CHFClBr (hydrogen, fluorine, chlorine, and bromine attached to a center carbon – similar to CH_4) for as many possible isomers as you can identify. Construct molecular models for each isomer and identify those that are truly different three-dimensional structures and thus real isomers. If there are isomers, characterize them as polar or non-polar. If there is more than one polar isomer, attempt to predict which is most polar.

After Laboratory Exercise

Use the **Valence Shell Electron Pair Repulsion** (VSEPR) theory <u>or</u> the **Hybrid Orbital** theory to transform the two dimensional Lewis diagrams into the molecular geometry in three dimensions. <u>Compare</u> your results with the molecular geometry and polarity determined using the molecular model kit.

Molecular Structure and Geometry
Advanced Problem Assignment

Name_____ Section_____ Date_____

READ THE EXPERIMENTAL DISCUSSION FIRST!

Draw Lewis diagrams for the molecules and molecule ions listed below. (You may employ the Lewis diagram procedure described in your lecture textbook or the principles/procedure outlined in **Tables 1, 2, and 3** earlier in this discussion.) Prepare these in a legible fashion on the following pages <u>BEFORE</u> <u>the</u> <u>class</u> <u>meets</u> for this laboratory exercise. There will not be sufficient time to draw the diagrams and determine molecular geometry and polarity in one laboratory period.

CH_4	H_2O	NH_3	C_2H_6	C_3H_4	H_2O_2	CH_4O
$C H_2F_2$	H_3O^+	C_2H_4	$C_2H_4F_2$	CO_2	SO_3	
HF	N_2	C_2H_2	$C_2H_2F_2$	SO_2	SO_4^{-2}	

For the molecules having three or more atoms, investigate the possibilities for isomers (there are several.) Can one have Lewis diagrams that meet valence, octet rule, and electron count requirements but have different arrangements of atoms in space? Draw Lewis diagrams for any isomers you may have identified.

Examine any diagram having multiple bonding to determine if RESONANCE exists (there are at least two). If yes, draw all the resonance forms and join them with double-ended arrows. Remember to justify any valence rule or octet rule exceptions.

Molecular Structure and Geometry
PART I Report

Name_____   Section_____   Date_____

Partner_____

	Lewis Diagram	Molecular Geometry	Polarity
CH_4			
CH_2F_2			
HF			
N_2			

	Lewis Diagram	Molecular Geometry	Polarity
C_2H_2			
H_2O			
H_3O^+			
C_2H_6			
$C_2H_4F_2$			

	Lewis Diagram	Molecular Geometry	Polarity
NH_3			
SO_3			
H_2O_2			
C_3H_4			
C_2H_4			

	Lewis Diagram	Molecular Geometry	Polarity
$C_2H_2F_2$			
CH_4O			
SO_2			
CO_2			
SO_4^{-2}			

Molecular Structure and Geometry
PART II Report

Name_____ Section_____ Date_____

Partner_____

Lewis Diagram	Molecular Geometry	Similarities

1.

NH_4^+

2.

NO_3^{-1}

CO_3^{-2}

3.

CHFClBr

THERMOCHEMISTRY I: HEAT EFFECTS AND CALORIMETRY

Heat is defined as that form of energy, sometimes called thermal energy, which flows spontaneously from a warmer body to a colder body. This definition allows one to measure only HEAT FLOW into or out of a body, not total heat content of the body before or after the flow has occurred. It also means that the determination of heat flow requires at least two "bodies," one warmer and one cooler, and some type of boundary, real or imagined, between them. Determination of heat flow also requires the ability to measure the temperature change ΔT (change in heat content) of each body.

Heat flow is ordinarily measured in a device called a calorimeter. A calorimeter is simply a container with insulating walls, made so that essentially no heat is exchanged between the contents of the calorimeter and the surroundings. That is; the boundary between the system and the surroundings is thermally insulating, and the system is isolated from the rest of the universe. Chemical or physical changes may occur or heat may pass from one part of the contents to another within the calorimeter, but no heat flows across that boundary from or to the surroundings. The calorimeter itself is also a "body" having a heat flow, and its heat effect must often be considered along with the heat effects of its contents. Fortunately, a Styrofoam cup calorimeter has a heat effect that is so small that it is negligible in comparison to that of its' contents and does not therefore have a significant effect on the experiment.

Recall that water was the substance used to define the mass unit GRAM; the mass contained in one cubic centimeter of water at 4°C (its temperature of maximum density). This same standard is also used to define a unit for heat energy. The energy required to change the temperature of exactly one gram of water from 3.5°C to 4.5°C is defined as 1.000 calorie or 4.184 JOULES. The SPECIFIC HEAT of a substance is the heat energy required to change a specific mass of the substance (one gram) by a specific temperature change (one degree centigrade), having the dimensions **joule/gram °C** (or calorie/g°C). Water therefore has a specific heat <u>defined</u> as **4.184 joule/g °C**. The specific heats of all other substances are relative to this defined standard. If, for instance, a substance requires half as much heat per gram per degree, its specific heat is 2.094 joule/g °C relative to the defined specific heat of water. Experimental determination of a specific heat therefore requires that water be one of the "bodies" involved in the heat flow measurement, either directly or indirectly.

The HEAT FLOW (usually given the symbol **q**) for a particular body depends on the mass of the body, its temperature change, and its specific heat:

Heat Flow q = [mass in grams] [specific heat in joule/g °C] [temperature change °C]   **(1)**

Heat flow also <u>**requires**</u> a **SIGN** which is defined from the **SYSTEM** point of view:

q is <u>positive</u> (+) if heat <u>enters</u> the body and <u>negative</u> (-) if heat flows <u>out of</u> the body

The "body" can be defined in any manner that is convenient to the nature of the heat effect experiment. For instance, if one is determining the potential energy change of a chemical or physical process, the calorimeter and contents are defined as one body and the surrounding universe becomes the other body. On the other hand, if one wishes to determine the specific heat of a metal, it is more convenient to view the metal sample as one body and a water sample as the other. Since both metal and water must be inside the calorimeter, the heat that leaves one must have the same value (but opposite sign) as the heat that enters the other.

PART A: Determination of a Specific Heat

The specific heat of a metal can be conveniently determined using a Styrofoam cup calorimeter. A known mass of metal is heated to a known temperature and then quickly transferred into a calorimeter that contains a known mass of water at a known temperature. Heat flows from the metal to the water, and the two reach some final temperature that is between the initial temperatures of the metal and the water. There is no physical or chemical change in either the metal or the water, only temperature changes. The experiment therefore measures change in KINETIC energy but not potential energy.

Assume that no heat is lost from the calorimeter to the surroundings (the calorimeter is truly insulating), and the heat effect of the calorimeter is negligible. Therefore, as the metal cools, the amount of heat that flows from the metal is equal to the amount of heat absorbed by the water.

$$q_{metal} \; = \; q_{water}$$

and thus:

$$[\text{mass metal}][\text{specific heat metal}][\Delta T \text{ metal}] \; = \; [\text{mass water}][4.184 \text{ J/g °C}][\Delta T \text{ water}]$$

Since the mass and temperature change of the metal and mass and temperature change of the water are experimentally measured, the above relationship can be solved for the metal's specific heat, the only unknown term:

$$[\text{specific heat metal}] \; = \; \frac{[\text{mass water}][4.184 \text{ J/g °C}][\Delta T \text{ water}]}{[\text{mass metal}][\Delta T \text{ metal}]}$$

The specific heat of a metal is also related in a simple way to its gram atomic weight. Dulong and Petit discovered many years ago that the amount of heat required to raise the temperature of one gram atomic weight of most metals was approximately 25 joules/°C. This relationship is know as the *Law of Dulong and Petit* and can be used to obtain the <u>approximate</u> gram atomic weight of a metal through the experimental determination of its specific heat as described above:

$$\text{Approximate Gram Atomic Weight} \; \cong \; \frac{25 \text{ joules/°C}}{\text{Specific Heat J/g °C}}$$

PART B: Determination of a Potential Energy Change – Heat of Solution

When a chemical or physical change takes place, the nature and energy content of the final system is different from that of the initial system. This energy difference is a POTENTIAL ENERGY change and is measured by observing the accompanying heat flow into or out of the system. When a potential energy change occurs inside a calorimeter, however, the temperature of the contents changes (KINETIC energy changes) because the insulating calorimeter walls prevent the flow of potential energy between the calorimeter and its surroundings. If the calorimeter and contents are defined as our system and the surrounding universe is defined as the other "body", q for our experiment is zero because the change occurs in an isolated system. As a result, the potential energy change is converted into a kinetic energy change and the temperature increases or decreases accordingly. To measure a potential energy change, however, one must observe the heat that would flow into or out of the system in order to maintain <u>constant temperature</u> (zero kinetic energy change).

To accomplish this one calculates the kinetic energy change of the <u>isolated system</u> using the mass, specific heat, and temperature change of the calorimeter contents. The SIGN of the energy change is then obtained by determining whether heat must leave (negative q) or enter (positive q) the calorimeter in order to restore it to the initial temperature. If, for instance, temperature increased because the reaction occurs in an isolated system ($q = 0$), heat would flow out and the temperature would remain constant in an <u>open</u> system. The heat flow would therefore be negative for this open (real) system, and this negative heat flow is the <u>potential energy</u> change for the process. In effect, one measures a kinetic energy change (temperature changes because $q = 0$) and translates it into the potential energy change ($q \neq 0$) that caused the temperature (kinetic energy) change.

If the physical or chemical change also takes place at <u>constant pressure</u>, as is the case for a Styrofoam cup calorimeter and for most normal (atmospheric pressure) processes, the heat flow is termed an ENTHALPY CHANGE ΔH. When the temperature is 25°C and the pressure is one atmosphere, the notation becomes $\Delta H°$ and is referred to as STANDARD ENTHALPY CHANGE:

$$\Delta H° = q_{REACTION} \text{ at 25°C and one atmosphere constant pressure}$$

The formation of an aqueous solution by dissolving an ionic solid in water is an example of a physical change that can easily be studied in a "coffee cup" calorimeter. The formation of aqueous NaOH, for instance, is exothermic by approximately 40 kJ/mole at constant temperature and pressure. Because the nature of an aqueous sodium hydroxide system is not the same as that of pure water and solid sodium hydroxide, this heat flow represents a POTENTIAL energy change. However, the calorimeter is an isolated system, and the potential energy evolved by the process cannot flow into the surroundings. As a result, it is absorbed by the calorimeter contents thus causing a temperature <u>increase</u>. (e.g. A decrease in potential energy in the reaction has resulted in an increase of kinetic energy in the calorimeter contents.) In this example, the kinetic energy change of the contents would be +40 kJ/mole NaOH. However, the potential energy change for the reaction is <u>negative</u> 40 kJ/mole: the heat that would have to flow out of the calorimeter in order to maintain constant temperature during the reaction (the heat flow for an open system).

The heat flow for a process is the sum of the heat effects for each component within the system (the calorimeter heat effect, 8-10 J/g °C, is negligible in our experiment for temperature changes less than ten degrees). When a known mass of NaOH solution is prepared in a calorimeter, the measured temperature change and the specific heat of the solution can be used to calculate heat flow (change in kinetic energy) via equation **(1): q** = [mass][Sp. Heat][ΔT].

(The specific heat of a dilute solution is essentially the same as the specific heat of water.)

$$\mathbf{q} = \mathbf{q_{SOLUTION}} = [\text{mass solution}][4.184 \text{J/g°C}][\Delta T]$$

Because, in a real system, heat would leave our calorimeter to maintain it at constant temperature, **q** would be <u>negative</u> for our NaOH example in an open (real) system.

Because the reaction occurred in a constant pressure device (Styrofoam calorimeter), **q** is also an ENTHALPY CHANGE (**ΔH**) (negative) for the solution process.

If the value of **ΔH**$_{SOLUTION}$ represents the heat flow associated with dissolving <u>one mole </u>of solid NaOH, its value can be written as part of the reaction that describes the process. This reaction is termed the BALANCED <u>THERMOCHEMICAL</u> EQUATION:

$$NaOH_{(s)} \rightarrow Na^+_{(aq)} + OH^-_{(aq)} \quad \Delta H_{SOLUTION} = -40 \text{ kjoule/mol}$$

WEAR YOUR SAFETY GOGGLES/LAB COAT!
WASH YOUR HANDS WHEN FINISHED!

Experimental Procedure

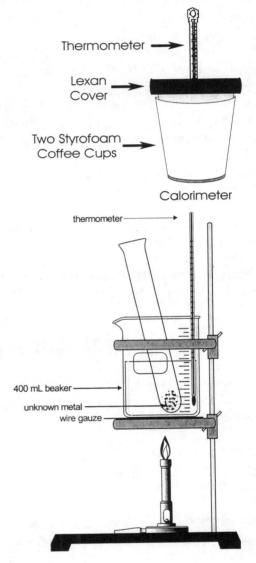

Thermometer →

Lexan Cover →

Two Styrofoam Coffee Cups →

Calorimeter

The Calorimeter: The calorimeter consists of two Styrofoam cups nested together and fitted with a black, hard plastic cover. While temperature measurements are being carried out the calorimeter rests inside a 400 mL beaker for stability. A thermometer is inserted through an opening in the cover. CAREFULLY EXAMINE both cups to ensure they are dry and that there are no openings (leaks) in the inner cup BEFORE you begin. WEIGH the Styrofoam cups/contents OR the empty calorimeter, NOT the cover and/or beaker.

The Thermometer: Examine the thermometer to be sure no separations are in the liquid column. While it is true that thermometers are not necessarily accurate, we will use temperature DIFFERENCE in our calculations. Therefore, any inaccuracy will not pose a problem so long as the SAME THERMOMETER is used for ALL temperature measurements. Read and record all temperatures to the nearest tenth of a degree (0.1°C).

DO NOT allow the thermometer to STAND UNATTENDED in any container. Hold the thermometer while measuring temperature, and then RETURN it to the protective case until needed for the next measurement. Because the Styrofoam calorimeter is easily punctured DO NOT use the thermometer to STIR the calorimeter contents. These techniques will avoid loss of both the thermometer and the experiment!

thermometer →

400 mL beaker →

unknown metal →

wire gauze →

The Water Bath: The water bath is a 400 mL beaker resting on a wire gauze pad that is supported by an iron ring (about the same diameter as the beaker) attached to a ring stand. A second, larger ring is fastened around the beaker about one or two inches from the top to prevent "tip over". The gauze pad should be about four inches above the Bunsen burner.

SUPPORT THE BATH WITH AN IRON RING AND WIRE GAUZE
ADD A SECOND "SAFETY RING" AROUND THE BATH
TWO STUDENTS MAY SHARE A BATH

PART A: Specific Heat of a Metal

Obtain a sample of dry metal in a large test tube, and record the identification number. Write a brief description. Place the tube containing the metal sample in the bath, add water to the bath until the beaker is about three-fourths full and begin heating to bring the water bath to boiling temperature. You will continue heating the tube and metal sample for about five minutes after the water boils to ensure that both the metal and boiling water are at the same temperature.

While the metal is heating, weigh the <u>empty</u> <u>calorimeter</u>. Add approximately 40 mL of water and <u>weigh</u> again. Record these weights, and replace the calorimeter in its support beaker. After the metal has been boiling four to five minutes, measure the temperature of the water in the calorimeter to 0.1°C precision and record as the <u>initial</u> <u>water</u> <u>temperature</u>.

Remove the test tube/metal sample from the bath (**HOT**!) by holding the tube with a folded paper towel, pour the metal into the calorimeter, and cover the calorimeter. Gently swirl to mix the contents. Record to 0.1° precision the <u>maximum</u> <u>temperature</u> reached.

Remove the thermometer and cover and WEIGH THE <u>CALORIMETER</u> <u>AND</u> <u>CONTENTS</u>, recording the mass to 0.001 g precision.

Measure the temperature (0.1°C precision) of the BOILING water in the bath and record this as the <u>initial</u> <u>metal</u> <u>temperature</u>.

Carefully decant the water off the metal, and transfer the metal onto paper towels. Also dry the calorimeter with paper towels – use care not to perforate the inner cup.

PART B: Heat of Solution of an Ionic Solid

Place approximately 2.5 grams of an ionic solid in a 50 mL beaker and crush into fine particles. Record the identification number of this solid, and obtain its formula and formula weight from your instructor.

Record the mass of the <u>empty</u>, dried <u>calorimeter</u>. Add your solid, and record the mass of <u>calorimeter</u> <u>and</u> <u>solid</u>. Return the calorimeter to the support beaker. Record all weights to 0.001 g precision.

Add about 50 mL of water to a separate, clean beaker and record its temperature. Pour the water into the calorimeter, cover, and swirl gently to mix the contents. Determine and record (to 0.1°C precision) the maximum or minimum temperature reached as the solid dissolves. Check to make sure that ALL of the solid has dissolved. (If not, the experiment will have to be repeated. Consult with your instructor before proceeding if this is the case.)

Remove the thermometer and cover, and WEIGH THE <u>CALORIMETER</u> <u>AND</u> <u>CONTENTS</u>, recording the mass to 0.001 g precision.

Dispose of the solution by washing it down the lab sink drain with flowing tap water. Rinse the calorimeter, cover and thermometer with tap water. Dry them with paper towels. Put the metal (Part A) back into the test tube and return it to the laboratory cart.

Calculations

Part A: Determine the specific heat of your metal sample.

Use the *Law of Dulong and Petit* to calculate an approximate gram atomic weight for your metal.

Part B: Calculate the Enthalpy of Solution (ΔH) for your ionic solid in kilojoules per mole of solid.

Give the balanced <u>thermochemical</u> equation for this process.

Record your data/results on the report forms provided at the end of this experiment.

Report your results in correct significant digits.

Include signs (+ or -) with <u>all</u> heat flow and ΔH values in Part B.

Heat Effects and Calorimetry
Advanced Problem Assignment

Name_____ Section_____ Date_____

READ THE EXPERIMENTAL DISCUSSION FIRST!
SHOW CALCULATION SET-UP on the next page.
Report ALL answers to correct significant figures.

PART A: Specific Heat of an Unknown Metal

Mass of Styrofoam calorimeter cup	5.676	g
Mass of Styrofoam calorimeter cup and water ($\cong$ 40-45mL water)	44.276	g
Initial water temperature	25.2	°C
Final temperature of metal/water mixture	32.5	°C
Mass of Styrofoam calorimeter cup, water, and metal	89.476	g
Initial metal temperature (Boiling water bath temperature)	100.0	°C

CALCULATION SUMMARY

Specific heat of water	4.184	J/g·°C
Temperature change of water	_____	°C
Mass of water	_____	g
Temperature change of metal	_____	°C
Mass of metal	_____	g
Specific Heat of a Metal (Show "set-up" below)	_____	J/g·°C

Approximate Gram Atomic Weight   _____ g/mole

PART B: Heat of Solution of an Ionic Solid

Mass of Styrofoam calorimeter cup	5.742	g
Mass of Styrofoam calorimeter cup and solid	8.242	g
Initial water temperature	24.0	°C
Final temperature of the solution	37.1	°C
Mass of Styrofoam calorimeter cup and solution	57.242	g

CALCULATION SUMMARY

Specific heat of solution	4.184	J/g·°C
Mass of solution	_____	g
Temperature change of solution ($\Delta T_{SOLUTION}$)	_____	°C
Mass of solid sample	_____	g
Formula _____ Formula mass of solid	_____	g/mol
Formula/formula mass of solid NaOH	40.00	g/mol
Moles of solid sample	_____	mol
Heat flow (**q**) for the above sample size *(SIGN required)*	_____	joules
Enthalpy change (ΔH) for the above sample size *(SIGN required)*	_____	joules
Enthalpy change (ΔH) for one gram of sample *(SIGN required)*	_____	joules
Enthalpy change (ΔH) for one mole of solid *(SIGN required)*	_____	kilojoules

BALANCED <u>THERMOCHEMICAL</u> EQUATION FOR THIS REACTION

_____ ΔH = _____

Heat Effects and Calorimetry
Experimental Data & Calculations

Name_____ Section_____ Date_____

SHOW CALCULATION SET-UP on the next page.

Report ALL answers to correct significant figures.

PART A: Specific Heat of an Unknown Metal

EXPERIMENTAL DATA IN ORDER OF MEASUREMENT

Unknown metal description _____ Unknown # _____

Mass of Styrofoam calorimeter cup _____ g

Mass of Styrofoam calorimeter cup and water ($\cong$ 40-45mL water) _____ g

Initial water temperature _____ °C

Final temperature of metal/water mixture _____ °C

Mass of Styrofoam calorimeter cup, water, and metal _____ g

Initial metal temperature (Boiling water bath temperature) _____ °C

CALCULATION SUMMARY

Specific Heat of water $\qquad$ 4.184 J/g·°C

Temperature change of water _____ °C

Mass of water _____ g

Temperature change of metal _____ °C

Mass of metal _____ g

Specific Heat of a Metal   (Show "set-up" below) _____ J/g·°C

Approximate Gram Atomic Weight _____ g/mole

PART B: Heat of Solution of an Ionic Solid

EXPERIMENTAL DATA IN ORDER OF MEASUREMENT

Unknown Solid Unknown # _____

Mass of Styrofoam calorimeter cup _____ g

Mass of Styrofoam calorimeter cup and solid _____ g

Initial water temperature _____ °C

Final temperature of the solution _____ °C

Mass of Styrofoam calorimeter cup and solution _____ g

CALCULATION SUMMARY

Specific Heat of solution 4.184 J/g·°C

Mass of solution _____ g

Temperature change of solution ($\Delta T_{SOLUTION}$) _____ °C

Mass of solid sample _____ g

Formula _____ Formula mass of solid _____ g/mol

Moles of solid sample _____ mol

Heat flow (**q**) for the above sample size _____ joules

Enthalpy change (ΔH) for the above sample size _____ joules

Enthalpy change (ΔH) for one gram of sample _____ joules

Enthalpy change (ΔH) for one mole of solid _____ kilojoules

BALANCED <u>THERMOCHEMICAL</u> EQUATION FOR THIS REACTION

_____ $\Delta H =$ _____

96

THERMOCHEMISTRY II:
Hess's Law of Constant Heat Summation

Prerequisite: Calorimetry Experiment/Heat Flow Calculations
Background: Molarity/Dilution Calculations
                  Thermochemical Equations/Enthalpy Calculations

Heat has been defined as that manifestation of energy that flows spontaneously from a warmer to a colder body. This definition implies that one is unable to determine the heat content of either body, but only the HEAT FLOW that crosses the boundary between them. This heat flow (q) is the change in heat content, and is calculated by multiplying the mass of the body by its specific heat and by its temperature change. The heat flow for a particular chemical process or physical change is the sum of the heat flows for each component in the system. For instance, the heat flow involved in forming an aqueous solution of solid sodium nitrate is the sum of the heat flows for solid sodium nitrate, water, aqueous sodium nitrate, and the calorimeter. The heat effect for a Styrofoam cup calorimeter is small and can usually be neglected (as is the case in this experiment.)

A SIGN specifying the direction of flow MUST accompany the value of a heat flow. The sign convention is from the system point of view, and it is positive (+) if heat will enter the system (endothermic) and negative (-) if heat will leave the system (exothermic) (when the process occurs in an open system where heat is able to cross the boundary between the system and its' surroundings). When the heat flow occurs at constant pressure, it is termed the ENTHALPY CHANGE and is given the symbol ΔH. The enthalpy change is the difference in heat content between initial and final states when the process occurs under constant pressure conditions. (A Styrofoam cup calorimeter is a constant pressure device and will be used in this experiment.) The value of the enthalpy change depends only on the <u>difference</u> between the initial and final states and is independent of the pathway between them.

Because of this independence, we may describe the process by any convenient pathway we choose even though it did not actually occur by that pathway. This experiment will determine the enthalpy change for the formation of solid sodium nitrate from its elements by describing the process as the algebraic sum of the following five thermochemical equations. (A thermochemical equation is a balanced equation with its associated heat flow):

A. The formation of aqueous sodium nitrate from aqueous sodium hydroxide and aqueous nitric acid (Equation **1**).

B. The formation of solid sodium nitrate from a solution of sodium nitrate in water (Equation **2**).

C. The formation of aqueous NaOH from the elements (Equation **3**).

D. The formation of aqueous HNO_3 from the elements (Equation **4**).

E. The decomposition of water into its elements [equation **5**].

1.	$NaOH_{(aq)} + HNO_{3(ag)}$	$\rightarrow$	$NaNO_{3(aq)} + H_2O_{(l)}$	Experiment, Part I
2.	$NaNO_{3(aq)}$	$\rightarrow$	$NaNO_{3(s)}$	Experiment, Part II
3.	$Na_{(s)} + \frac{1}{2}\,O_{2(g)} + \frac{1}{2}\,H_{2(g)}$	$\rightarrow$	$NaOH_{(aq)}$	$\Delta H = -470.1$ kJ/mole
4.	$\frac{1}{2}\,H_{2(g)} + \frac{1}{2}\,N_{2(g)} + 1\frac{1}{2}\,O_{2(g)}$	$\rightarrow$	$HNO_{3(aq)}$	$\Delta H = -207.4$ kJ/mole
5.	$H_2O_{(l)}$	$\rightarrow$	$H_{2(g)} + \frac{1}{2}\,O_{2(g)}$	$\Delta H = +285.8$ kJ/mole

---

6.	$Na_{(s)} + \frac{1}{2}\,N_{2(g)} + 1\frac{1}{2}\,O_{2(g)}$	$\rightarrow$	$NaNO_{3(s)}$	$\Delta H = ?$

Equation **6** describes the formation of ONE mole of solid sodium nitrate from the elements each in their standard state. This is a FORMATION reaction, and the accompanying heat flow is termed the ENTHALPY OF FORMATION ($\Delta H_{formation}$) of sodium nitrate. Since this formation reaction is the sum of the other five, the enthalpy of formation will equal the SUM of the enthalpy changes for each of these five reactions. This principle is termed the HESS LAW OF CONSTANT HEAT SUMMATION.

The enthalpy changes for reactions (**3**), (**4**) and (**5**) have been provided from the chemical literature. The enthalpy changes for reactions (**1**) and (**2**) are values determined by your calorimeter measurements in Parts I and II of this experiment. (Refer to Advanced Problems 2 and 3 for calculation examples). The enthalpy of formation of solid sodium nitrate will then be calculated via the algebraic summation process described above (Refer to Advanced Problem 4).

Calorimetry

The heat flow for any process occurring in a calorimeter is the sum of the heat flows for each component within the calorimeter. The heat flow for the styrofoam cup calorimeter will be negligible in this experiment. For each component the heat flow (**q**) equals its **MASS** multiplied by its **SPECIFIC HEAT** and by the **TEMPERATURE CHANGE**. [ie: **q** = (mass)(sp.ht.)(ΔT)]. Because enthalpy is path independent, and because our experiment does not involve pressure volume work, we can imagine that part of our process occurs at constant temperature (zero ΔT = zero heat flow) and thus simplify calculations of the heat flow for the remainder of the process.

The formation of aqueous sodium nitrate by mixing solutions of nitric acid and aqueous sodium hydroxide can be viewed as a constant temperature process. The NaOH and HNO_3 heat flows would then be zero at constant temperature. The aqueous sodium nitrate then changes from the initial temperature T_1 to the final temperature T_2. The heat flow for reaction 1 is then only the heat flow for the AQUEOUS SODIUM NITRATE. (Advanced Problem 2)

100 mL $HNO_{3\;(aq)}$ at T_2

$\uparrow$

$50 \text{ mL NaOH} + 50 \text{ mL HNO}_3 \text{ at } T_1 \rightarrow \quad 100 \text{ mL NaNO}_{3(aq)} \text{ at } T_1$

$q = $ Heat flow of aqueous $NaNO_3$

$q = (\text{mass aq } NaNO_3)(4.184 \text{ J/g.deg})(\Delta T) = $ Heat flow in joules

$$\Delta H = \frac{\left(\dfrac{q}{1000}\right)}{\text{mole } NaNO_3 \text{ formed}} = \text{Enthalpy change in kjoule/mole}$$

The SIGN of q and of ΔH is NEGATIVE because heat must leave the calorimeter in order to restore the system to T_1.

To determine the heat of solution for solid sodium nitrate we imagine that the solid and the solvent (water) react at constant temperature to form aqueous sodium nitrate first. The solid and the water heat flows would be zero at constant temperature. The aqueous sodium nitrate then changes temperature from T_1 to T_2. The heat flow for the reaction is then only the heat flow for AQUEOUS SODIUM NITRATE. (Advanced Problem 3)

$$\text{WATER and SOLID at } T_1 \quad \rightarrow \quad \text{AQUEOUS NaNO}_3 \text{ at } T_2$$

$$\downarrow$$

$$\text{AQUEOUS NaNO}_3 \text{ at } T_2$$

$q = $ Heat flow of aqueous $NaNO_3$

$q = (\text{mass solution})(4.184 \text{ J/g.deg})(\Delta T) = $ heat flow in joules

$$\text{mole } NaNO_3 = \text{mass } NaNO_3 \left[\frac{1 \text{ mole } NaNO_3}{84.995 \text{ g } NaNO_3}\right]$$

$$\Delta H = \frac{\left(\dfrac{q}{1000}\right)}{\text{mole } NaNO_3 \text{ used}} = \text{Enthalpy change in kjoule/mole}$$

The SIGN of q and of ΔH is POSITIVE because heat must enter the calorimeter in order to restore the system to T_1.

We measure the heat flow for DISSOLVING the solid but use the REVERSE reaction in the algebraic summation process.

WEAR YOUR SAFETY GOGGLES/LAB COAT!
WASH YOUR HANDS WHEN FINISHED!

Experimental Procedure

Temperature Measurement: The rate at which the reaction or solution process occurs in the calorimeter is NOT necessarily the same as the speed at which we mix the contents to obtain temperature uniformity. As a result, final temperature readings must be recorded at one minute intervals until they become constant within plus or minus 0.2 degrees OR until the temperature change becomes LINEAR with time (usually five minutes or less). The constant temperature value is then recorded as the final system temperature. If temperature values are changing with time, a temperature-time graph must be constructed. The LINEAR portion of this graph is extrapolated backward to zero time to obtain the final system temperature. (Advanced Problem 2 contains an example of this type of changing but linear temperature-time behavior.)

The Calorimeter: The calorimeter consists of TWO Styrofoam cups nested together and fitted with a hard plastic cover. When temperature measurements are being taken, the calorimeter rests inside a 400 mL beaker for stability. Examine both cups to be sure they are dry and that there is no opening (leak) in the inner cup before you begin. WEIGH ONLY the calorimeter or the calorimeter and contents, NOT the cover or beaker. MIX the contents by gently swirling the calorimeter, cover and beaker. Do NOT use the thermometer to stir the contents. The cups are fragile and puncture easily.

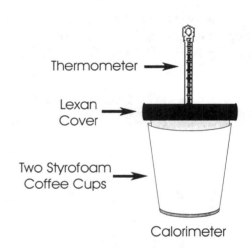

The Thermometer: Examine the thermometer to be sure there are no separations in the liguid column. While it is true that thermometers are not accurate, we use temperature DIFFERENCE, not temperature, in our calculations. Therefore, any inaccuracy will not pose a problem so long as the SAME thermometer is used for ALL measurements.

Read and record all temperature values to the nearest tenth of a degree (0.1°C) precision.

CAUTION

DO NOT allow the thermometer to STAND UNATTENDED in the calorimeter or other container. Hold the thermometer while measuring temperature and then RETURN it to the PROTECTIVE CASE until needed for the next measurement.

NOTICE

If the thermometer breaks or the calorimeter cup is punctured during the course of an experiment, the trial must be discarded and the experiment repeated.

PART I: Reaction of NaOH $_{(aq)}$ with HNO$_3$ $_{(aq)}$

1. Dry and weigh the calorimeter. Record this mass to 0.001 g precision.

2. Put approximately 10 mL of water into your 50 mL graduated cylinder. Calculate the volume of 6.00 M nitric acid needed to prepare 50.0 mL of 1.0 M solution. (Advance Problem 1.) Add this acid volume (use your 10 mL graduated cylinder) into the 50 mL graduated cylinder. Rinse the 10 mL cylinder three times with about 5 mL of water, adding the rinse into your 50 mL cylinder each time. Finally, add water to the 50.0 mL mark of the 50 mL cylinder. Transfer this solution into your calorimeter.

3. Rinse the 50 mL cylinder, and prepare 50.0 mL of 1.00 M sodium hydroxide by diluting 6.00 M sodium hydroxide solution in the same manner as the nitric acid above. Retain this solution in your cylinder until ready to run the reaction.

4. Measure the temperature (to the nearest 0.1 deg precision) of <u>each solution</u>, and RECORD THEIR <u>AVERAGE</u> as the initial temperature of the sodium hydroxide-nitric acid mixture. The thermometer must be RINSED and DRIED before it is inserted into either solution.

5. Pour the 50.0 mL sodium hydroxide into the nitric acid, cover the calorimeter, and swirl gently to mix. Record the temperature after mixing every minute until the temperature becomes constant OR becomes linear. (five minutes maximum)

6. Weigh the calorimeter cup and contents. Record to 0.001 g precision.

 **DISPOSAL** of reaction products: Discard all waste solutions in the sink as directed by your instructor.

7. Rinse the sodium nitrate solution into the sink with flowing tap water, and rinse/dry the calorimeter. Weigh the empty calorimeter. REPEAT this process to obtain a second trial.

8. Determine the final temperature and the temperature change for each trial.

9. Calculate the heat flow for the number of moles of aqueous sodium nitrate formed in THIS experiment, and then calculate the heat flow for the formation of ONE MOLE. Write the balanced THERMOCHEMICAL equation for this reaction. Record the enthalpy change in kjoules per mole for <u>each</u> trial. (Refer to Advanced Problem 2.)

The SPECIFIC HEAT of aqueous sodium nitrate is **4.184 J/g.deg.**, the same as water.

101

PART II: Formation of NaNO$_3$ (aq) from SOLID NaNO$_3$

1. Dry and weigh the calorimeter, recording to 0.001 g precision.

2. Add approximately 5.0 grams of solid sodium nitrate into a 50-mL beaker, and crush into fine crystals using the handle of a scoopula. (See *Appendix: Preparation of Weighed Samples*) Transfer approximately 2.5 g of the solid into the calorimeter and weigh and record the calorimeter and contents. Save the remaining solid for the second trial.

3. Put approximately 50 mL of water in a calibrated beaker. Determine the water temperature to the nearest 0.1 degree, and record as the initial temperature.

4. Transfer the water into the calorimeter, cover, and swirl gently to mix. Record the temperature after mixing every minute until it becomes constant OR linear (maximum of five minutes.) WEIGH and record the calorimeter and contents.

 **DISPOSAL** of reaction products: Rinse all waste solutions into the sink with flowing tap water as directed by your instructor.

5. Rinse the sodium nitrate solution into the sink with flowing tap water and rinse and dry the calorimeter. Weigh the empty calorimeter again, and REPEAT this experiment using the remaining solid to obtain a second trial.

6. Determine the final temperature and the temperature change for each trial.

7. Calculate the heat flow for the mass of solid dissolved in this experiment and then calculate the heat flow for dissolving ONE MOLE of solid (Sodium nitrate = 84.995 g/mol). Write the balanced THERMOCHEMICAL equation for this reaction, reporting the enthalpy change for EACH TRIAL in kjoules per mole. What is the enthalpy change per mole for the <u>REVERSE</u> reaction? (Refer to Advanced Problem 3)

TEMPERATURE DATA				
	PART I: Heat of reaction		**PART II:** Heat of solution	
<u>Time (Min.)</u>	Trial 1	Trial 2	Trial 1	Trial 2
1.0	_____ °C	_____ °C	_____ °C	_____ °C
2.0	_____ °C	_____ °C	_____ °C	_____ °C
3.0	_____ °C	_____ °C	_____ °C	_____ °C
4.0	_____ °C	_____ °C	_____ °C	_____ °C
5.0	_____ °C	_____ °C	_____ °C	_____ °C
FINAL TEMP.	_____ °C	_____ °C	_____ °C	_____ °C
INITIAL TEMP.	_____ °C	_____ °C	_____ °C	_____ °C
TEMP. CHANGE	_____ °C	_____ °C	_____ °C	_____ °C
SPECIFIC HEAT: Aqueous Sodium Nitrate = **4.184 J/g.deg**.				

PART III: Calculation of Enthalpy of Formation of NaNO₃ (s)

Algebraically add the balanced thermochemical equations that describe the reactions in **PART I** and **PART II** to the thermochemical equations for the formation of aqueous sodium hydroxide (reaction **3**), the formation of aqueous nitric acid (reaction **4**), and the dissociation of water into its elements [reaction **5**]. Complete this in a manner which yields the reaction forming ONE MOLE of SOLID sodium nitrate from the elements nitrogen, oxygen, and sodium in their standard states. Calculate the enthalpy change (**ΔH**) for the formation of one mole solid sodium nitrate. Record this for each trial in the Part III data section of your report. (Refer to Advanced Problem 4.)

Hess's Law of Constant Heat Summation
Advanced Problem Assignment

Name_____ Section_____ Date_____

READ THE EXPERIMENTAL DISCUSSION FIRST!
SHOW CALCULATION SET-UP!   SIGNS!   SIGNIFICANT FIGURES!

1. The 1.00 M solutions of HNO_3 and NaOH used in this experiment are prepared by diluting 6.00 M stock solutions.

   a) What volume of 6.00 M stock solution, and what volume of water is required to prepare 50.0 mL of 1.0 M HNO_3 and of 1.0 M NaOH solution?

_____ mL 6.00 M HNO_3	_____ mL 6.00 M NaOH	_____ mL H_2O

   b) How many moles of solute are contained in 50.0 mL of 1.0 M solution?

   _____moles

2. 50.0 mL of 1.00 M HNO_3 (initial temperature 22.4) are mixed with 50.0 mL of 1.00 M sodium hydroxide (initial temperature 21.2) in a Styrofoam calorimeter.

The mass of the resulting sodium nitrate solution was 100.120 g.

Temperature readings after mixing were:

1 min – **28.6**   2 min – **28.2**   3 min – **27.8**   4 min – **27.4**   5 min – **27.0** °C

a) Determine the average initial temperature.

Average Initial Temperature = _____

b) Construct a temperature-time graph, and extrapolate back to zero time to determine the final temperature. Then calculate the moles of the aqueous sodium nitrate formed, the heat flow for this quantity, and the enthalpy change in kjoules to form **ONE MOLE** of aqueous sodium nitrate. [**SIGNS!**]   *Appendix: The Graph – A Data Analysis Tool*

_____ moles formed | **q** = _____ J | **ΔH** = _____ kJ/mole

c) Write the balanced THERMOCHEMICAL equation for the reaction.

3. When 3.890 g of solid sodium nitrate are dissolved in 50.00 g of water in a Styrofoam calorimeter to form 53.89 g of aqueous sodium nitrate, the temperature decreases by 3.5 degrees. Determine the heat flow (q) for this mass of solid, and then calculate the enthalpy change in kjoules for dissolving ONE MOLE of solid. [**SIGNS!**] [$NaNO_3$ = 84.995 g/mol]

$q =$ _____ J $\Delta H =$ _____ kJ/mole

a) Write the balanced THERMOCHEMICAL equation for this reaction.

b) What is the balanced THERMOCHEMICAL equation for the <u>reverse</u> reaction?

4. The enthalpies of formation of aqueous sodium hydroxide, aqueous nitric acid and water are −470.1 kJ/mole, −207.4 kJ/mole, and −285.8 kJ/mole respectively (Reactions 3, 4, and the reverse of 5). Use these values, your answers from questions 2 and 3, and the balanced thermochemical equations to calculate the enthalpy of formation of <u>solid</u> sodium nitrate in kJ/moles per mole of sodium nitrate by the algebraic summation method (HESS LAW) described earlier in the experimental discussion.

1. $NaOH_{(aq)} + HNO_{3(ag)} \rightarrow NaNO_{3(aq)} + H_2O_{(l)}$	_____	kJ/mol
2. $NaNO_{3(aq)} \rightarrow NaNO_{3(s)}$	_____	kJ/mol
3. $Na_{(s)} + \frac{1}{2} O_{2(g)} + \frac{1}{2} H_{2(g)} \rightarrow NaOH_{(aq)}$	− 470.1	kJ/mol
4. $\frac{1}{2} H_{2(g)} + \frac{1}{2} N_{2(g)} + 1\frac{1}{2} O_{2(g)} \rightarrow HNO_{3(aq)}$	− 207.4	kJ/mol
5. $H_2O_{(l)} \rightarrow H_{2(g)} + \frac{1}{2} O_{2(g)}$	+ 285.8	kJ/mol
_____	_____	kJ/mol

Calculations

Hess's Law of Constant Heat Summation
Experimental Data & Calculations

Name_____   Section_____   Date_____

PART I: ENTHALPY OF REACTION:

	Trial 1		Trial 2	
Mass of Calorimeter	_____	g	_____	g
Mass of Calorimeter, Solution	_____	g	_____	g
Mass of Solution	_____	g	_____	g
Temperature Change	_____	°C	_____	°C
Moles $NaNO_3$ Formed	_____	moles	_____	moles
Heat Flow (q)	_____	joule	_____	joule
ΔH of Reaction	_____	kJ/mol	_____	kJ/mol

THERMOCHEMICAL EQUATION:

PART II: ENTHALPY OF SOLUTION:

	Trial 1		Trial 2	
Mass of Calorimeter	_____	g	_____	g
Mass of Calorimeter, Solid	_____	g	_____	g
Mass of Calorimeter, Solution	_____	g	_____	g
Mass Solid $NaNO_3$	_____	g	_____	g
Moles Solid $NaNO_3$	_____	mol	_____	mol
Mass Solution	_____	g	_____	g
Temperature Change	_____	°C	_____	°C
Heat Flow (q)	_____	joule	_____	joule
ΔH of Solution	_____	kJ/mol	_____	kJ/mol

THERMOCHEMICAL EQUATION

REVERSE THERMOCHEMICAL EQUATION

PART III: ENTHALPY OF FORMATION:

	Trial 1		Trial 2	
1. $NaOH_{(aq)} + HNO_{3(ag)} \rightarrow NaNO_{3(aq)} + H_2O_{(l)}$	_____	kJ/mol	_____	kJ/mol
2. $NaNO_{3(aq)} \rightarrow NaNO_{3(s)}$	_____	kJ/mol	_____	kJ/mol
3. $Na_{(s)} + \frac{1}{2} O_{2(g)} + \frac{1}{2} H_{2(g)} \rightarrow NaOH_{(aq)}$	− 470.1	kJ/mol	− 470.1	kJ/mol
4. $\frac{1}{2} H_{2(g)} + \frac{1}{2} N_{2(g)} + 1\frac{1}{2} O_{2(g)} \rightarrow HNO_{3(aq)}$	− 207.4	kJ/mol	− 207.4	kJ/mol
5. $H_2O_{(l)} \rightarrow H_{2(g)} + \frac{1}{2} O_{2(g)}$	+ 285.8	kJ/mol	+ 285.8	kJ/mol
_____	_____	kJ/mol	_____	kJ/mol
Balanced THERMOCHEMICAL equation for the formation of solid NaNO$_3$	Trial 1		Trial 2	

THE EMPIRICAL GAS LAWS

Several investigators studied the effect of pressure and temperature on the volume of a gas phase sample during the seventeenth and eighteenth centuries. Their experiments were designed to hold one of the variables constant, change the other variable, and observe the effect of this change on volume. Robert Boyle first observed the impact of pressure change on volume (at constant temperature) in the seventeenth century. He found that the relationship between <u>pressure</u> and <u>volume</u> was <u>inverse</u> – increasing pressure caused a volume decrease. This relationship is known as Boyle's Law and can be expressed in equation form as: $P \times V = k$. The value of the constant k (the Boyle's Law constant) depends on the size and the temperature of the gas sample. For a specific sample of gas at a specific temperature, however, its value remains the same as pressure is changed. (Any change in pressure causes an opposite but equal change in volume.)

The relationship between gas temperature and gas volume (at constant pressure) was studied by Jacques Alexandre Charles in the eighteenth century and then later by Joseph Gay-Lussac and John Dalton. They observed that <u>volume</u> was a <u>direct</u> function of (Kelvin) <u>temperature</u>. This relationship, often known as Charles' Law, is expressed in equation form as $V / T = k$. The value of the constant k (the Charles' Law constant) depends on the size and the pressure of the gas sample. For a specific sample of gas at a specific pressure, however, its value remains the same as temperature is changed. (Any change in temperature causes an equal change in volume.) The volume of a gas sample at constant pressure decreases linearly with decreasing temperature. Extrapolation of this volume–temperature behavior to (a theoretical) zero gas volume identifies –273.15 °C as the temperature of zero heat content and the centigrade–Kelvin temperature scale relationship.

These gas laws are based on experimental observation of gas behavior, not on some theoretical model of gas structure. Accordingly, they are termed "<u>empirical</u>" laws. Note also that the amount of gas in the sample (as well as temperature for Boyle's Law or pressure for Charles' Law) is unknown; it needed only to be held constant as the other variables (pressure or temperature) were changed. Empirical gas laws, therefore, did not address the relationships between the mass of a sample and its pressure, volume, or temperature.

Part I of this experiment will attempt to demonstrate the validity of Boyle's Law by measuring the volume of a gas sample (at constant temperature and mass) at different pressures and then calculating a value of the Boyle's Law constant for each trial. We will then use the standard deviation to evaluate the agreement between these values. Part II of the experiment demonstrates the temperature–volume relationship (at constant pressure and mass) by determining Charles' Law constants for several trials. The agreement between these values will be evaluated as well.

WEAR YOUR SAFETY GLASSES!

Experimental Procedure

PART I: Pressure – Volume Relationship (Boyle's Law)

Assemble the gas buret apparatus according to the diagram in **Figure One** with the leveling bulb on a separate ring stand. Disconnect the flask and raise the bulb until the water level is near the top of the gas buret. Then lower the bulb until the water level is near the bottom of the buret. Repeat several times to ensure there are no air bubbles trapped in the connecting hose.

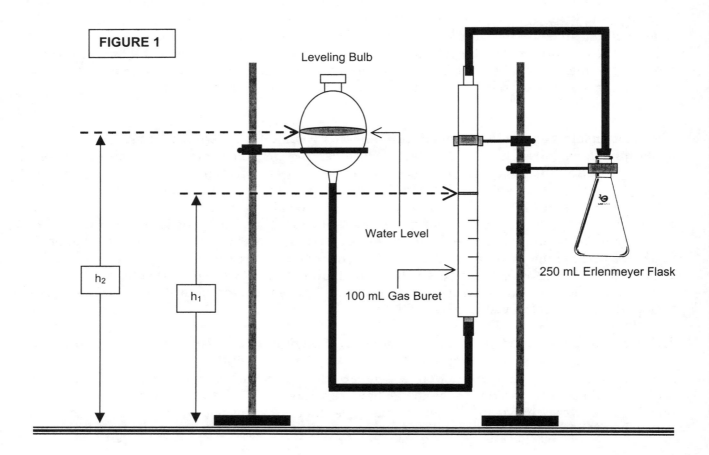

FIGURE 1

Leveling Bulb

Water Level

100 mL Gas Buret

250 mL Erlenmeyer Flask

h_2

h_1

Adjust the bulb so the water level is at the <u>middle</u> of the <u>buret</u>, and close the system by inserting the stopper firmly in the flask. Mark the flask at the bottom of the stopper with a grease pencil. Check the system for leaks as described below before starting the experiment.

<u>LEAK</u> <u>TEST</u>: Elevate the bulb above the water level in the buret (the gas is above atmospheric pressure). Observe the buret water level for one or two minutes. If the level rises slowly, air is leaking from the system. Check all connections and then retest for leaks. If the level remains constant, the system is free of leaks. Return the bulb to its original position (buret water level and bulb water level approximately the same.)

Your apparatus now contains a gas sample of fixed mass occupying the flask volume plus the measurable buret volume. The volume of air in the tubing that connects the flask to the buret is negligible. Therefore, there is no measurable impact on the experimental results and can be ignored. The volume of the gas sample at any pressure is the sum of the flask volume (the same for all trials) and the buret volume (which changes as the pressure is changed.)

For each of the five trials summarized below, record the following measurements.

(a) Volume of gas in the buret to the nearest 0.1 ml.

(b) Distance from the bench top to the buret water level (h_1).

(c) Distance from the bench top to the bulb water level (h_2).

Distances are measured with a meter stick to the nearest 0.1 cm precision.

TRIAL	WATER LEVEL POSITIONS
1	Bulb and Buret levels about the same.
2	Bulb level maximum distance <u>above</u> the Buret level.
3	Bulb approximately half way between Trial I and II positions.
4	Bulb level maximum distance <u>below</u> the Buret level
5	Bulb approximately half way between Trial I and IV positions.

<u>Verify</u> that the pressure difference (water level difference) between each and every trial is at least 10.0 centimeters. Repeat trials that fall below a 10.0 cm difference.

Once you are certain you have recorded measurement **a.**, **b.**, and **c.** for EACH trial, and that the pressures all differ by at least 10 centimeters, return the water levels to their Trial 1 positions (bulb and buret levels about the same). Then remove the stopper from the flask and the flask from its clamp. Fill the flask to the "grease pencil" reference mark with water, transfer the water to a graduated cylinder, and record its volume as the <u>flask</u> <u>volume</u>. Measure the temperature of the water in the bulb and use it to obtain the <u>vapor pressure</u> of water (Refer to the *APPENDIX: Properties of Water*). Record the <u>atmospheric pressure</u> provided by your instructor.

Calculation:
Determine the volume, dry gas pressure, and the Boyle's Law constant for each trial. Recall that atmospheric pressure and vapor pressure are in **millimeters of mercury**, while pressure differences ($h_2 - h_1$) are in **centimeters of water**. Make these dimensions consistent before attempting to calculate dry gas pressure. Express the Boyle's Law constants in standard scientific notation and correct significant figures. Evaluate the agreement between trials by calculating an average value for the constant and the standard deviation. (Standard deviation is discussed in the first experiment: *Significant Figures – Mass-Volume Exercise*.)

113

PART II: Temperature – Volume Relationship (Charles' Law)

Set up a water bath using a one liter beaker, wire gauze, and a ring stand with iron rings as shown in **Figure Two**. The bottom of the beaker should be three to four inches above the top of the Bunsen burner to achieve efficient heating. Clamp the Erlenmeyer flask inside the beaker in a position for maximum immersion. Adjust the leveling bulb so that the buret water level is near the 10 mL mark of the gas buret. Insert the stopper to its previous ("grease pencil" reference) depth. Conduct a leak test as before, returning the buret water level to the 10 mL mark when finished. Use another beaker or flask to fill the water bath with tap water.

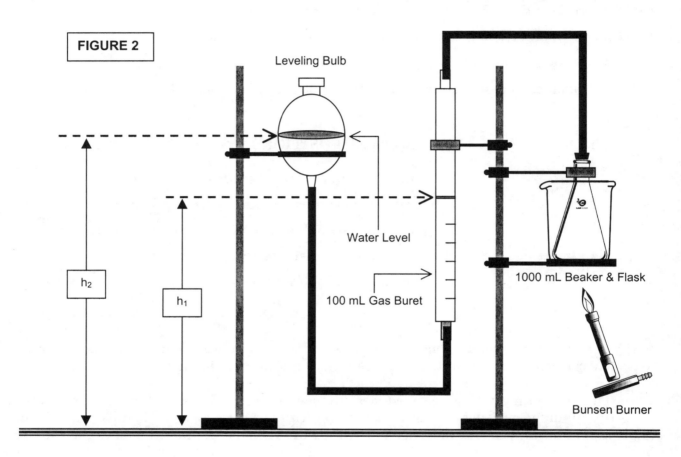

FIGURE 2

Leveling Bulb

Water Level

h_2

h_1

100 mL Gas Buret

1000 mL Beaker & Flask

Bunsen Burner

Record the gas buret volume and the water bath temperature for each of the five trials described below. In every case one must equalize pressure by adjusting the leveling bulb so that the water levels in the buret and the bulb are identical. Gas volume and gas temperature (water bath temperature) can then be measured and recorded. Measurements should be taken at tap water temperature and at four additional temperatures as summarized below.

Temperature is changed by gently heating the water bath with the Bunsen burner until the temperature increases about ten degrees Celsius. HEAT SLOWLY! The temperature should only increase about ten degrees for each trial. When the temperature has changed about ten degrees, remove the thermometer and the burner. Use a glass rod to stir the bath for several minutes to equalize bath and flask temperatures.

Then, adjust the leveling bulb so that the bulb and buret water levels are identical, and record the water bath temperature and the gas buret volume. Repeat this process, warming the bath about ten degrees each time, until five sets of temperature-volume points have been measured and recorded.

114

TRIAL	TEMPERATURE	
1	Tap water	(about 20 °C)
2	Tap water + 10° C	
3	Tap water + 20° C	
4	Tap water + 30° C	
5	Tap water + 40° C	(about 60 °C)

When you have recorded all data, remove the flask from the bath and return it to the ring stand that supports the gas buret. Return the leveling bulb and clamp to the same ring stand as well. When the bath apparatus is COOL, empty the bath and return rings, ring stand, and beaker to their appropriate laboratory storage areas.

Calculation:

Determine the absolute temperature (Celsius temperature + 273) and the total gas volume (Flask volume + Buret volume) for each trial. Divide total volume by temperature to obtain a "Charles Law Constant" for each trial. Evaluate the agreement between trials by calculating an average value for the constant and the standard deviation of the trials.

Construct a graph of Celsius temperature (vertical axis) vs total gas volume (horizontal axis.) To obtain a valid graph, your temperature axis must include a +75 °C to −300 °C range. Draw the best straight line through these points, and extrapolate this line to obtain its intersection with the temperature axis at zero gas volume. What is the value and the significance of this temperature?

For further information refer to the Appendix — The Graph: A data Analysis Tool

The Empirical Gas Laws
Advanced Study Assignment

Name_____ Date_____

READ THE EXPERIMENTAL DISCUSSION FIRST!
Complete the data page below.

PART I: Pressure – Volume Relationship (Boyle's Law)

1. Density: Mercury = **13.6** g/cm^3 Water = **1.00** g/cm^3

2. Flask Volume (use in PART II and PART II) **232** mL

3. Water Temperature **24.5** °C

4. Atmospheric Pressure **76.0** cm Hg = _____ cm H$_2$O

5. Water Vapor Pressure **2.30** cm Hg = _____ cm H$_2$O

VOLUME

Buret Volume **26.0** mL

Flask Volume **232.** mL

Total Gas Volume _____ **mL**

PRESSURE

Leveling Bulb (h$_2$) **96.5** cm H$_2$O

Buret (h$_1$) **36.5** cm H$_2$O

Difference (h$_2$ – h$_1$) _____ cm H$_2$O

$P_{total} = P_{atm} + (h_2 - h_1)$ _____ cm H$_2$O

$P_{dry} = P_{total} - P_{vapor}$ _____ **cm H$_2$O**

> REFER TO FIGURE 1 on page 112

Boyle's Constant

$P_{dry} \times V_{total}$ _____ $\times 10^5$

PART II: Pressure – Temperature Relationship (Charles' Law)

Buret Volume   26.0   mL

Flask Volume   232.0   mL

Total Gas Volume   _____   mL

Temperature, °C   22.0   °C

Temperature, K   _____   **K**

Charles' Constant

  [V$_{total}$ ÷ T]   _____   **mL/K**

The Kelvin Experiment:

Construct a graph of Celsius temperature (vertical axis) vs total gas volume (horizontal axis.) To obtain a valid graph, your temperature axis must include a +65 °C to –280 °C range. Draw the best straight line through these five points, and extrapolate this line to obtain its intersection with the temperature axis at <u>zero gas volume</u>. What is the value and the significance of this temperature? Refer to *Appendix: The Graph – A Data Analysis Tool*

Volume (mL)	240.0	249.0	255.0	263.0	270.0
Temperature (°C)	20.0	30.0	40.0	50.0	60.0

Celsius Temperature at Zero Volume (graph)

(Include your graph as part of your answer)   _____   °C

118

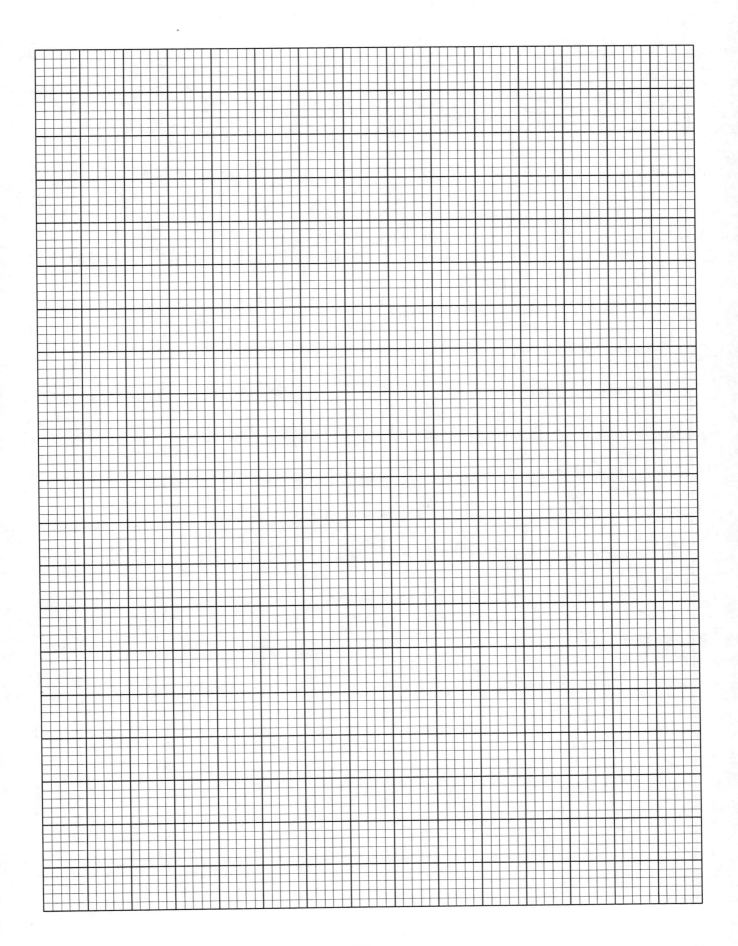

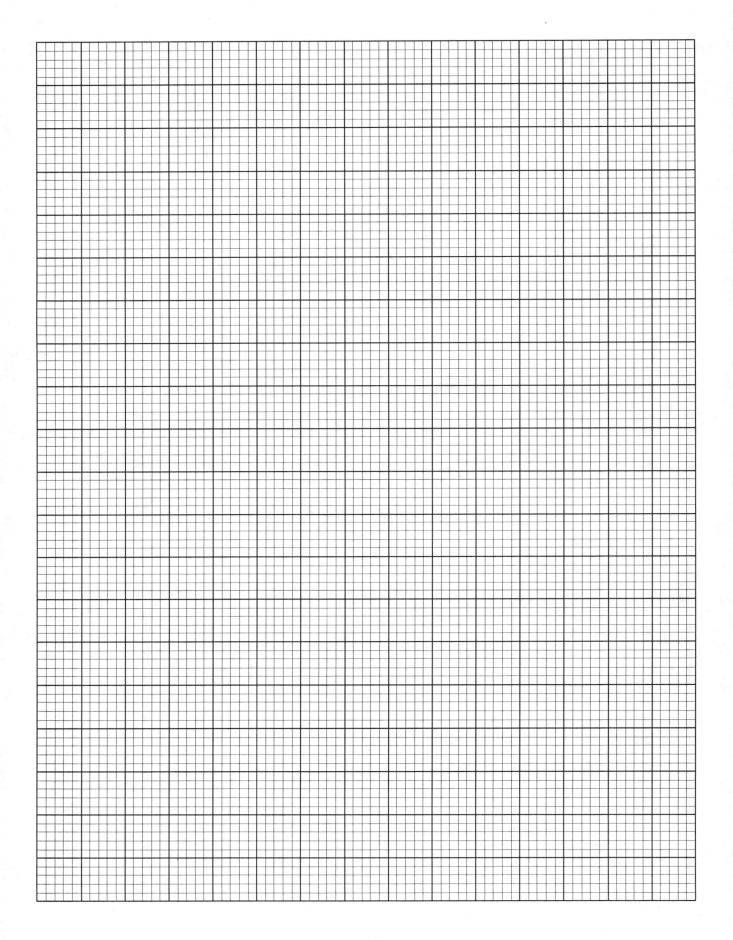

The Empirical Gas Laws
Experimental Data & Calculations

Name_____ Date_____

Partner_____ Section_____

READ THE EXPERIMENTAL DISCUSSION FIRST!

Complete the data page below.

Use scientific notation and correct significant figures.

PART I: Pressure – Volume Relationship (Boyle's Law)

1. Density: Mercury = 13.6 g/cm^3 Water = 1.00 g/cm^3

2. Flask Volume (use in PART I and PART II)   _____ mL

3. Water Temperature   _____ °C

4. Atmospheric Pressure   _____ cm Hg = _____ cm H$_2$O

5. Water Vapor Pressure   _____ cm Hg = _____ cm H$_2$O

VOLUME

	1	2	3	4	5	
Buret Volume	_____	_____	_____	_____	_____	mL
Flask Volume	_____	_____	_____	_____	_____	mL
Total Gas Volume	_____	_____	_____	_____	_____	**mL**

PRESSURE

	1	2	3	4	5	
Leveling Bulb (h_2)	_____	_____	_____	_____	_____	cm H$_2$O
Buret (h_1)	_____	_____	_____	_____	_____	cm H$_2$O
Difference ($h_2 - h_1$)	_____	_____	_____	_____	_____	cm H$_2$O
$P_{total} = P_{atm} + (h_2 - h_1)$	_____	_____	_____	_____	_____	**cm H$_2$O**
$P_{dry} = P_{total} - P_{vapor}$	_____	_____	_____	_____	_____	**cm H$_2$O**
Boyle's Constant $P_{dry} \times V_{total}$	_____	_____	_____	_____	_____	$\times 10^5$

Statistical Analysis				
Boyle's Constants	Average Value	Deviation	(Deviation)^2	Standard Deviation
	Total			Total

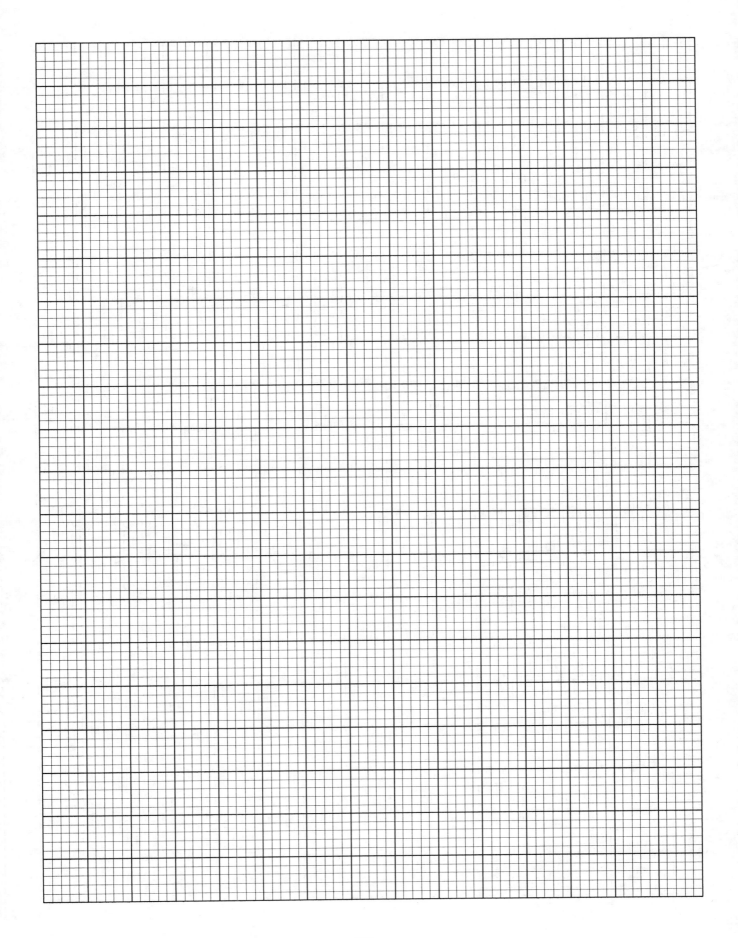

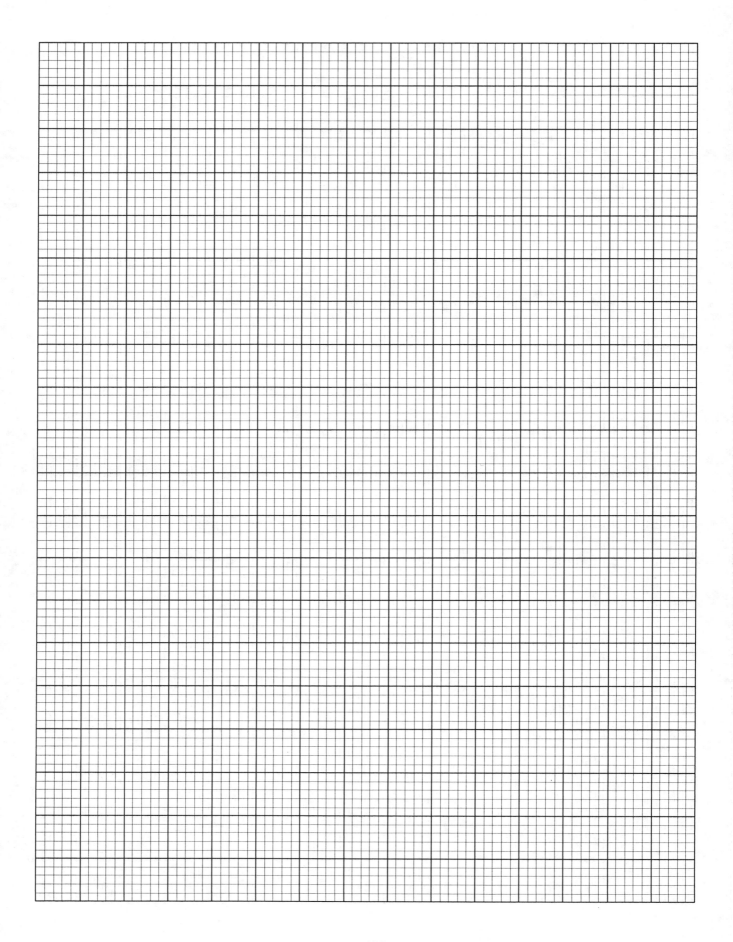

Name_____ Date_____

Partner_____ Section_____

PART II: Temperature – Volume Relationship (Charles' Law)

	1	2	3	4	5	
Buret Volume	_____	_____	_____	_____	_____	mL
Flask Volume	_____	_____	_____	_____	_____	mL
Total Gas Volume	_____	_____	_____	_____	_____	**mL**
Temperature, °C	_____	_____	_____	_____	_____	°C
Temperature, K	_____	_____	_____	_____	_____	**K**
Charles' Constant $[V_{total} \div T]$	_____	_____	_____	_____	_____	**mL/K**

Statistical Analysis				
Charles' Constants	**Average Value**	**Deviation**	**(Deviation)²**	**Standard Deviation**
	Total			Total

Celsius Temperature at Zero Volume (graph)

(Include your graph as part of your answer)   _____ °C

MOLECULAR MASS OF A VOLATILE LIQUID

In this experiment we make use of the ideal gas equation:

$$PV = nRT \tag{1}$$

where P is the pressure, V is the volume, n is the number of moles, T is the Kelvin temperature and R is the universal gas constant. The value of R is 0.08206 L-atm/mol-K. The units given with R dictate the units that must be used in this equation. This equation, which is for an ideal gas, holds quite nicely for real gases under the conditions of this experiment.

A small sample of a volatile liquid is introduced into the flask and the flask assembly is placed in a hot water bath as shown in the figure. At the beginning of the experiment the flask is filled with air plus this small amount of liquid. While in the hot water bath, the liquid boils and produces vapor which forces the air out of the flask through the pinhole in the foil cap. When the liquid appears to be gone, the flask now contains vapor only. Its' temperature is the temperature of the water in the bath; its' volume is the volume of the flask, and its' pressure is atmospheric pressure.

At this point the flask is cooled and the air, which had been displaced, returns into the flask so that the increase in mass is the mass of what had been vapor. We calculate the number of moles of vapor by rearranging equation 1:

$$n = \frac{PV}{RT} \tag{2}$$

We then calculate the molecular mass, M, by dividing the mass of vapor, g, by the number of moles, n:

$$M = \frac{g}{n} \tag{3}$$

By combining the empirical formula and the molecular mass, the molecular formula for a compound can be found.

WEAR YOUR SAFETY GOGGLES/LAB COAT!
WASH YOUR HANDS WHEN FINISHED!

Experimental Procedure

Obtain a DRY 250 mL Erlenmeyer flask, and remove any paper labels from it. The flask will be sitting in hot water, and any labels would soak off thus changing the weight. Obtain an aluminum foil square and rubber band from the laboratory cart. Without assembling the flask, foil and rubber band, weigh the combination. Add about 2 mL of the unknown liquid to the flask, attach the aluminum foil cover and rubber band tightly and make a pinhole in the cover. Be sure this hole is small.

Clamp the flask and assemble the apparatus as shown in the figure to the right. Adjust the flask and water level so that the flask is immersed as well as possible in the water bath. Heat the water to boiling and make note of when the liquid in the flask appears to have completely boiled away. Continue to boil the flask for an additional three minutes after the liquid is completely vaporized.

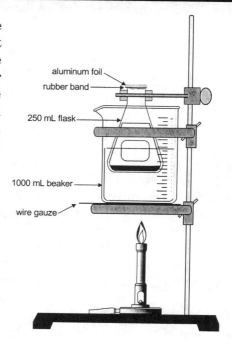

NOTE: The temperature of the vapor is the temperature of the boiling water bath. The boiling point of water at today's barometric pressure is found in APPENDIX: *Properties of Water* at the end of this manual.

At this point, release the clamp from the ring stand, and cool the flask under running cold water for about one minute. Do not allow any water to get on the aluminum cap. Carefully and thoroughly dry the flask and its' cap, especially under the edge of the foil, but do not open the cap. Weigh the flask, cap and rubber band. The increase in mass is the mass of condensed vapor. Remove the aluminum foil cover and rubber band, and discard them in the garbage can. Discard the condensed liquid into the waste bottle provided by your instructor.

Fill the flask to the very top with water and pour the water into a 500 mL graduated cylinder to obtain the volume of the flask. Record the barometric pressure reading provided by your instructor. This is the gas pressure. The gas temperature is the bath temperature found by using the *APPENDIX: Properties of Water* to obtain the boiling temperature of water at today's barometric pressure. Calculate the number of moles of vapor using equation 2 and the molecular mass using equation 3.

Repeat the procedure on another 2 mL sample of the SAME unknown using a different clean, dry flask.

DISPOSAL OF WASTE: Put the unknown liquid into the WASTE CONTAINER provided by your instructor.

Molecular Mass of a Volatile Liquid
Advanced Problem Assignment

Name_____   Section_____   Date_____

READ THE EXPERIMENTAL DISCUSSION FIRST!

1. Complete the data/calculations table below.

Mass of flask + cover	95.522g
Mass of flask + cover + condensed vapor	96.246g
Flask volume	255mL
Barometric pressure	784mm Hg
Temperature of boiling water bath	100.0°C
Pressure of vapor (P)	_____ atm
Volume of flask (vapor, V)	_____L
Temperature of vapor (T)	_____ K
Mass of vapor (g)	_____g
Moles unknown (n)	_____mol
Molecular mass (M)	_____

Calculations

2. The vapor in question 1 was found to be 85.7% carbon and 14.3 % hydrogen by mass. What are the empirical and molecular formulas of this vapor?

3. How would each of the following procedural errors affect the value obtained for the molecular mass? Give your reasoning in each case.
   a) Not all of the liquid was vaporized when the flask was removed from the hot water bath.

   b) The flask was not dried thoroughly before weighing it at the end of the experiment.

   c) The flask was left in the hot water bath for an additional thirty minutes after the liquid was completely vaporized.

   d) The flask was not cooled after removal from the hot water bath .

Molecular Mass of a Volatile Liquid
Experimental Data & Calculations

Name_____   Section_____   Date_____

READ THE EXPERIMENTAL DISCUSSION FIRST!
Complete the calculation summary in the space provided below.
Be sure to write your unknown # on your report sheet.

UNKNOWN #____

	Trial 1	Trial 2
Mass of flask + cover	_____g	_____g
Mass of flask + cover + condensed vapor	_____g	_____g
Flask volume	_____mL	_____mL
Barometric pressure	_____mm Hg	_____mm Hg
Temperature of boiling water bath	_____°C	_____°C
Pressure of vapor (P)	_____ atm	_____ atm
Volume of flask (vapor, V)	_____L	_____L
Temperature of vapor (T)	_____ K	_____ K
Mass of vapor (g)	_____g	_____g
Moles unknown (n)	_____mol	_____mol
Molecular mass (M)	_____	_____

Calculations

GAS PHASE STOICHIOMETRY AND THE MOLAR VOLUME OF AN IDEAL GAS

Prerequisite: Equation Stoichiometry and Ideal Gas Equations

During the seventeenth and eighteenth centuries, several investigators studied the behavior of gases as a function of their pressure, volume, and temperature. It was found that the relationship between pressure and volume was an inverse function while pressure-temperature and volume-temperature relationships were a direct function of KELVIN temperature. These observations are expressed by what is termed the COMBINED GAS EQUATION (Eq. 1).

$$\frac{P_1 \times V_1}{T_1} = \frac{P_2 \times V_2}{T_2} \tag{1}$$

Where the subscripts refer to initial (1) and final (2) state.

Among other things, this equation allows us to predict the volume of a gas sample resulting from a change in the gas pressure and absolute temperature (Eq. 2):

$$\frac{P_1 \times T_2 \times V_1}{P_2 \times T_1} = V_2 \tag{2}$$

Equation 1 solved for volume at the new conditions of pressure and temperature.

There is also a relationship that includes, as a fourth variable, the number of moles (**n**) of gas particles (Eq. 3). This equation is based on one rather than two states for the gas and is termed the IDEAL GAS EQUATION OF STATE.

$$PV = nRT \tag{3}$$

where the Gas Constant **R** *has a value of* **0.08206 L •atm / mole•K**

An IDEAL gas is a gas sample at conditions where the molecules are relatively far apart, and inter-molecular forces are not observable. For gas samples that are at low temperatures or at high pressures, inter-molecular forces ARE significant and the samples are non-ideal. Their behavior can therefore NOT be predicted by equation 1, 2, or 3.

The **MOLAR VOLUME** is defined as the volume of ONE MOLE of gas. The molar volume of an ideal gas is independent of the nature of the gas. Its value depends only on temperature and pressure and is the same for all ideal gases at the same conditions of temperature and pressure. At zero degrees Celsius (273 K) and one atmosphere [termed Standard Temperature and Pressure **S.T.P.**)], the molar volume of an ideal gas is **22.41 liters**.

In this experiment a solid <u>mixture</u> containing potassium chlorate and another inert solid (non-reacting potassium chloride) will be heated in the presence of a catalyst to decompose the potassium chlorate. Potassium chloride and oxygen gas are the products. The catalyst [Manganese (IV) oxide, MnO_2] lowers the energy required for the reaction but is not consumed. The oxygen produced is collected by water displacement at known conditions of temperature and pressure.

The potassium chlorate (molar mass = **122.5** g/mol) reaction is:

$$2KClO_3(s) \xrightarrow{\text{heat}+MnO_2} 2KCl(s) + 3O_2(g) \qquad (4)$$

If the number of MOLES of oxygen produced is known, then the MASS of potassium chlorate in the original mixture can be calculated using the relationships established in the balanced equation. [2(122.5) g $KClO_3$ for every **3** moles O_2 produced]

The percent potassium chlorate in the mixture is then obtained by dividing the mass of the mixture into the mass of potassium chlorate and multiplying by one hundred.

We will determine the moles of oxygen produced in our experiment TWO different ways. First, the moles of oxygen are calculated based on the MASS of oxygen lost when the sample was heated (and the gram molecular mass 32.00). This will then be used to calculate the mass of $KClO_3$ decomposed and the percent $KClO_3$ in the mixture via the balanced equation stoichiometry.

Second, the moles will be calculated from the volume, temperature, and pressure of the oxygen COLLECTED using the Ideal Gas Equation (Eq.3). Note that since the gas is collected by water displacement the pressure will have to be corrected for the presence of water vapor before it can be used in the Ideal Gas Equation. Once the moles of oxygen have been calculated, this value will also be used to determine the mass and percent $KClO_3$ in our sample as before. We will then compare the resulting values of percent $KClO_3$.

In order to evaluate the accuracy of our experiment we will also calculate the molar volume of oxygen at S.T.P. from the measured volume, temperature, pressure, and mass of oxygen produced in our experiment. Our result will be compared with the theoretical value of **22.41 L** to determine the RELATIVE ERROR:

$$\text{Relative error} = \frac{\text{difference between experimental and theoretical value}}{\text{theoretical value}} \times 100 \qquad (5)$$

134

WEAR YOUR SAFETY GOGGLES/LAB COAT!
WASH YOUR HANDS WHEN FINISHED!

Experimental Procedure

1. Obtain a gas collection and Mohr pinchcock clamp apparatus from the laboratory cart, and a 500 mL flask, 400 mL beaker and large, DRY test tube from your locker. Verify that the stoppers on the gas collection apparatus FIT your flask and your test tube.

2. Place the test tube in a 250 mL beaker for support, and weigh to the nearest milligram. Add your potassium chlorate/potassium chloride unknown mixture to the test tube, and weigh the tube, beaker, and contents. The SAMPLE SIZE must be within the mass range specified for your unknown. (See *APPENDIX: Preparation of Weighed Samples*.) Record the weighings and the unknown identification number in section **B**.

3. Add approximately 0.2 g of MnO_2 to the test tube. Visually, this is approximately the same volume as half of a pencil eraser. The mixture should yield a medium gray solid when the unknown and the MnO_2 are mixed. Weigh and record the mass of the test tube, beaker and contents in section **B**.

4. Set up the experimental apparatus as shown in Figure I. The test tube used to contain the sample is attached LAST to avoid water contamination. Attach the test tube to the apparatus, OPEN the clamp between the flask and water collection beaker, and have your instructor check the set-up.

Your instructor MUST APPROVE your Set up BEFORE you begin heating.

After receiving approval, heat the test tube in the outer Bunsen flame to decompose the potassium chlorate, thereby producing oxygen. Continue heating until the water levels no longer change (oxygen production has stopped) and then allow the system to cool.

5. Equalize the flask and beaker water levels, close the clamp between flask and beaker, and measure the volume of water in the beaker using a graduated cylinder. This is the volume of oxygen produced at the reaction conditions.

6. Measure the water temperature; obtain the barometric pressure from your instructor and the water vapor pressure from the APPENDIX. Record this information in Section **A** of the data page. The water temperature is also the gas temperature.

7. Disconnect the test tube, support it in the 250 mL beaker, and weigh the tube, beaker, and residue to the nearest milligram. Record this value in Section **C**.

 DISPOSAL OF WASTE: Measure 10 mL of tap water using your 10 mL graduated cylinder and add it to the solid residue in your test tube. Stir to dissolve the solid and transfer the mixture into the waste container provided by your instructor.

135

8. Determine the mass and moles of oxygen produced and the molar volume at **S.T.P.** (Eq.2) based on this information. Determine the relative error in your result (Eq.5).

9. Calculate the experimental moles of oxygen and percent potassium chlorate based on MASS data.

10. Calculate the moles of oxygen and the percent potassium chlorate based on volume-pressure-temperature data using the Ideal Gas Equation of State.

11. Calculate the percent difference between these values via:

$$\frac{\text{Difference between \% KClO}_3}{\text{\% KClO}_3 \text{ from Mass data}} \times 100 \qquad (6)$$

NOTICE

If this percent difference and the relative error calculated in step 7 are not approximately the same, you may have a calculation error somewhere in your report.

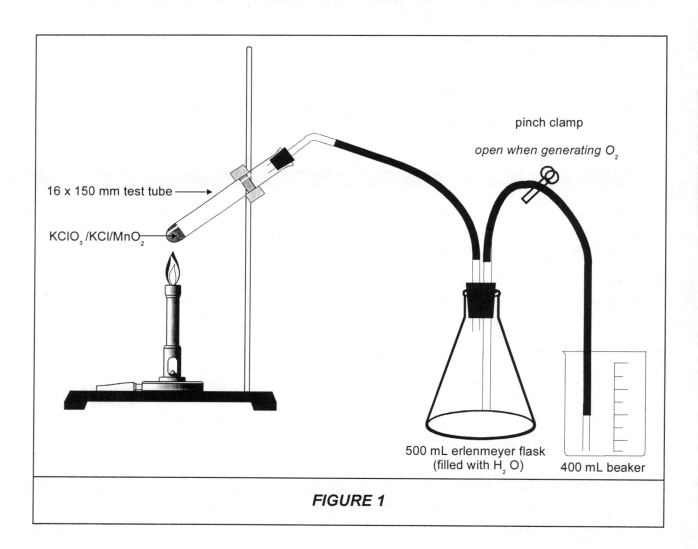

16 x 150 mm test tube

$KClO_3/KCl/MnO_2$

pinch clamp

open when generating O_2

500 mL erlenmeyer flask (filled with H_2O)

400 mL beaker

FIGURE 1

Molar Volume of an Ideal Gas
Advanced Problem Assignment

Name_____ Section_____ Date_____

	READ THE EXPERIMENTAL DISCUSSION FIRST!
	Complete the data table below using correct significant digits.
	Show the calculations on a separate page.

A	Gas Data		
1.	Barometric Pressure (torr)	768	torr
2.	Temperature O_2 gas	24.0	°C
3.	Vapor Pressure of Water (torr) (See table in the APPENDIX)	24.3	torr
4.	Volume of O_2 gas collected (mL)	354.0	mL
5.	Dry O_2 Pressure *(A1-A3)/760.0*	_____	atm

B.	Mass Data Before Reaction		
1.	Weight of beaker, test tube, $KClO_3$/KCl, MnO_2	44.445	g
2.	Weight of beaker, test tube, $KClO_3$/KCl	44.306	g
3.	Weight of beaker, test tube	42.000	g
4.	Weight of $KClO_3$/KCl sample *(B2-B3)*	_____	g

C.	Mass Data After Reaction		
1.	Weight of beaker, test tube, MnO_2, residue	43.998	g
2.	Weight of O_2 produced during reaction *(B1-C1)*	_____	g

D.	Calculation Summary		
1.	The moles of O_2 gas formed based on the mass of O_2 produced *(mass oxygen) × (1 mol/32.00 g)*	_____	mol
2.	The volume of O_2 gas produced at 0°C & 1.00 atm pressure (S.T.P.) *(refer to equations 1 and 2)*	_____	Liter
3.	The MOLAR VOLUME of O_2 gas based on the experimental data: *(S.T.P volume)/(moles O_2 produced)*	_____	Liter
4.	Accepted value for the MOLAR VOLUME at S.T.P.	22.41	Liter
5.	RELATIVE ERROR	_____	%

Use the balanced chemical equation shown below to calculate the mass of $KClO_3$ and the percent $KClO_3$ in your unknown sample from TWO different experimental data sets:

A. The moles of oxygen produced calculated using the MASS of oxygen lost on heating.

B. The moles of oxygen produced calculated using the VOLUME, TEMPERATURE, and PRESSURE of the gas collected.

$$KClO_3 = 122.5 \text{ g/mol}$$
$$O_2 = 32.00 \text{ g/mol}$$

$$2KClO_3\,(s) \xrightarrow{\text{heat} + MnO_2} 2KCl(s) \;+\; 3O_2\,(g)$$

	A. From MASS data	**B. From GAS data**
1. MOLES Oxygen Produced	_____ mol *(Section D-1)*	_____ mol *(Equation 3)*
2. Mass of $KClO_3$ in sample *(moles O_2) × [(2 x 122.5 g)/(3 mole)]*	_____ g	_____ g
3. Percent $KClO_3$ in sample *[(mass $KClO_3$)/(mass $KClO_3$/KCl)] × 100*	_____ %	_____ %
4. PERCENT DIFFERENCE between Part **A** and Part **B** results: *[(DIFFERENCE)/(KClO₃ from MASS data)] × 100*		_____ %

5. Which of the above would you expect to be more precise and why?

Molar Volume of an Ideal Gas
Experimental Data & Calculations

Name_____   Section_____   Date_____

EXPERIMENTAL MEASUREMENTS		
A.	**Gas Data**	
1. Barometric Pressure (torr)	_____	torr
2. Temperature O_2 gas	_____	°C
3. Vapor Pressure of Water (torr) (See table in the APPENDIX)	_____	torr
4. Volume of O_2 gas collected (mL)	_____	mL
5. Dry O_2 Pressure	_____	atm
B.	**Mass Data Before Reaction**	
Unknown Number_____		
1. Weight of beaker, test tube, $KClO_3/KCl$, MnO_2	_____	g
2. Weight of beaker, test tube, $KClO_3/KCl$	_____	g
3. Weight of beaker, test tube	_____	g
4. Weight of $KClO_3/KCl$ sample	_____	g
C.	**Mass Data After Reaction**	
1. Weight of beaker, test tube, MnO_2, residue	_____	g
2. Weight of O_2 produced during reaction	_____	g
D.	**Calculation Summary**	
1. The moles of O_2 gas formed based on the mass of O_2 produced	_____	Mol
2. The volume of O_2 gas produced at 0°C & 1.00 atm pressure (S.T.P.)	_____	Liter
3. The MOLAR VOLUME of O_2 gas based on the experimental data:	_____	Liter
4. Accepted value for the MOLAR VOLUME at S.T.P.	**22.41**	Liter
5. RELATIVE ERROR	_____	%

Use the balanced chemical equation shown below to calculate the mass of $KClO_3$ and the percent $KClO_3$ in your unknown sample from TWO different experimental data sets:

A. The moles of oxygen produced calculated using the MASS of oxygen lost on heating.

B. The moles of oxygen produced calculated using the VOLUME, TEMPERATURE, and PRESSURE of the gas collected.

$$KClO_3 = 122.5 \text{ g/mol}$$
$$O_2 = 32.00 \text{ g/mol}$$

$$2KClO_3(s) \xrightarrow{\text{heat} + MnO_2} 2KCl(s) + 3O_2(g)$$

	A. From MASS data	B. From GAS data
1. MOLES Oxygen Produced	_____ mol	_____ mol
2. Mass of $KClO_3$ in sample	_____ g	_____ g
3. Percent $KClO_3$ in sample	_____ %	_____ %
4. PERCENT DIFFERENCE between Part **A** and Part **B** results:		_____ %

5. Which of the above would you expect to be more accurate and why?

CHEMICAL KINETICS
The Iodine Clock Reaction

Prerequisite: Solution Concentration Calculations: Dilution
Background: Chemical Kinetics: Instantaneous Rate Equations
                  Chemical Kinetics: Activation Energy

In the study of chemical reactions, the ability to discover the kinetics of the reaction being investigated is the key to understanding the overall chemistry. In a kinetic study, one investigates the speed at which reactions occur and how this rate is affected by changes in the concentration of reactants and by changes in temperature. Once these factors are understood, the conditions at which the reaction is carried out are then optimized to improve the reaction rate or the yield of products.

In this experiment, the reaction between iodide ion (I^-) and bromate ion (BrO_3^-) in acid solution is evaluated:

$$6\ I^-_{(aq)} + BrO_3^-_{(aq)} + 6\ H^+_{(aq)} \longrightarrow 3\ I_2{}_{(aq)} + Br^-_{(aq)} + 3\ H_2O \qquad\qquad (1)$$

The INSTANTANEOUS RATE EQUATION for this reaction takes the form:

$$\textbf{Reaction Rate} = \Delta[I_2]/\Delta t = k\ [I^-]^x[BrO_3^-]^y[H^+]^z$$

Where **k** is the rate constant, the terms in brackets [ ] are concentration in moles per liter, and the exponents **x, y,** and **z** are termed the reaction order with respect to each reactant and generally have values of 0, 1, 2, or 3. If, for instance, **x** has a value of two, the reaction is said to be second order with respect to iodide ion concentration. The reaction rate for each trial will be determined by measuring the change in iodine (I_2) molarity with time in moles per liter per second: $\Delta[I_2]/\Delta t$.

For reactions occurring in solution, the rate depends upon a number of factors, the most important being the concentrations of the reactants and the rate constant, **k**. The value of the rate constant is a function of the specific nature of the reaction and, for any given reaction, varies only with temperature. The order with respect to a particular reactant determines how the rate changes with changing reactant molarity. For instance, multiplying the concentration by two will double the rate if first order $([2]^1)$ but will increase the rate four times if second order $([2]^2)$ and eight times if third order $([2]^3)$.

The reaction rate also depends on the temperature at which the reaction occurs because the value of **k** changes with temperature. As an approximation, a ten-degree rise in temperature doubles the reaction rate. That is, the value of **k** is approximately doubled by a ten-degree temperature increase. The relationship between temperature and rate constant is based on the idea that reactants must collide with some minimum amount of energy (the activation energy E_A) in order to go on to form products. The system kinetic energy increases with increasing absolute temperature, and thus more collisions per second achieve this energy, causing the reaction to proceed at a faster rate.

The equation relating **k** and absolute temperature (the *Arrhenius Equation* presented here in the form of the equation for a straight line: y = mx + b) is:

$$\textbf{ln k} = \textbf{–}E_A/\textbf{RT} + \textbf{constant}$$

Where **R** is the Rydberg Gas Constant (**R=8.314 X 10^{-3} kJ/mol·K**) and **T** is <u>Kelvin</u> temperature. In practice, **k** is determined at several different temperatures, and values for the natural log of **k** and of **1/T** are then calculated. A graph of **ln k** (vertical axis) against **1/T** (horizontal axis) yields a straight line having a (negative) slope equal to **–E_A/R**. The activation energy can then be calculated from the value of this slope.

$$\textbf{Slope} \; = \; \frac{-\,\textbf{E}_A}{\textbf{R}}$$

$$\textbf{R} \; = \; 8.314 \times 10^{-3} \; \textbf{kJ/mole}$$

The reaction speed can be measured by what is termed the **method of initial rates**, that is, by observing the amount of time it takes for a specific fixed amount of product (**I_2**) to form. To do so we utilize a starch solution as an indicator and a second, extremely fast, reaction:

$$2\,S_2O_3^{-2}{}_{(aq)} \; + \; I_{2(aq)} \; \text{--->} \; 2\,I^-{}_{(aq)} \; + \; S_4O_6^{-2}{}_{(aq)} \tag{2}$$

This reaction is essentially instantaneous, and therefore removes the iodine produced by reaction 1) so long as thiosulfate ion ($S_2O_3^{-2}$) is present in the system. When the thiosulfate is gone, iodine remains in the system and adsorbs on the starch indicator. The iodine–starch reaction produces an <u>intense</u> <u>blue</u> <u>color</u>, the signal for us to stop timing the reaction. The amount of thiosulfate ion added is exactly the same for each trial. In the time it takes for the blue color to appear, the amount of iodine produced by **reaction 1** is also the same for each trial. Faster reactions require less time; the "CLOCK" in our iodine clock reaction.

Measuring the time interval for two reaction trials where the concentration of only ONE reactant changes and the others remain the same allows one to obtain a numerical value for the reaction order with respect to that reactant. (i.e.: if doubling iodide molarity makes the reaction four times faster, it is second order in iodide.) Once the order for each reactant has been determined, a value for the rate constant can be calculated for each trial (rate constants should be the same for each trial, of course, so long as temperature is constant.) These are averaged to obtain the rate constant for the reaction.

The rate is calculated as a change in concentration over a time interval, $\Delta[I_2]/\Delta t$, and has the units $mol\cdot L^{-1}s^{-1}$. During each of several runs under different conditions, we will measure the length of time (Δt) in seconds required for the concentration of one product (I_2) to change by a certain fixed amount ($\Delta[I_2]$). Each trial will contain the <u>same</u> amount of <u>thiosulfate</u> <u>ion</u>: (10.0mL)(0.0010 M $Na_2S_2O_3$)/(50.0 mL) = 2.0×10^{-4} M $S_2O_3^{-2}$. The starch indicator turns blue when half as much iodine (see reaction 2) is produced by the reaction. The value of $\Delta[I_2]$ is therefore always **1.0 X 10^{-4} mole·L^{-1}** in each trial. Only the time (Δt) will change from trial to trial.

We note here that a rate determined in this manner is an AVERAGE rate, not an INSTANTANEOUS rate, because the concentrations of reactants MUST CHANGE during the time elapsed. However, note that this change in concentration is very small. For instance, $[BrO_3^-]$ changes by only 1/6 of 1.0×10^{-4} mole·L^{-1}. (See **Reaction 1**) during this time. For our purposes, therefore, the AVERAGE rate is a reasonable approximation for INSTANTANEOUS rate.

Determining the Order of Reaction

As a demonstration of how a reaction order is experimentally determined, assume that the times for Trial 1 and Trial 2 in TABLE 1 below were measured to be: Trial **1 = 131 s**, Trial **2 = 32 s**. Since Trial 2 required less time, it is the faster reaction. While other reactants remained the same, Table 1 also tells us that the amount of iodide ion in Trial 2 is TWICE that of Trial 1. We next write the rate equation for each trial, and then divide the FASTER trial by the slower trial.

$$\Delta[I_2]/\Delta t = \underline{1.0 \times 10^{-4}/32} = \underline{3.1_2 10^{-6}\ mol\cdot L^{-1}s^{-1}} = k[2.0]^x[BrO_3^-]^y[H^+]^z$$
$$\Delta[I_2]/\Delta t = 1.0 \times 10^{-4}/131 = 7.6_3 10^{-7}\ mol\cdot L^{-1}s^{-1} = k[1.0]^x[BrO_3^-]^y[H^+]^z$$

Since the value of k, $[BrO_3^-]^y$, and $[H^+]^z$ are identical in both cases, the division yields:

$$4.0_8 = [2.0]^x$$

The order must be 0, 1, 2, or 3, therefore the reaction is SECOND order (X=2) in iodide concentration (in this example).

The same process is followed for Trials 1 and 3, and Trials 1 and 4 to obtain the orders with respect to bromate ion and hydrogen ion.

Determining the Rate Constant

Once the orders have been determined, a value of the rate constant FOR EACH of trials one through four is calculated. For each trial we substitute the reactant concentrations, the orders, and the reaction rate into the rate equation, and solve for k. The AVERAGE of these four values is the rate constant for this rate equation at this temperature (room temperature) .

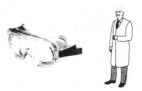

WEAR YOUR SAFETY GOGGLES/LAB COAT!
WASH YOUR HANDS WHEN FINISHED!

Experimental Procedure

DISPOSAL: Put all waste solutions in a 400 mL beaker at your workstation. Save this solution mixture for PART III.

PART I: Concentration Dependence of Reaction Rate

Determination of the Instantaneous Rate Equation

TABLE 1 below summarizes the volumes of each reactant solution needed to prepare five trials of reaction 1. Note that each solution has been diluted to a total of 25.0 mL by virtue of mixing. It is therefore necessary for you to calculate the molarity of each component after mixing, but before any reaction has occurred. Volumes must be measured using BURETS or PIPETS and must be precise to 0.1 mL. Graduated cylinders are not appropriate. It is recommended that you prepare and run one trial at a time.

Work in PAIRS. One student should prepare *FLASK A* while, at the same time, the other student prepares *FLASK B*.

Trials one through four are used to determine the reaction orders and the average rate constant. We will then use these to calculate the rate for trial five. Comparison of the calculated trial five rate with the observed rate allows one to evaluate the validity of the rate equation derived from trials one through four.

TABLE I: Preparation of Solutions for Determining Reaction Rate

Table 1	Reaction Flask A (125 mL)			Reaction Flask B (50.0 mL)	
Trial	KI 0.010 M	Na$_2$S$_2$O$_3$ 0.0010 M	H$_2$O --------	KBrO$_3$ 0.040 M	HCl 0.10 M
1	5.0 mL	5.0 mL	5.0 mL	5.0 mL	5.0 mL
2	10.0 mL	5.0 mL	0.0 mL	5.0 mL	5.0 mL
3	5.0 mL	5.0 mL	0.0 mL	10.0 mL	5.0 mL
4	5.0 mL	5.0 mL	0.0 mL	5.0 mL	10.0 mL
5	5.0 mL	5.0 mL	2.0 mL	10.0 mL	3.0 mL
	Four Drops of Starch Solution				

144

$M_1 V_1 = M_2 V_2$

$(.01)(5) = (.00)(25)$

$M_2 = .002$

$(.04)(5) = M_2(25)$

$M_2 = .008$

To measure the reaction rate of a trial, invert *FLASK B* into the neck of *FLASK A* and BEGIN TIMING. Gently swirl FLASK A to mix the solutions. Note the TIME of the initial appearance of the BLUE starch indicator color. (If the solution turns yellow, the starch indicator was absent; repeat the trial.) Record the TEMPERATURE of TRIAL 1 (only) to 0.1 degree precision.

Calculate the rate of reaction by dividing 1.0×10^{-4} M I_2 (see the above discussion) by the measured time in seconds. Calculate the molarity of each reactant after mixing for each trial (*Advance Problem 1.*) Determine the reaction orders, rate constants, and average rate constant using trials 1-4. Then calculate the trial 5 theoretical rate and relative error.

PART II: Temperature Dependence of Reaction Rate

Determination of Activation Energy

The time of the Trial I reaction mixture will be measured at several different temperatures. The reaction rate and temperature of the Trial I reaction in PART I above will also serve as one of the experiments for this PART II analysis.

Prepare another set of Trial I solutions as above, but DO NOT MIX them. Put the reaction flasks in a hot water bath drawn from the hot water tap. The bath temperature should be about 10 degrees higher than the room temperature of the Trial 1 reaction in Part I above (30-35 °C). When both reaction flasks have achieved this temperature, mix the solutions and record the time required to observe the blue color as before. RECORD THE TEMPERATURE of the resulting mixture.

REPEAT THIS EXPERIMENT on another Trial 1 mixture at a temperature that is about 10 degrees LOWER than the room temperature experiment in PART I (8-12 °C). RECORD THE TEMPERATURE of this experiment.

Calculate the reaction rate and the rate constant for each of the above experiments. (The constant should be larger at the higher temperature and smaller at the lower temperature). Convert each temperature to <u>Kelvin</u>, and obtain the natural logarithm of each rate constant. Prepare a graph of **ln k** (vertical axis) vs. **1/T** (horizontal axis). Determine a value for the slope of this line, and use it to calculate a value for the activation energy (E_A) of the reaction.

$$\mathbf{Slope} \ = \ \frac{-E_A}{R} \qquad\qquad \mathbf{R} \ = \ 8.314 \times 10^{-3} \ \mathbf{kJ/mole}$$

$$\frac{.01 \ mol}{1 L} \times \frac{x \ ml}{.05 L} \qquad \frac{.01 \ mol}{1 L} \times \frac{1 L}{1000 ml} = 10 \ ml$$

$$5 \times 10^{-4} \ M$$

145

PART III: Waste Disposal Instructions

Collect all waste solutions, including leftover reactant solutions, in a beaker at your workstation. The solution should appear blue in color and have a pH of about 1.3 to 1.6 (acid.) Add 5–6 drops of 6.0 M NaOH to the mixture in the Waste Beaker with stirring (Add only 3–4 drops if you did only PART I of the experiment). Use the stirring rod to place a drop of solution on a piece of pH test paper. Determine the pH by comparison with the color chart provided with the test paper. If the pH of the mixture is not between 5.5 and 9.5, continue adding 6.0 M NaOH drop by drop, testing the pH every two drops.

- If you achieve a pH between 5.5 and 9.5, the solution can be rinsed into the sink drain with flowing tap water.

- If the pH becomes 9.5 or higher, add 1.0 M HCl one drop at a time until the value is under 9.5, then rinse the solution into the sink drain with flowing tap water.

The Iodine Clock Reaction
Advanced Problem Assignment

Part I: CONCENTRATION DEPENDENCE

1.	Calculate the molarity of each reactant (I^-, BrO_3^-, H^+) for all five trials based on the information contained in TABLE 1. Summarize your answers on the following page.
2.	Use the time specified for trials one through four to calculate reaction rates for each trial, the reaction order for each reactant, a rate constant for each trial, and the average rate constant. Summarize your answers on the following page.
3.	Calculate the theoretical rate expected for trial five based on the INSTANTANEOUS RATE LAW you determined in question 2. Calculate the observed rate of trial five based on the time specified for trial five.
4.	What is the RELATIVE ERROR for trial five? (Relative error is defined in the *Mass-Volume Exercise*, experiment one in this book.)

$$S_2O_3^{-2} = 5\times10^{-6}\,mol$$

$$\frac{5\times10^{-6}mol}{.025L} = 2\times10^{-4}\,M$$

$$\frac{\Delta I_2}{\Delta t}$$

$$\frac{1\times10^{-4}}{t} = Rate$$

146

VOLUMETRIC CHEMICAL ANALYSIS I:
Solution Standardization Exercise

A titration is the procedure for carrying out a chemical reaction by the controlled addition of one reactant (the titrant) to a fixed amount of the other reactant (the sample). The technique requires that the amount of titrant added is exactly what is required to consume the amount of the sample present (i.e., there is no excess of either reactant present in the system). This condition is termed the "EQUIVALENCE POINT" or the "ENDPOINT". To accurately control the addition of reactant, the titrant is in solution form and is dispensed from a buret. The sample can be either a solution OR a weighed solid dissolved in water and is held in a 125 mL or 250 mL Erlenmeyer flask.

At the ENDPOINT, the relationship between the number of moles of titrant added from the buret and the number of moles of sample originally present in the flask is identical to the stoichiometry (equation coefficients of the BALANCED chemical equation for the reaction.

NUMBER OF MOLES OF TITRANT

The number of moles of titrant or sample is determined from:

For solutions: (Molarity) × (Volume in liters) = Moles of solute

For solids: (Sample mass) ÷ (Gram Molecular Weight) = Moles

The operational form of the ENDPOINT EQUATION therefore becomes:

n ·(Moles of Titrant) = **m** ·(Moles of Sample)

Where **n** and **m** refer to the mole relationship between reactants.
(coefficients in the balanced chemical equation)

A chemical substance that changes color at the endpoint (an INDICATOR) is added to the sample solution before the titration is begun. When ONE DROP of titrant results in a permanent color change in the sample solution, the endpoint has been reached and the titration has been completed.

In every case, three variables are determined by the experiment and the fourth variable is calculated using one of the above expressions.

EXAMPLE

35.00 mL of NaOH solution (titrant) are required to neutralize 30.00 mL of a 0.1200 M HCl solution (sample). Determine the molarity (M) of the NaOH solution (the titrant).

EQUATION: $\quad$ 1 NaOH$_{(aq)}$ + 1 HCl$_{(aq)}$ $\rightarrow$ 1 NaCl$_{(aq)}$ + 1 H$_2$O(l)

ANSWER: $\quad$ The moles of NaOH and HCl are identical at the endpoint.
(n and m are identical at 1 each)

The operational form of the ENDPOINT EQUATION therefore becomes:

$$n \cdot (\text{Moles of Titrant}) = m \cdot (\text{Moles of Sample})$$

Mol HCl $\quad = \quad 0.01200 \text{ mol/L} \times 0.0300 \text{ L} \quad = \quad 0.003600_0 \text{ mol HCl}$

Mol NaOH $\quad = \quad 0.003600_0 \text{ mol} \times \left[\dfrac{1 \text{ mol NaOH}}{1 \text{ mol HCl}} \right] = \quad 0.003600_0 \text{ mol NaOH}$

Molarity NaOH $\quad = \quad \dfrac{0.003600_0 \text{ mol}}{0.0300 \text{ L}} \quad = \quad 0.1028_5 \text{ mol/L NaOH}$

NOTE

If the acid were H$_2$SO$_4$, for instance, the balanced chemical equation becomes:

$$2 \text{ NaOH}_{(aq)} + 1 \text{ H}_2\text{SO}_{4(aq)} \rightarrow 1 \text{ Na}_2\text{SO}_{4(aq)} + 2 \text{ H}_2\text{O(l)}$$

Every **1** mole H$_2$SO$_4$ requires **2** moles NaOH

If, as in the above example:

the moles of H$_2$SO$_4$ = (0.1200 mol/L) × (0.0300 L) = 0.003600$_0$

Then the moles of NaOH would become:

Mol NaOH $\quad = \quad 0.003600_0 \text{ mol H}_2\text{SO}_4 \times \left[\dfrac{\textbf{2 mol NaOH}}{\textbf{1} \text{ mol H}_2\text{SO}_4} \right] = \quad 0.007200_0 \text{ mol}$

Molarity NaOH $\quad = \quad \dfrac{0.007200_0 \text{ mol}}{0.03500 \text{ L}} \quad = \quad 0.2057_1 \text{ mol/L}$

Whenever this technique is used to determine the <u>molarity</u> of a titrant solution, the process is termed a **STANDARIZATION.**

Since a "true" or accepted value for the molarity is generally not available, the accuracy of the result cannot be measured. The validity of the result must therefore be determined by evaluating the precision of the work.

Precision is used to express the reproducibility of a measurement. That is, the agreement between several measurements of the same object or property. Since the same property should theoretically give the same result every time it is measured, differences between results allow one to determine the reliability of an experiment even when there is no true or accepted value. The quantities used in this evaluation are defined as follows:

Mean (Average)   - Average of the experimental values of all trials.

Range   - Maximum difference between values
(i.e., the highest value minus the lowest value)

Deviation   - Difference between the mean and the value of an individual trial.

Average Deviation   - Sum of the deviations without regard to sign divided by the total number of trials.

Standard Deviation - $\sqrt[2]{\dfrac{\text{Sum of (deviations)}^2}{\text{number of trials} - 1}}$

In addition, the application of correct significant figures is as important to experimental quality as is precise measurement and accurate results. Significant figure rules must be followed in all calculation steps. Refer to the first experiment in this lab textbook (*Mass –Volume Exercise*) for a summary of these rules and an example of precision calculations.

WEAR YOUR SAFETY GOGGLES/LAB COAT!
WASH YOUR HANDS WHEN FINISHED!

Experimental Procedure

1. Prepare 150 mL of 0.1000 M Hydrochloric Acid by diluting the 6 M stock HCl solution as follows:

   Put approximately 50 mL of distilled water in a 250 mL beaker, add about 2.5 mL of the 6.0 M stock HCl solution (measure in a 10 mL graduated cylinder), and mix with your glass stirring rod. Rinse the residual acid from the cylinder into the beaker, add an additional 50 mL of distilled water, and continue mixing. Finally, add water to the 150 mL calibration mark on the beaker, and thoroughly mix the solution. This is our SAMPLE and will be assigned a concentration of 0.1000 M.

2. Prepare 150 mL of approximately 0.1 M Sodium Hydroxide by diluting 6.0 M NaOH in the same manner as described above. Prepare this solution in a 250 mL Erlenmeyer flask and take care to insure it is uniformly mixed. This is our TITRANT. Its' exact concentration will be determined in this experiment.

3. Clean one 25 mL or 50 ml buret and one 10.00 mL pipet. Rinse thoroughly with tap water, and then with two SMALL volumes of distilled water. Check to be sure that water flows smoothly through the buret tip and the pipet tip.

NOTE

A small beaker is used as a waste container to receive solutions that are used to rinse the buret or that are wasted in the process of adjusting the buret volume.

4. Rinse the buret twice with 4 mL portions of the NaOH solution and save the rinse in a waste beaker. Fill the buret with the NaOH solution. Drain some solution through the tip to eliminate air bubbles, and then adjust the level to some value between 0.0 mL and 1.0 mL. DO NOT attempt to achieve exactly 0.00 mL.

5. **SAMPLE**: THE 10.00 mL pipet will be used to dispense the acid solution into a 125 or 250 mL Erlenmeyer flask. DO NOT pipet by mouth. A pipet pump or bulb (suction device) is used to draw liquid into a pipet and dispense liquids from the pipet. Refer to the lab textbook, *APPENDIX: Use of a Volumetric Pipet*, for instructions on the use of a pipet and pump. Ask your instructor to explain its operation if you are uncertain about its use.

   Use the pipet to transfer 10.00 mL of your 0.1000 M HCl into a 125 or 250 mL flask, and add 3-5 drops of PHENOLPHTHALEIN indicator. Place a sheet of white paper behind and beneath the flask to improve endpoint visibility.

6. **TITRANT**: Adjust the BASE BURET level to between 0.0 mL and 1.0 mL, read this level to the nearest 0.01 mL (use a meniscus reader to locate the bottom of the meniscus), and record this as the <u>initial</u> NaOH volume. Add the NaOH solution into the acid in the flask while CONTINUOUSLY swirling the flask. If you are right-handed, use your left hand to control the stopcock and your right hand to swirl the flask (opposite if you are left-handed). When ONE DROP of NaOH causes a permanent pink color throughout the sample, the endpoint has been reached. Read and record the endpoint buret level as the <u>final</u> NaOH volume. Subtract the two readings to obtain the exact volume of the titrant added.

NOTE

If your solutions were prepared correctly, you can expect the endpoint to occur around 10 mL of base added. You should also be able to complete two trials (25 mL buret) or four trials (50 mL buret) before having to refill the buret.

7. Perform at least nine additional trials by repeating procedures 5 and 6 above. The final volume reading for a trial can serve as the initial reading for the following trial. Remember to REFILL the buret every two to four trials, recording the new initial NaOH volume (between 0.0 mL and 1.0 mL) each time you refill. Do not begin a trial unless you can finish without refilling.

DISPOSAL: Follow the instructions in Sections 8 and 9 to properly dispose of your waste materials.

8. Each titration trial is a neutralized sodium chloride solution at the endpoint and can therefore be poured into the sink and flushed down the drain with running tap water at the end of each trial. The sample flask should be rinsed with tap water and then with two small volumes of distilled water before being used for another sample.

After you have finished all ten trials, add all the left over sodium hydroxide solution (from the buret, flask and waste beaker) to the left over hydrochloric acid solution WHILE THE ACID CONTAINER IS IN THE SINK.

- Add 4–6 drops of **phenolphthalein indicator** to the mixture in the beaker.

- If the solution remains pink in color add 1.0 M HCl one drop at a time with stirring until one drop causes the pink color to fade clear (water-white). **Caution:** Do not add excess HCl.

- If the solution remains clear (water-white) in color add 6 M NaOH one drop at a time with stirring until one drop turns the solution pink.

- Then add 1 M HCl one drop at a time with stirring until one drop turns the solution clear. **Caution:** Do not add excess HCl.

- Rinse the neutralized mixture into the sink drain with flowing tap water.

9. RINSE the pipet with tap water at least four times and return. RINSE the buret with tap water at least four times (including the tip), fill the buret with tap water, insert a stopper, and return.

10. The ACID molarity is defined as 0.1000_0 M.

For trials **1** through **5** determine:

1. The molarity of NaOH for each trial.
2. The average molarity.
3. The deviation of each trial from the average.
4. The square of each deviation
5. The sum of the squared deviations.
6. The range of the NaOH molarity values.
7. The average deviation.
8. The standard deviation.

11. REPEAT the above calculation for trials **6** through **10.**

12. Report your measurements and calculated results on the CALCULATION SUMMARY TABLE using correct significant digits. The completed CALCULATION SUMMARY TABLE is your experimental report.

VOLUMETRIC CHEMICAL ANALYSIS II:
Acid Content of An Unknown Mixture

A titration is the procedure for carrying out a chemical reaction by the controlled addition of one reactant (the titrant) to a fixed amount of the other reactant (the sample). The technique requires that the amount of titrant added is exactly what is needed to consume the amount of the sample present (i.e., there is no excess of either reactant present in the system). This condition is termed the EQUIVALENCE POINT or the ENDPOINT. In order to accurately control the addition of reactant, the TITRANT is in solution form and is dispensed from a buret. The SAMPLE can be either a solution or weighed solid dissolved in water and is held in a 150 or a 250 mL Erlenmeyer flask.

At the ENDPOINT, the number of moles of titrant added from the buret equals the number of moles of sample originally present in the flask ADJUSTED FOR the reaction stoichiometry (equation coefficients) established by the BALANCED chemical equation for the reaction.

NUMBER OF MOLES OF TITRANT

The number of moles of titrant or sample is determined from:

For solutions: (Molarity) × (Volume in liters) = Moles of solute

For solids: (Sample mass) ÷ (Gram Molecular Weight) = Moles

A chemical substance that changes color at the endpoint (an INDICATOR) is added to the sample solution before the titration is begun. When ONE DROP of titrant results in a permanent color change, the endpoint has been reached and the titration has been completed.

In every case, the number of moles of one reactant is determined by measured experimental quantities such as mass or volume, and the moles of the other reactant are then calculated from its balanced equation (stoichiometric) relationship to the first reactant. Specific variables of the second reactant, such as its molarity, mass, volume, or gram molecular weight can then be evaluated.

If the experiment is used to determine the CONCENTRATION (Molarity M) of a solution the process is determined STANDARDIZATION. The other reactant used to accomplish this is often a pure solid compound known as a PRIMARY STANDARD. Once the concentration of the titrant has been determined (once the solution has been standardized), it can then be used to analyze a substance of unknown composition (e.g. such as a sample of impure solid acid).

EXAMPLE

28.96 mL of NaOH solution (titrant) is required to neutralize 0.127 grams of HCl (sample). Determine the molarity (M) of the NaOH solution (titrant). (Gram Molecular Weight HCl = 36.454)

EQUATION: $1 \text{ NaOH}_{(aq)} + 1 \text{ HCl}_{(aq)} \rightarrow 1 \text{ NaCl}_{(aq)} + 1 \text{ H}_2\text{O(l)}$

ANSWER: The moles of NaOH and HCl are identical at the endpoint.

$$\text{Mol HCl} = \frac{0.127 \text{ g}}{36.454 \text{ g/mol}} = 0.00348_3 \text{ mol HCl}$$

$$\text{Mol NaOH} = 0.00348_3 \text{ mol HCl} \times \left[\frac{1 \text{ mol NaOH}}{1 \text{ mol HCl}} \right] = 0.00348_3 \text{ mol NaOH}$$

$$\text{Molarity NaOH} = \frac{0.00348_3 \text{ mol}}{0.02896 \text{ L}} = 0.102_2 \text{ mol/L NaOH}$$

EXAMPLE

35.00 mL of the 0.120_2 M NaOH solution (titrant) is required to neutralize 0.252 grams of an unknown mixture containing the acid HCl (sample). Determine the percent HCl in the mixture. This acid contains one mole of "replaceable hydrogen" per mole of compound and therefore the reaction coefficients are all one:

EQUATION: $1 \text{ NaOH}_{(aq)} + 1 \text{ HA}_{(aq)} \rightarrow 1 \text{ NaA}_{(aq)} + 1 \text{ H}_2\text{O(l)}$

ANSWER: The moles of NaOH and of HA are equal at the endpoint.

$$\text{Mol NaOH} = 0.120_2 \text{ mol/L} \times 0.03500 \text{ L} = 0.00420_7 \text{ mol NaOH}$$

$$\text{Mol HCl} = 0.00420_7 \text{ mol NaOH} \times \left[\frac{1 \text{ mol HCl}}{1 \text{ mol NaOH}} \right] = 0.00420_7 \text{ mol HCl}$$

$$\text{Mass HCl} = 0.00420_7 \text{ mol HCl} \times \left[\frac{36.454 \text{ g HCl}}{1 \text{ mol HCl}} \right] = 0.1533 \text{ g HCl}$$

$$\textbf{Percent HCl} = \left[\frac{0.1533 \text{ g HCl}}{0.252 \text{ g mixture}} \right] \times 100 = 60.8_3 \text{ \%}$$

Acids such as HNO_3 and HCl provide one mole of acidic hydrogen per mole of compound and are termed *MONOPROTIC* acids. However, many acids are polyprotic, providing more than one mole of acidic hydrogen per mole of acid. For instance, H_2CO_3 provides two moles (*DIPROTIC*) and H_3PO_4 can provide up to three moles (*TRIPROTIC*) of acidic hydrogen per mole of acid.

When limited quantities of a base such as sodium or potassium hydroxide are added to a polyprotic acid, only part of the acidic hydrogen is converted to water, and an ACID SALT is formed:

$$1 \text{ KOH}_{(aq)} + 1 \text{ H}_2\text{SO}_{4(aq)} \rightarrow 1 \text{ H}_2\text{O} + 1 \text{ KHSO}_{4(aq)} \text{ (acid salt)}$$

Acid salts are stable, easily purified crystalline solids containing acidic hydrogens that are still available to react with additional base. As such, they are excellent samples to use when standardizing base solutions.

The sodium hydroxide solution in this experiment will be standardized using a compound of this type, potassium hydrogen phthalate ($KHC_8H_4O_4$) which is sometimes represented by the common, although technically incorrect, formula KHP. This is an *acid salt* formed by reaction of potassium hydroxide with diprotic phthalic acid ($H_2C_8H_4O_4$). The structural formulas are shown below. Note that only hydrogens bonded to oxygen are acidic enough to react with a base.

$$\text{H-O-}\overset{\overset{\displaystyle O}{\|}}{\text{C}}\text{-C}_6\text{H}_4\text{-}\overset{\overset{\displaystyle O}{\|}}{\text{C}}\text{-O-H}$$

$\text{HOC}_8\text{H}_4\text{O}_2\text{OH}$
PHTHALIC ACID

$$\text{H-O-}\overset{\overset{\displaystyle O}{\|}}{\text{C}}\text{-C}_6\text{H}_4\text{-}\overset{\overset{\displaystyle O}{\|}}{\text{C}}\text{-O}^-\text{K}^+$$

$\text{HOC}_8\text{H}_4\text{O}_2\text{O}^-\text{K}^+$
POTASSIUM HYDROGEN PHTHALATE

The gram molecular weight of potassium hydrogen phthalate (KHP) is 204.23 grams. This compound contains only one mole of acidic hydrogen per mole of compound, and thus the coefficients in its reaction with sodium hydroxide are all one. The equation for the standardization of sodium hydroxide with KHP is:

$$1 \text{ NaOH}_{(aq)} + 1 \text{ KHC}_8\text{H}_4\text{O}_{4(aq)} \rightarrow 1 \text{ NaKC}_8\text{H}_4\text{O}_{4(aq)} + 1 \text{ H}_2\text{O}_{(l)}$$

One the sodium hydroxide solution has been standardized with pure potassium hydrogen phthalate – a primary standard, it will be used to determine the percent composition of an impure mixture containing the same acid.

WEAR YOUR SAFETY GLASSES/LAB COAT!
WASH YOUR HANDS WHEN FINISHED!

EXPERIMENTAL PROCEDURE

1. TITRANT: Prepare 150 mL of approximately 0.1 M NaOH by diluting the 4 M stock NaOH solution as follows: Put approximately 50 mL of distilled water in a 250 mL beaker or flask, addapproximately 4.0 mL of 4 M NaOH, and mix by gently swirling the flask contents. Rinse the residual base from the cylinder into the container, add an additional 50 mL of water, and continue mixing. Finally, add water to the 150 mL calibration mark on the flask and thoroughly mix the solution. This is our TITRANT. Its' exact concentration will be determined by this experiment.

2. Clean one 25 or 50 mL buret. Rinse thoroughly with tap water, and then with two successive SMALL volumes of distilled water. Clean three 125 or 250 mL Erlenmeyer flasks. Rinse thoroughly with tap water and then with two successful SMALL volumes of distilled water. Dry the outside top lip of the flasks.

3. A small beaker is used as a waste container to receive solutions that are used to rinse the buret or that are wasted in the proces of adjusting the buret volume. Rinse the buret with two 5 mL portions of the NaOH titrant solution and then fill the buret with the NAOH solution. Drain some solution through the tip to eliminate air bubbles and then adjust the level to some value between 0.0 and 10 mL. Do NOT attempt to achieve exactly 0.00 mL.

4. SAMPLE: Transfer approximately two grams of solid potassium hydrogen phthalate (KHP) into a clean, DRY 50 mL beaker. (Add solid to a little <u>less</u> than <u>half</u> <u>way</u> to the 10 mL calibration mark on the beaker.) Use the method of successive mass difference (*Appendix: Preparation of Weighed Samples*) to prepare THREE samples of solid KHP in your 250 mL Erlenmeyer flasks. Each sample should weigh between 0.25 and 0.45 grams and be known (and recorded) to the nearest milligram.

TRANSFER THE SOLID WHILE OUTSIDE OF THE BALANCE
NOT WITHIN THE DRAFT SHIELD

Set the 50 mL beaker containing the excess solid aside for later treatment in Step 8.

5. Add approximately 50 mL of distilled water to your first sample, and then add five drops of PHENOLPHTHALEIN indicator and swirl to mix.

Adjust the BASE BURET level to between zero and one mL, and read and record this (to the nearest 0.01 mL precision) as the initial buret volume. Use a meniscus reader to locate the bottom of the meniscus). Place a piece of white paper behind/beneath the flask as you titrate. The white background makes the pink phenolphthalein color more visible, allowing easy determination of the endpoint. Add the NaOH solution into the sample while continuously swirling the solution in the flask. If you are right-handed, use your left hand to control the stopcock and your right hand to swirl the flask (opposite if you are left-handed). When one drop of NaOH causes a permanent pink color throughout the sample, the endpoint has been reached.

CHECK THE SAMPLE TO BE CERTAIN ALL THE SOLID HAS DISSOLVED

Read and record this final volume ($\pm$ 0.02 mL), and subtract the two readings to obtain the exact volume of titrant added. NOTE: If your solution was prepared correctly, you can expect the endpoint to occur between 10 and 22 mL of NaOH added.

Each titration trial is a neutralized solution at the endpoint and can be flushed down the drain with flowing tap water. Rinse the flask with tap water and then with two or three small volumes of distilled water. Remember to dry the top lip of the flask before using it for another sample.

REPEAT this titration with your other samples.

Calculate the NaOH molarity for each trial, the range of molarities, and the average molarity of the titrant.

6. Obtain a sample of an UNKNOWN impure acid and the sample size range from your instructor. Prepare three weighed samples in flasks as in item 4 above.

OBTAIN THE CORRECT SAMPLE SIZE FROM YOUR INSTRUCTOR!

Titrate each sample to the pink phenolphthalein endpoint as described in Step 5.

Calculate the mass and mass percent of potassium hydrogen phthalate for each trial. Calculate the range of mass percent values, and the average mass percent acid.

7. Each titration trial is a neutralized solution at the endpoint and can therefore be flushed down the sink drain with running tap water. However, all leftover NaOH solution must be neutralized before sink disposal.

 **DISPOSAL:** Follow the instructions in Section 8 to properly dispose of your waste materials.

8. **After you have finished all trials**, drain any remaining sodium hydroxide solution from your buret into any remaining left over sodium hydroxide. Transfer any excess solid KHP sample remaining from **Step 4** into the left over sodium hydroxide. Add three drops of phenolphthalein to this solution.

   - If the solution turns pink in color, add 6 M HCl drop by drop with stirring until one drop makes the pink color turn clear. Add one drop of 6 M NaOH to restore the pink color. Then add 1 M HCl drop by drop with stirring until one drop turns the solution clear.

- If the solution remains clear, add 6 M NaOH drop by drop with stirring until one drop turns the solution pink. Then add 1 M HCl drop by drop with stirring until one drop turns the solution clear.

This neutralized solution can then be flushed down the drain.

Rinse the BURET and all other containers with running tap water. Fill the buret with tap water, stopper, and return the buret to the storage bin.

9. Report your results on the attached data summary page using correct significant figures.

VOLUMETRIC CHEMICAL ANALYSIS III:
Equivalent Mass of an Unknown Acid

Titration, the procedure for carrying out a chemical reaction by the controlled addition of one reactant (the titrant) to a fixed amount of the other reactant (the sample), can also be used to determine the gram formula mass of an acid. As was the case for *Volumetric Analysis I* and *Volumetric Analysis II*, the amount of titrant added must be exactly what is needed to consume the amount of the sample present. The unknown acid sample must be pure so that the mass of the sample is directly related to the gram formula weight of the compound.

Acids such as HNO_3 and HCl provide one mole of acidic hydrogen per mole of compound and are termed *MONOPROTIC* acids. However, many acids are polyprotic, providing more than one mole of acidic hydrogen per mole of acid. For instance, H_2CO_3 provides two moles (*DIPROTIC*) and H_3PO_4 can provide up to three moles (*TRIPROTIC*) of acidic hydrogen per mole of acid. When the formula of the sample is unknown (this experiment), it is not possible to determine correct stoichiometry (coefficients) for the reaction or the correct endpoint relationship. In this case, we <u>assume</u> the acid is a *MONOPROTIC* acid, and that the number of moles of acid equals the number of moles of base at the endpoint.

Because the acid formula is unknown, determination of a gram formular mass in this case is not possible. Instead, one determines the EQUIVALENT MASS of the acid. This is the mass of compound that contains one mole of acidic hydrogen – the mass that is chemically equivalent to one mole of *MONOPROTIC* acid.

In order to analyze an unknown acid, we must first standardize a base solution with a known acid sample as in *Volumetric Analysis II*. We will use potassium hydrogen phthalate (KHP), the same primary standard we utilized in *Volumetric Analysis II*. Please refer to that experiment for a discussion of the structure and chemistry of this compound.

EXAMPLE

28.96 mL of NaOH solution (titrant) is required to neutralize 0.711 grams of KHP (sample). Determine the molarity (M) of the NaOH solution (titrant). (Gram Formula Weight KHP = 204.23)

EQUATION: $1\,NaOH_{(aq)} + 1\,KHP_{(s)} \rightarrow 1\,NaKP_{(aq)} + 1\,H_2O(l)$

ANSWER: The moles of NaOH and KHP are identical at the endpoint.

$$\text{Mol KHP} = \frac{0.711\,g}{204.23\,g/mol} = 0.00348_1\,mol\,KHP$$

$$\text{Mol NaOH} = 0.00348_1\,mol\,KHP \times \left[\frac{1\,mol\,NaOH}{1\,mol\,KHP}\right] = 0.00348_1\,mol\,NaOH$$

$$\text{Molarity NaOH} = \frac{0.00348_1\,mol}{0.02896\,L} = 0.102_2\,mol/L\,NaOH$$

EXAMPLE

35.00 mL of the 0.120_2 M NaOH solution (titrant) is required to neutralize 0.252 grams of an unknown mixture containing the acid HA (sample). Determine the Gram Formular Mass of the acid. We assume this acid contains one mole of "replaceable hydrogen" per mole of compound and therefore the reaction coefficients are all one:

EQUATION: $1\,NaOH_{(aq)} + 1\,HA_{(aq)} \rightarrow 1\,NaA_{(aq)} + 1\,H_2O(l)$

ANSWER: The moles of NaOH and of HA are equal at the endpoint.

$$\text{Mol NaOH} = 0.120_2\,mol/L \times 0.03500\,L = 0.00420_7\,mol\,NaOH$$

$$\text{Mol HA} = 0.00420_7\,mol\,NaOH \times \left[\frac{1\,mol\,HA}{1\,mol\,NaOH}\right] = 0.00420_7\,mol\,HA$$

$$\text{GFW HA} = \left[\frac{mass\,HA}{mol\,HA}\right] = \left[\frac{0.252\,g}{0.00420_7\,mol}\right] = 59.9_0\,g/mol\,HA$$

NOTE

For the case where the acid is POLYPROTIC the balanced equation coefficients are not identical:

$$2\,NaOH_{(aq)} + 1\,H_2SO_{4(aq)} \rightarrow 1\,Na_2SO_{4(aq)} + 2\,H_2O(l)$$
$$3\,NaOH_{(aq)} + 1\,H_3PO_{4(aq)} \rightarrow 1\,Na_3PO_{4(aq)} + 3\,H_2O(l)$$

If the acid is of unknown formula, the coefficients cannot be determined. Therefore, the endpoint equation is treated as if the acid were MONOPROTIC (all coefficients are one.) In this case, the analysis determines the GRAM EQUIVALENT MASS not the Gram Formula Mass.

WEAR YOUR SAFETY GLASSES/LAB COAT!
WASH YOUR HANDS WHEN FINISHED!

EXPERIMENTAL PROCEDURE

1. TITRANT: Prepare 150 mL of approximately 0.1 M NaOH by diluting the 4 M stock NaOH solution as follows: Put approximately 50 mL of distilled water in a 250 mL beaker or flask, add approximately 4.0 mL of 4 M NaOH, and mix by gently swirling the flask contents. Rinse the residual base from the cylinder into the container, add an additional 50 mL of water, and continue mixing. Finally, add water to the 150 mL calibration mark on the flask and thoroughly mix the solution. This is our TITRANT. Its' exact concentration will be determined by this experiment.

2. Clean one 25 or 50 mL buret. Rinse thoroughly with tap water, and then with two successive SMALL volumes of distilled water. Clean three 125 or 250 mL Erlenmeyer flasks. Rinse thoroughly with tap water and then with two successful SMALL volumes of distilled water. Dry the outside top lip of the flasks.

3. A small beaker is used as a waste container to receive solutions that are used to rinse the buret or that are wasted in the proces of adjusting the buret volume. Rinse the buret with two 5 mL portions of the NaOH titrant solution and then fill the buret with the NAOH solution. Drain some solution through the tip to eliminate air bubbles and then adjust the level to some value between 0.0 and 10 mL. Do NOT attempt to achieve exactly 0.00 mL.

4. SAMPLE: Transfer approximately two grams of solid potassium hydrogen phthalate (KHP) into a clean, DRY 50 mL beaker. (Add solid to a little <u>less</u> <u>than</u> <u>half</u> <u>way</u> to the 10 mL calibration mark on the beaker.) Use the method of successive mass difference (*Appendix: Preparation of Weighed Samples*) to prepare THREE samples of solid KHP in your 250 mL Erlenmeyer flasks. Each sample should weigh between 0.25 and 0.45 grams and be known (and recorded) to the nearest milligram.

   Set the 50 mL beaker containing the excess solid aside for later treatment in Step 8.

5. Add approximately 50 mL of distilled water to your first sample, and then add five drops of PHENOLPHTHALEIN indicator and swirl to mix.

   Adjust the BASE BURET level to between zero and one mL, and read and record this (to the nearest 0.01 mL precision) as the initial buret volume. Use a meniscus reader to locate the bottom of the meniscus). Place a piece of white paper behind/beneath the flask as you titrate. The white background makes the pink phenolphthalein color more visible, allowing easy determination of the endpoint. Add the NaOH solution into the sample while continuously swirling the solution in the flask. If you are right-handed, use your left hand to control the stopcock and your right hand to swirl the flask (opposite if you are left-handed). When one drop of NaOH causes a permanent pink color throughout the sample, the endpoint has been reached.

CHECK THE SAMPLE TO BE CERTAIN ALL THE SOLID HAS DISSOLVED

179

Read and record this final volume ($\pm$ 0.02 mL), and subtract the two readings to obtain the exact volume of titrant added. NOTE: If your solution was prepared correctly, you can expect the endpoint to occur between 10 and 22 mL of NaOH added.

Each titration trial is a neutralized solution at the endpoint and can be flushed down the drain with flowing tap water. Rinse the flask with tap water and then with two or three small volumes of distilled water. Remember to dry the top lip of the flask before using it for another sample.

REPEAT this titration with your other samples.

Calculate the NaOH molarity for each trial, the range of molarities, and the average molarity of the titrant.

6. Obtain a sample of an UNKNOWN ~~impure~~ acid and the sample size range from your instructor. Prepare three weighed samples in flasks as in item 4 above.

OBTAIN THE CORRECT SAMPLE SIZE FROM YOUR INSTRUCTOR!

Titrate each sample to the pink phenolphthalein endpoint as described in Step 5.

Calculate the equivalent mass for each trial. Calculate the range of equivalent mass values and the average equivalent mass.

7. Each titration trial is a neutralized solution at the endpoint and can therefore be flushed down the sink drain with running tap water. However, all leftover NaOH solution must be neutralized before sink disposal.

DISPOSAL: Follow the instructions in Section 8 to properly dispose of your waste materials.

8. **After you have finished all trials**, drain any remaining sodium hydroxide solution from your buret into any remaining left over sodium hydroxide. Transfer any excess solid KHP sample remaining from **Step 4** into the left over sodium hydroxide. Add three drops of phenolphthalein to this solution.

   • If the solution turns pink in color, add 6 M HCl drop by drop with stirring until one drop makes the pink color turn clear. Add one drop of 6 M NaOH to restore the pink color. Then add 1 M HCl drop by drop with stirring until one drop turns the solution clear.

   • If the solution remains clear, add 6 M NaOH drop by drop with stirring until one drop turns the solution pink. Then add 1 M HCl drop by drop with stirring until one drop turns the solution clear.

This neutralized solution can then be flushed down the drain.

Rinse the BURET and all other containers with running tap water. Fill the buret with tap water, stopper, and return the buret to the storage bin.

9. Report your results on the attached data summary page using correct significant figures.

VOLUMETRIC CHEMICAL ANALYSIS IV:
Determination of Percent Iron

Aqueous solutions of potassium permanganate ($KMnO_4$), an oxidizing agent, are often employed as a titrant in volumetric analysis. In acid solution the permanganate ion undergoes reduction to manganese (II) ion via:

$$8 \ H^+ + MnO_4^- + 5 \ e^- \ \rightarrow \ Mn^{+2} + 4 \ H_2O$$

This experiment utilizes permanganate ion to determine the percent iron in a solid mixture that contains some unknown quantity of the iron containing compound, iron(II) ammonium sulfate hexahydrate [$Fe(NH_4)_2(SO_4)_2 \cdot 6H_2O$]. The iron (II) ion is oxidized to iron(III) ion by permanganate via:

$$Fe^{+2} \ \rightarrow \ Fe^{+3} + e^-$$

The overall reaction is therefore:

$$8 \ H^+ + MnO_4^- + 5 \ Fe^{+2} \ \rightarrow \ Mn^{+2} + 5 \ Fe^{+3} + 4 \ H_2O$$

The reaction is carried out in 0.5 M sulfuric acid to insure that the permanganate ion is completely reduced to manganese (II), rather than to some intermediate product such as MnO_2. The MnO_4^- ion is intense purple in color, while Mn^{+2} is essentially colorless (very pale pink). An indicator is not needed for this analysis; the intense purple color makes the titrant self-indicating. The purple color disappears on contact with the sample solution as long as Fe^{+2} is present. The endpoint is achieved when ONE DROP of titrant imparts a permanent faint pink color to the solution caused by the slight excess of the purple $KMnO_4$.

The iron (III) ion is yellow in color and would tend to mask the faint pink endpoint color. The addition of phosphoric acid causes the iron to form a colorless complex thus preventing its' color from the interfering with endpoint identification. The phosphoric acid is not added until the yellow color is visible in the sample. The disappearance of the yellow color verifies formation of the colorless compound.

The potassium permanganate solution will be standardized using pure iron (II) ammonium sulfate hexahydrate [$Fe(NH_4)_2(SO_4)_2 \cdot 6H_2O$]. It is sometimes referred to by its common name, ferrous ammonium sulfate, and given the notation FAS. It has gram molecular weight of 392.15 and contains one mole of Fe^{+2} per mole of compound. Therefore, at the endpoint the moles of iron present (FAS) are FIVE times the moles of titrant added.

EXAMPLE

28.96 mL of solution is required to oxidize all the Fe^{2+} in a 1.212-gram sample of $Fe(NH_4)_2(SO_4)_2*6H_2O$ [FAS]. Determine the solution molarity.

From the balanced equation: mol FAS $= 5 \times$ (mol $KMnO_4$)

$$\text{Mol of FAS} = \text{Mol of iron} = \frac{1.212 \text{ g}}{392.15 \text{ g/mol}} = 3.090_6 \times 10^{-3} \text{mol iron}$$

$$\text{Mol } KMnO_4 = 3.090_6 \times 10^{-3} \text{mol iron} \times \left[\frac{1 \text{ mol } KMnO_4}{5 \text{ mol iron}} \right] = 6.181_3 \times 10^{-4} \text{mol } KMnO_4$$

$$\text{Molarity } KMnO_4 = \frac{6.181_3 \times 10^{-4} \text{mol } KMnO_4}{0.02896 \text{ L}} = 0.02134_4 \text{ M}$$

Once the concentration of the titrant has been determined (once the solution has been STANDARDIZED), it is then used to analyze some unknown compound or mixture:

EXAMPLE

35.00 mL of the 0.02134_4 M $KMnO_4$ solution (titrant) is required to oxidize the Fe^{2+} contained in a mixture weighing 1.642 grams. What is the mass and the percent iron in this sample?

As above, at the endpoint: mol FAS $= 5 \times$ (mol $KMnO_4$)

$$M_T \cdot V_T = (0.02134_4 \text{ mol } KMnO_4/L) \times (0.03500 \text{ L}) = 7.470_5 \times 10^{-4} \text{ mol } KMnO_4$$

$$\text{Mol Fe} = 7.470_5 \times 10^{-4} \text{ mol } KMnO_4 \times \left[\frac{5 \text{ mol iron}}{1 \text{ mol } KMnO_4} \right] = 3.735_2 \times 10^{-3} \text{mol Fe}$$

$$\text{Mass Iron} = (3.735_2 \times 10^{-3} \text{mol Fe}) \times (55.847 \text{ g/mol}) = 0.208_6 \text{ grams iron}$$

NOTE: We were only able to weigh the mixture sample to the nearest milligram. Therefore, we cannot report the mass of iron to any more (or less) precision than the nearest milligram.

$$\text{Percent Iron} = \frac{\text{mass iron}}{\text{mass iron}} \times 100 = \frac{0.208_6 \text{ g iron}}{1.642 \text{ g sample}} \times 100 = 12.7_0 \text{ \%}$$

WEAR YOUR SAFETY GOGGLES/LAB COAT!
WASH YOUR HANDS WHEN FINISHED!

EXPERIMENTAL PROCEDURE

1. _Titrant:_ Prepare a titrant solution by dissolving approximately 0.50 grams of $KMnO_4$ in about 150 mL of distilled water. (Use a 250 mL Erlenmeyer flask.) Swirl the solution in the flask to thoroughly mix its contents. Allow the solution to stand and settle. Then carefully pour (without mixing) into a <u>one-liter</u> beaker. Examine the flask in which the solution was stored for any signs of undissolved solid. If no solid is present, return the solution to the 250 mL flask and proceed to the next step.

   If solid is visible, it must be dissolved. Thoroughly mix the solution that is in the beaker, allow it to settle, and carefully pour it back into the 250 mL flask. Examine the beaker for any sign of undissolved solid. Continue this process until no evidence of solid potassium permanganate is visible, and then return the solution to the flask. Repeat the procedure described above until ALL of the solid has dissolved, and then proceed to step 2.

   LEAVE THE ONE LITER BEAKER AT YOUR WORKSTATION TO SERVE AS A WASTE CONTAINER.
   DISSOLVE ALL SOLIDS TO ENSURE THAT THE SOLUTION IS OF UNIFORM CONCENTRATION

2. Place a 250 mL beaker in a SINK and prepare 150 mL of approximately 0.5 M sulfuric acid (H_2SO_4) by slowly pouring about 4 mL (use a 10 mL cylinder) of concentrated (18 M) acid into the beaker containing 150 mL of distilled water. (Acid into water always!) Use 4-5 mL of distilled water to rinse the remaining acid from the cylinder into the beaker.

   Transfer 4.0 mL of 85% phosphoric acid into a 50 mL beaker, label the beaker and insert a dropper.

   Clean one 50 mL buret. Rinse thoroughly with tap water and then with two successive SMALL volumes of distilled water. Clean three 125 mL or 250 mL Erlenmeyer flasks. Rinse thoroughly with tap water and then with two successive SMALL volumes of distilled water. Dry the outside top lip of each flask.

3. Rinse the buret with two 3 mL portions of the $KMnO_4$ solution, and then fill the buret with the solution. Drain some solution through the tip (into your <u>waste container</u>) to eliminate air bubbles, and then adjust the level to some value between 0.0 and 1.0 mL. Do NOT attempt to achieve exactly 0.00 mL.

4. _Sample_: Transfer approximately 2.5 grams of solid $Fe(NH_4)_2(SO_4)_2 \cdot 6H_2O$ (FAS) into a clean, DRY 50 mL beaker. (Add solid to about the 5 mL mark of a 50 mL calibrated beaker.) Use the method of successive mass difference (_Appendix: Preparation of Weighed Samples_) to prepare THREE samples of solid FAS in the Erlenmeyer flasks. Each sample should weigh between 0.5 and 0.8 grams and be known to the nearest milligram (0.001 g) precision. When you have finished the entire experiment discard the excess FAS into your <u>waste container</u>. (See Step 9.)

189

5. Add about 20-25 mL of your 0.5 M sulfuric acid to your first sample, and swirl gently to mix (Do not add acid to the next sample until you are about to begin its titration.) Place a piece of white paper behind/beneath the flask to facilitate endpoint identification.

6. Adjust the BURET level to between 0.0 and 1.0 mL, and read/record this (to the nearest 0.01 mL) as the initial buret volume. Add the $KMnO_4$ solution to the sample while CONTINUOUSLY swirling the solution in the flask. If you are right-handed, use your left hand to control the stopcock and your right hand to swirl the flask (opposite if you are left-handed).

When the yellow Fe^{+3} color becomes visible in the sample, stop the titration and add approximately 10 drops of concentrated (85%) phosphoric acid (H_3PO_4). Gently mix the solution, and verify the disappearance of the yellow color. Continue the titration. When one drop of $KMnO_4$ causes a permanent pink color throughout the sample, the endpoint has been reached. (If the yellow color reappears, add 5-6 additional drops of concentrated phosphoric acid. If the gelatinous brown solid MnO_2 appears, consult your instructor.)

CHECK THE SAMPLE TO BE CERTAIN THAT ALL THE SOLID HAS DISSOLVED

7. Read/record this final volume ($\pm$ 0.02 mL), and subtract the two readings to obtain the exact volume of $KMnO_4$ added. NOTE: If your solution was prepared correctly, you can expect the endpoint to occur between 10 and 22 mL of titrant added. (See Step 9)

   REPEAT this titration with your other samples. CALCULATE the $KMnO_4$ molarity for each trial, the range of molarities, and the average molarity.

8. Obtain an UNKNOWN iron sample from your instructor, clean the flasks, and prepare three weighed samples in flasks as in Step 5 above. The unknown sample should be between 1.0 and 1.2 grams. Titrate each sample to the pink endpoint as described in Step 7 above. (See Step 9)

 **DISPOSAL:** Follow the instructions in Section 9 to properly dispose of your waste materials.

9. After an endpoint has been reached and the volumes recorded, each titration trial must be poured into the waste container. The flask should then be rinsed with tap water and then with distilled water if it is to be used for another trial (Discard the tap/distilled water rinses in the sink.) Remember to dry the top lip of the flask before using it to prepare a new sample.

   After all trials are completed, add all the left over $KMnO_4$ solution to the waste container. Also, add any left over phosphoric and sulfuric acid solution to the waste container.

Add solid iron(II) ammonium sulfate (FAS) to the waste solution in SMALL INCREMENTS, stirring the solution between additions, until the intense purple color of permanganate ion disappears. (A 50 mL excess of $KMnO_4$ solution would require approximately 0.4 grams of FAS – visually about a one-half pencil eraser volume. AVOID USING EXCESS SOLID.) The solution should appear yellow in color caused by the presence of iron(III) ion.

Add any leftover sulfuric and phosphoric acid solutions to your Waste Beaker.

Transfer the resulting solution into the waste container provided in the hood area.

Rinse the one-liter beaker and acid containers with tap water, flushing the rinse down the drain with flowing tap water, and return the beaker to the laboratory cabinet.

The buret MUST be thoroughly rinsed with tap water, and stored full of water.

10. CALCULATE the MASS of Iron and the PERCENT of IRON in each sample of your unknown. Then determine the range of PERCENT of IRON and the average PERCENT of IRON.

Report your results on the attached data summary page using correct significant figures.

Determination of Percent Iron
Advanced Problem Assignment

Name_____   Section_____   Date_____

READ THE EXPERIMENTAL DISCUSSION FIRST!
Complete the data tables below using the correct significant digits.
SHOW CALCULATION SET-UP ON THE NEXT PAGE.

A. Standardization of a Potassium Permanganate Solution:

SAMPLE: Iron(II)ammonium sulfate hexahydrate [$Fe(NH_4)_2(SO_4)_2 \cdot 6H_2O$]
Gram Molecular Weight: 392.15

	Sample 1	Sample 2	Sample 3	
Mass of Sample	0.786	0.847	0.715	grams
Moles of Iron				mole
Initial Buret Volume	1.02	1.40	1.35	mL
Final Buret Volume	22.33	24.16	20.87	mL
Total Volume				Liters
Moles of $KMnO_4$				mole
$KMnO_4$ Molarity				mole/L
Average Molarity				mole/L
Range of Molarities				mole/L

B. Percent Iron in an Unknown Mixture of Iron Compounds:

Gram Atomic Weight of Iron: 55.847

	Sample 1	Sample 2	Sample 3	
Mass of Unknown	0.914	0.733	0.926	grams
Initial Buret Volume	1.52	0.75	1.35	mL
Final Buret Volume	26.88	21.44	27.12	mL
Total Volume				Liters
Moles of $KMnO_4$				mole
Moles of Iron				mole
Mass of Iron				grams
Percent Iron				%
Average Percent Iron				%
Range of Percent Iron				%
Unknown Number				**********

Determination of Percent Iron
Experimental Data & Calculations

Name_____   Section_____   Date_____

A. Standardization of a Potassium Permanganate Solution:

SAMPLE: Iron(II)ammonium sulfate hexahydrate [$Fe(NH_4)_2(SO_4)_2 \cdot 6H_2O$]
Gram Molecular Weight: 392.15

	Sample 1	Sample 2	Sample 3	
Mass of Sample				grams
Moles of Iron				mole
Initial Buret Volume				mL
Final Buret Volume				mL
Total Volume				Liters
Moles of $KMnO_4$				mole
$KMnO_4$ Molarity				mole/L
Average Molarity				mole/L
Range of Molarities				mole/L

B. Percent Iron in an Unknown Mixture of Iron Compounds:

Gram Atomic Weight of Iron: 55.847

	Sample 1	Sample 2	Sample 3	
Mass of Unknown				grams
Initial Buret Volume				mL
Final Buret Volume				mL
Total Volume				Liters
Moles of $KMnO_4$				mole
Moles of Iron				mole
Mass of Iron				grams
Percent Iron				%
Average Percent Iron				%
Range of Percent Iron				%
Unknown Number				

195

Calculations

CHEMICAL ANALYSIS BY SPECTROPHOTOMETRIC METHODS

Whenever a beam of polychromatic radiation (white light) travels through a liquid or gas medium, loss of beam intensity occurs via several processes. Light reflection occurs at phase boundaries as a result of refractive index differences, and light scattering is caused by thermal fluctuations in the medium. In addition, the medium itself can absorb light wavelengths that promote energy changes within molecules, significantly reducing the power of the transmitted beam at those wavelengths (*FIGURE 1*). The degree of absorption is related to the number of absorbing molecules in the light path and is therefore a function of the concentration of the energy absorbing solute.

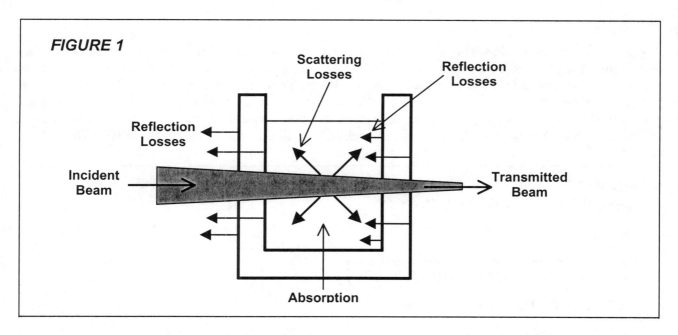

FIGURE 1

If the energy absorbed corresponds to wavelengths in the visible region of light (400 nm to 700 nm), the emergent beam will appear colored. The apparent color of the medium is the compliment of the color absorbed (*FIGURE 4*). Thus, a copper ion solution that appears blue is absorbing wavelengths in the yellow region (600 nm) while a solution that absorbs in the green region (530 nm) will appear purple.

The amount of light energy absorbed (the reduction in the intensity of the light beam) is proportional to the number of absorbing molecules in the light path. Measurement of the energy absorbed in the visible region can therefore be used to determine the concentration of colored species in the light path.

The change in light intensity caused by energy absorption is summarized by a relationship known as the BEER-LAMBERT LAW or simply BEER'S LAW:

$$\text{ABSORBANCE} = \text{Log}(I_o/I) = a \times b \times C$$

<u>WHERE</u>:

I_o = Light intensity without absorbing molecules.

I = Light intensity with absorbing molecules.

I/I_o = <u>TRANSMITTANCE</u> - the fraction of light transmitted. A non-linear, inverse function of concentration.
(High concentration = Low transmittance)

a = <u>MOLAR ABSORBITIVITY</u> - a characteristic of the particular solute/solvent used.

b = The <u>PATH LENGTH</u> of light through the sample.

C = The <u>MOLARITY</u> of the colored solute.

$\text{Log}(I_o/I)$ = <u>ABSORBANCE</u> – a measure of light absorbed. A linear, direct function of concentration.
(High concentration = High absorbance)

According to this equation, the absorbance of colored solutes that follow the Beer-Lambert Law is a linear function of solute CONCENTRATION. A graph of solution absorbance at a fixed wavelength vs. the solute molarity is termed a "Beer's Law calibration curve." Once established by measuring the absorbances of solutions having known concentrations (at constant wavelength), this graph can be used to determine the concentration of an unknown solution containing the same solute based on the absorbance of the unknown solution (*FIGURE 2*).

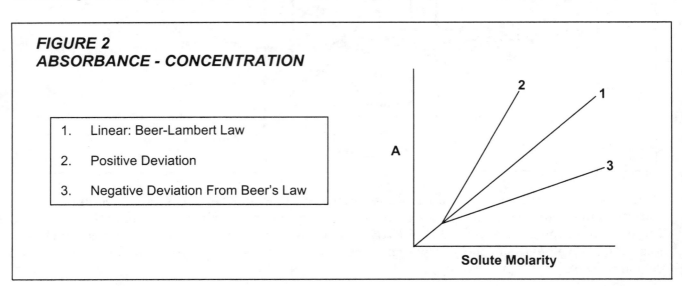

FIGURE 2
ABSORBANCE - CONCENTRATION

1. Linear: Beer-Lambert Law
2. Positive Deviation
3. Negative Deviation From Beer's Law

The ABSORPTION SPECTRUM (*FIGURE 3*) measures the absorbance of a colored solute as a function of the WAVELENGTH of incident light (at constant solute concentration). The wavelength at which absorption is a <u>maximum</u> is the *wavelength* selected for the absorbance-concentration measurements required to obtain a Beer's Law calibration graph.

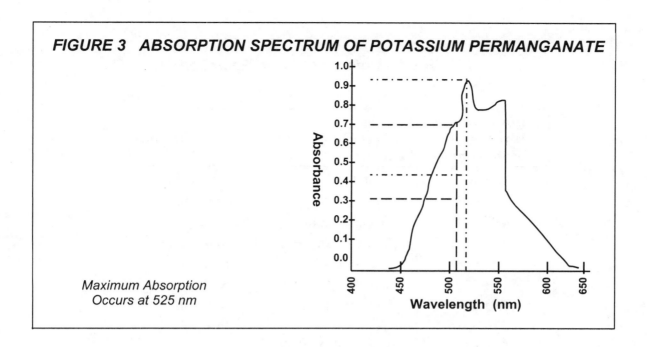

FIGURE 3 ABSORPTION SPECTRUM OF POTASSIUM PERMANGANATE

Maximum Absorption Occurs at 525 nm

The ABSORBANCE of light by a solution (or the light TRANSMITTED through a solution) is measured using a SPECTROPHOTOMETER, often termed a COLORIMETER if used in the visible (colored) region of light (refer to *APPENDIX*). This device allows one to select the wavelength of light that is passed through a solution, and then to measure the intensity of the light beam as it exits the sample.

In practice, the instrument is first adjusted to read zero ABSORBANCE (100% TRANSMITTANCE) with distilled water in the sample chamber, and then used to measure the light absorbed by the colored solution. Measurements are carried out in a series of test tubes that have been matched to eliminate differences in their path lengths and in their reflection losses. Once matched, the test tubes are termed cuvettes. Since the molar absorbitivity and the path length will therefore be identical for all samples, any change in the amount of light absorbed depends only on the change in concentration.

This experiment will demonstrate the techniques used to obtain a Beer's Law calibration curve for aqueous potassium permanganate ($KMnO_4$). The curve will then be used to determine the molarity of a permanganate solution of unknown concentration. In addition, the ABSORPTION SPECTRUM and wavelength of maximum absorption will be determined in PART **B** of the experiment.

FIGURE 4 **Colors of Visible Radiation**

Approximate Wavelength Range, nm	Color	Complement
400-465	Violet	Yellow-green
465-482	Blue	Yellow
482-487	Greenish blue	Orange
487-493	Blue-green	Red-orange
493-498	Bluish green	Red
498-530	Green	Red-purple
530-559	Yellowish green	Reddish purple
559-571	Yellow-green	Purple
571-576	Greenish Yellow	Violet
576-580	Yellow	Blue
580-587	Yellowish orange	Blue
587-597	Orange	Greenish blue
597-617	Reddish orange	Blue-green
617-780	Red	Blue-green

WEAR YOUR SAFETY GOGGLES/LAB COAT!
WASH YOUR HANDS WHEN FINISHED!

DISPOSAL: Place all used and unused solutions into a 400 mL Waste Beaker at your workstation. Save these for Part C Step 4.

Experimental Procedure

STUDENTS SHOULD WORK IN PAIRS FOR PART A, PART B AND PART C.

One student prepares the matched test tubes (cuvettes) while, at the same time, the other student begins to prepare TABLE I solutions (with PRECISION!)

Once the cuvettes have been matched, that student uses SOLUTION 1 (of the TABLE I solutions) to complete **PART C** of the experiment (ABSORBANCE vs. WAVELENGTH). Remember that the ZERO Absorbance point MUST be adjusted using a water blank EVERY time the wavelength is changed.

After all TABLE I solutions have been prepared, **PART B** measurements (ABSORBANCE vs. CONCENTRATION) are then taken by both partners at 525 nm.

EACH student prepares and submits his or her own graphs and lab report for PART B and PART C.

Part A: Preparation of Matched Test Tubes (cuvettes)

1. Thoroughly clean six or seven (13 × 100 mm) test tubes, affix labels at the very top of each tube, and fill the bottom half with distilled water. Check to be sure the Spectronic 20 wavelength is set at 525 nm, and set the MODE switch to TRANSMITTANCE. Adjust the Spectronic 20 to read 0.0 % Transmittance when the sample chamber is empty and closed (**LEFT front** control knob).

2. Insert the first test tube in the same chamber, close the lid, and adjust the TRANSMITTANCE reading to 100.0% (**RIGHT front** control knob). Mark the test tube label opposite the reference mark that is on the surface of the sample chamber, and set the tube aside for later use.

   Insert another tube (do not adjust the front control knobs), and turn it in the chamber until the TRANSMITTANCE is 100.0% (within one unit, sample chamber closed). This tube now matches the first. Mark the tube at the reference point, and set it aside.

REPEAT this process until you obtain a set of five matched tubes (now called "cuvettes"). Although it may be necessary to discard tubes that cannot be matched, you should not need to try more than eight or nine to obtain five that match. Discard the water from four of the tubes, and save the fifth to serve as your "blank" for the ABSORBANCE measurements. *Save these cuvettes for other experiments.*

3. Empty and dry four cuvettes in preparation for the next part of the experiment. Remember that a cuvette must be dry before filling it with potassium permanganate solution.

Part B: Preparation of a Beer's Law Calibration Curve

1. You will be provided with a solution that is 3.0×10^{-4} M potassium permanganate. Using your 50.0 mL graduated cylinder, carefully measure 25 – 30 mL of this 3.0×10^{-4} M solution and take it to your workstation. This solution will serve as the STOCK SOLUTION and will be used to prepare the TABLE I mixtures for this experiment.

Set up a 400 mL beaker at your workstation to serve as a Waste Container. All waste solution must be held in this container until the experiment is complete.

Obtain two 5.0 mL pipets and a pipet pump from the laboratory cart. Rinse one pipet with a very small amount of your stock solution (discard the rinse into your waste beaker) and rinse the other with distilled water.

Rinse three LARGE (approximately 20 mL or more) test tubes with distilled water and thoroughly dry the inside.

2. Prepare mixtures 1 through 4 as follows:

Solution 1:	Pipet 5.0 mL of your $KMnO_4$ into a dry cuvette, mark as Solution 1, and have your laboratory partner use this solution for Part C.
Solution 2:	Mix 5.0 mL of $KMnO_4$ stock solution and 5.0 mL of water in a large test tube. Label this as Solution 2.
Solution 3:	Mix 5.0 mL of $KMnO_4$ stock solution and 10.0 mL of water in a large test tube. Label this as Solution 3.
Unknown Solution:	Pipet 5.0 mL of stock $KMnO_4$ solution into a large test tube. Rinse the pipet twice with distilled water. Rinse again with a very small sample of Solution 3. Discard the rinse into your Waste Container. Use this pipet to transfer 5.0 mL of Solution 3 into the test tube containing the 5.0 mL sample of your stock solution. Label this mixture as Unknown Solution.

3. Transfer Solution 2, Solution 3 and the Unknown Solution into dry cuvettes. Fill each cuvette about two-thirds full and label each.

Your instructor will explain the operation of the Spectronic 20 Spectrophotometer. The procedure is summarized in the Appendix of this book. Make sure you use the same spectrophotometer throughout the experiment.

4. Measure the absorbance of all four solutions <u>at</u> a <u>wavelength</u> setting of <u>525 nm</u>. Record these absorbance values on TABLE I.

5. Examine your absorbance values for the Part B Solutions. Are they consistent with the specified concentrations? The molarity of Solution 2 is one half that of Solution 1. Are these absorbance values in the same relationship? The molarity of Solution 3 is one third that of Solution 1. Are these absorbance values in the same relationship?

   Repeat solution preparation and absorbance measurement for any absorbance values that are not consistent with the solution molarity.

6. Prepare a graph having absorbance as the vertical axis (the ordinate) and solution molarity as the horizontal axis (the abscissa). Refer to *Appendix: The Graph – A Data Analysis Tool*.

   Plot ABSORBANCE vs. MOLARITY data for mixtures 1 through 3 on this graph, and draw the best straight line through these three points <u>and the origin</u>. Then use this Beer's Law calibration curve to determine the molarity of the Unknown Solution from its absorbance.

7. Calculate the theoretical molarity of the unknown solution from the concentrations and volumes of stock solution and the volume of Solution 3 used to prepare it. Determine the RELATIVE ERROR between this theoretical value and the actual molarity determined from the Beer's Law Curve. Refer to the Mass-Volume Exercise experiment for a discussion of Relative Error.

Part C. Determination of the Absorption Spectrum

1. Set the spectrophotometer wavelength control at 500 nm and adjust the 0% and 100% TRANSMITTANCE using a distilled water blank. Insert the cuvette containing Solution 1 (prepared in Part B) and record its absorbance at 500 nm.

2. Reset the wavelength control to 515 nm and repeat this process. Continue until you have recorded the ABSORBANCE of Solution 1 over the range 500 nm to 560 nm as indicated in the chart below. (REMEMBER: The 100 % TRANSMITTANCE must be adjusted every time the wavelength is changed.)

Wavelength in nm	Absorbance
500	.524
515	.704
520	.790
525	~~0.80~~ .758
530	.780
535	.774
540	.746
545	.708
550	.652
560	.494

3. Prepare a graph having absorbance as the ordinate and wavelength as the abscissa. Plot the absorbance–wavelength data to obtain the absorption spectrum of potassium permanganate. Determine the wavelength at which absorbance is a maximum. Record this wavelength on your data page and attach the graph to your report.

4. Once you have completed both Part B and Part C discard all solutions into your Waste Beaker. Fill the beaker with tap water and flush the contents into the sink with running tap water.

EQUILIBRIUM CONSTANT DETERMINATION

Prerequisite: Chemical Analysis by Spectrophotometric Methods
Background: Molarity Calculations
                         Law of Chemical Equilibrium

When a chemical process takes place in a closed system (one which prevents the escape or further reaction of components), product molecules can collide with sufficient energy to form reactant molecules. Eventually, the rate of this reverse reaction becomes identical to the rate of the forward reaction, and a state of dynamic equilibrium is thus established in the system. Under this condition, the concentrations of all components become constant, and the product to the reactant ratio is a fixed number termed an <u>equilibrium constant.</u>

For a reaction having the general form:

$$aA + bB \quad \Leftrightarrow \quad dD + eE$$

The equilibrium constant in terms of concentration (K_c) is defined using the <u>equilibrium</u> molarities of the products divided by the equilibrium molarities of the reactants, each raised to the power of its' coefficient:

$$K_c = \frac{[D]^d [E]^e}{[A]^a [B]^b}$$ The symbol **[ ]** means MOLAR concentration of the reactant or product AT EQUILIBRIUM.

Experimentally, the value of the equilibrium constant is obtained by allowing the reaction to achieve equilibrium at a fixed temperature. The molarity of each component is then experimentally measured and its' value substituted into the equilibrium expression for calculation of K_c. Usually several trials are performed thus allowing the reaction to achieve equilibrium from various starting reactant concentrations. A value of K_c is calculated for each trial, and these are averaged to obtain the equilibrium constant for the reaction.

For our experiment we will observe the reaction of iron(III) ion with thiocyanic acid (HSCN) to form the iron(III)thiocyanate complex ion which is colored in aqueous solution:

$$Fe^{+3}_{(aq)} + HSCN_{(aq)} \quad \Leftrightarrow \quad Fe(SCN)^{+2}_{(aq)} + H^+_{(aq)} \tag{1}$$

$$\text{Where} \qquad K_c = \frac{[Fe(SCN)^{+2}][H^+]}{[Fe^{3+}][HSCN]}$$

Since the iron thiocyanate complex is colored, the equilibrium concentration can be determined by measuring the absorbance with a spectrophotometer (colorimeter). The equilibrium concentration of the other reaction components can then be calculated from their initial concentrations and the equilibrium molarity of $FeSCN^{+2}$. Substitution of the equilibrium concentrations into the K_C expression yields a value for the equilibrium constant. The following example illustrates the calculations involved:

10.0 mL of 0.00400 M iron(III)nitrate is mixed with 10.0 mL of 0.00400 M thiocyanic acid and 5.0 mL of 0.25 M nitric acid. (Both the iron and the thiocyanic acid solutions were prepared in 0.25 M nitric acid, allowing the H^+ molarity to remain constant at 0.25 M.) These react to form the iron thiocyanate complex ion according to reaction **(1)**. At equilibrium, the complex ion molarity was found to be 0.00050 M by colorimetric analysis. Calculate the equilibrium constant K_C:

(a) The <u>initial</u> molarities of Fe^{+3} <u>and</u> of HSCN are identical at:

$$\frac{\left(4.00 \times 10^{-3} \text{ M}\right)\left(1.00 \times 10^{-2} \text{ liters}\right)}{\left(2.50 \times 10^{-2} \text{ liters}\right)} = 1.60 \times 10^{-3} \text{ M}$$

(b) The <u>initial</u> molarity of H^+ is fixed at 0.25 M.

(c) The amount of Fe^{+3} and of HSCN consumed in reaching equilibrium (X) is identical to the amount of the $FeSCN^{+2}$ (and H^+) formed:

$$\textbf{Fe}^{+3} \quad + \quad \textbf{HSCN} \quad \Leftrightarrow \quad \textbf{FeSCN}^{+2} \quad + \quad \textbf{H}^+$$

Initial–X   Initial–X   0+X   0.25+X $\Leftarrow$ *Equilibrium Concentrations*

The value of X is the $FeSCN^{+2}$ complex ion molarity found by colorimetric analysis (0.00050 M in this example). The equilibrium molarities are thus:

(d) $[FeSCN^{+2}] = X$ $\qquad\qquad\qquad\qquad\qquad\qquad\qquad\qquad = 0.50 \times 10^{-3}$ M

$[Fe^{+3}] = [HSCN] = (1.60 \text{ X } 10^{-3}) - (0.50 \text{ X } 10^{-3})$ $\qquad = 1.10 \times 10^{-3}$ M

$[H^+] = 0.25 + 0.50 \text{ X } 10^{-3}$ $\qquad\qquad\qquad\qquad\qquad = 0.25 \qquad$ M

The equilibrium constant can be then evaluated:

(e) $\quad K_c = \dfrac{\left[Fe(SCN)^{+2}\right]\left[H^+\right]}{\left[Fe^{3+}\right]\left[HSCN\right]} \qquad K_c = \dfrac{\left[0.50 \times 10^{-3}\right]\left[0.25\right]}{\left[1.10 \times 10^{-3}\right]\left[1.10 \times 10^{-3}\right]} = 1.0_3 \times 10^{+2}$

In the above example, we assumed the reaction occurred according to equation **(1)**. However, the formation of the colored iron thiocyanate complex ion <u>may</u> have occurred via the reaction:

$$\textbf{Fe}^{+3}{}_{(aq)} \quad + \quad 3 \textbf{ HSCN}_{(aq)} \quad \Leftrightarrow \quad \textbf{Fe(SCN)}_{3(aq)} \quad + \quad 3 \textbf{ H}^+{}_{(aq)} \qquad\qquad (2)$$

Initial–X   Initial–3X   0+X   0.25+3X $\Leftarrow$ *Equilibrium Concentrations*

214

If this were the case, then the equilibrium molarities become:

$[Fe(SCN)_3] = X$ $= 0.50 \times 10^{-3}$ M

$[Fe^{+3}] = (1.60 \times 10^{-3}) - (0.50 \times 10^{-3})$ $= 1.10 \times 10^{-3}$ M

$[HSCN] = (1.60 \times 10^{-3}) - 3(0.50 \times 10^{-3})$ $= 0.10 \times 10^{-3}$ M

$[H^+] = 0.25 + 3(0.50 \times 10^{-3})$ $= 0.25$ M

And the value of K_c then becomes:

$$K_c = \frac{[Fe(SCN)^{+2}][H^+]^3}{[Fe^{3+}][HSCN]^3} \qquad K_c = \frac{[0.50 \times 10^{-3}][0.25]^3}{[1.10 \times 10^{-3}][0.10 \times 10^{-3}]^3} = 7.1_0 \times 10^{+9}$$

By comparing the K_c values for several different trials, one can <u>identify</u> the <u>correct</u> equilibrium <u>reaction</u>. If the balanced equation used is not correct, then the K_c values will be different for each trial. The correct equation yields equilibrium constant values that are the same (within experimental error) for every trial.

FORMULAS:

Thiocyanic Acid: HSCN
Iron(III)nitrate: $Fe(NO_3)_3$
Iron(III)thiocyanate ion: $FeSCN^{+2}$
Nitric Acid: HNO_3

WEAR YOUR SAFETY GOGGLES/LAB COAT!

WASH YOUR HANDS WHEN FINISHED!

DISPOSAL of reaction products: Put all waste solutions in a 1 Liter beaker at your workstation. Save the solutions for PART B.

Experimental Procedure

PART A: Preparation of a Standard Curve for a Spectrophotometer

1. You or your laboratory partner should have a set of matched cuvettes from a prior experiment. If you do not have a set of matched cuvettes refer to the Experiment *Chemical Analysis by Spectrophotometric Methods* for the procedure for matching cuvettes. These cuvettes will be used for future experiments. Make sure that you SAVE them.

> **Your instructor will explain the operation of the Spectronic 20 Spectrophotometer. The procedure is summarized in the Appendix. Make sure you use the same spectrophotometer throughout the experiment.**

2. Use a 50 mL graduated cylinder to obtain 12–14 mL of 0.00300 M Fe^{+3} solution. Use a 10 mL graduated cylinder to obtain 10 mL of 0.00300 M HSCN solution. Take the solutions, a pipet pump and the necessary pipettes back to your workstation.

> **Set up a 1 Liter beaker at your workstation to serve as a Waste Beaker. All waste solutions must be held in this beaker until the experiment is completed.**

3. Prepare three different solutions of iron thiocyanate complex ion by mixing volumes of iron(III)nitrate, thiocyanic acid, and nitric acid as summarized in **Table I** on the next page.

   Please note that the stock solution of thiocyanic acid is 0.200 M.

   The stock solutions are dispensed from pipets or burets. The solutions in **Table I** should be dispensed into clean and dry small beakers. Since the buret volumes are read to 0.01 mL precision, a meniscus reader should be used.

   Measure and record the absorbance of each solution prepared according to **Table I**. The wavelength should be maintained at 447 nm. Each cuvette must be dried and then be filled about two-thirds.

4. Graph the absorbance versus the molar concentration of iron thiocyanate of the **Table I** solutions to obtain the Beer-Lambert calibration curve. Plot absorbance on the vertical axis and the concentration on the horizontal axis. The graph should yield a "best straight line" passing through the origin. If your data points do not result in an acceptable straight line graph you will have to redo **PART A** of this experiment in its entirety. For more information about graphing refer to *Appendix: The Graph – A Data Analysis Tool.*

TABLE I: Preparation of Solutions for a Spectrophotometer Calibration Curve

Trial	HSCN 0.200 M	Fe³⁺ 0.00300 M	HNO₃ 0.25 M	[FeSCN⁺²]	ABSORBANCE
A	10.00 mL	1.00 mL	9.00 mL	1.50×10^{-4} M	1.120
B	10.00 mL	1.00 mL	14.00 mL	1.20×10^{-4} M	.855
C	10.00 mL	1.00 mL	19.00 mL	1.00×10^{-4} M	.68
	BURET	PIPET	BURET		

$\frac{.003}{20} = 1.5 \times 10^{-4}$

$\frac{.003}{25} = 1.2 \times 10^{-4}$

PART B: Preparation of the Iron Thiocyanate Equilibrium System

1. Prepare three different iron thiocyanate equilibrium systems by mixing volumes of iron(III)nitrate, thiocyanic acid, and nitric acid as summarized in **TABLE II** below. The solutions are dispensed from pipets or burets and should be measured to the nearest 0.01 mL. Prepare each mixture in a clean, dry large test tube, and mix thoroughly to ensure that equilibrium is achieved. Note that the thiocyanic acid solution used in this part of the experiment is 0.00300 M, NOT 0.200 M as in **TABLE I**.

TABLE II: Preparation of the Iron Thiocyanate Complex Equilibrium System

Trial	HSCN 0.00300 M	Fe⁺³ 0.00300 M	HNO₃ 0.25 M	Initial Fe⁺³ Molarity	Initial HSCN Molarity	Absorbance	[FeSCN⁺²] Molarity
1	4.00 mL	2.00 mL	4.00 mL	6×10^{-4}	12×10^{-4}	.592	$.82 \times 10^{-4}$
2	3.00 mL	2.00 mL	5.00 mL	6×10^{-4}	9×10^{-4}	.305	$.425 \times 10^{-4}$
3	2.00 mL	2.00 mL	6.00 mL	6×10^{-4}	6×10^{-4}	.384	$.53 \times 10^{-4}$
	PIPET	PIPET	BURET				GRAPH

$\frac{.003 \times 2}{10} = 6 \times 10^{-4}$

2. Determine the absorbance of each of these trials at a wavelength of 447 nm. The absorbance measurements must be made in the matched cuvettes you prepared in the first part of this experiment.

3. When you have finished all parts of the experiment combine all leftover and waste solutions in the 1 Liter Waste Beaker. Use your 10 mL graduated cylinder to measure 6–7 mL of NaOH and add it to the mixture in the beaker. The color of the waste solution should fade indicating that the solution has become basic. If not add 6 M NaOH in 1 mL increments until the color fades, then add 10 drops of phenolphthalein indicator. The solution should become pink in color.

Add 1.0 M HCl <u>one drop at a time</u> with stirring until one drop causes the pink color to disappear. Do NOT add excess HCl.

Fill the beaker to the top with tap water and rinse into the sink.

Thoroughly rinse each pipet with water and return the pipets and pipet pump to the laboratory cart.

4. Use the calibration curve prepared in **PART A** to obtain the concentrations of the iron(III) thiocyanate complex from these absorbance values. Calculate the initial concentration of the iron(III) ion and thiocyanic acid. Based on **Reaction (1)**, for each trial calculate the equilibrium concentration of each component and then a value for the equilibrium constant. (Note that the H^+ ion concentration remains constant at 0.25 M. Any increase caused by the reaction is negligible in comparison to 0.25 M.)

Calculate the average value of K_C for trials one through three, **Reaction (1)**.

Determine the range of K_C for trials one through three, **Reaction (1)**.

5. Calculate the equilibrium constant assuming the reaction proceeded via equation **(2)**. Determine the range of K_C for trials one through three, **Reaction (2)**.

PART C: Identification of the Correct Equilibrium Reaction

Which equilibrium model is the correct reaction for this equilibrium?

- **Reaction (1)** represents the correct equilibrium.

- **Reaction (2)** represents the correct equilibrium.

- The correct equilibrium model cannot be identified.

- **Justify** your choice using the results of your experimental determination of the K_C values.

218

QUALITATIVE ANALYSIS OF AQUEOUS SOLUTIONS
An Introduction

There are many instances in chemistry where the composition of a substance must be determined or the identity of a material must be determined. This process first requires one to identify WHAT elements, ions, or compounds are present. Once these are identified, measurement of the QUANTITY (often as percent composition) of each component is then undertaken. The process of identifying what components are present is the area known as QUALITATIVE ANALYSIS. Determination of how much is present is known as QUANTITATIVE ANALYSIS and requires the ability to accurately measure mass and/or volume.

The following experimental sequence is concerned with identifying which cations (positive ions) or anions (negative ions) are present in an aqueous solution and serves to demonstrate many of the principles involved in qualitative chemical analysis. Qualitative analysis utilizes one or more types of reaction to separate the ions in the aqueous mixture. Once separated, a reaction that forms a product that is characteristic of the particular ion confirms its presence.

Reactions Involved in Inorganic Qualitative Analysis

Most reactions taking place in aqueous solution occur between charged atoms such as Cl^{-1} and Na^{+1} or molecular ions such as NO_3^{-1} or SO_4^{-2}. Some of the compounds utilized in the analysis process, however, exist as neutral molecules in solution. The general principles are as follows:

- Dissolved ionic compounds and the strong electrolyte acids, HCl, HBr, HI, H_2SO_4, and HNO_3, are completely ionized in solution.

- Water, ammonia (NH_3), dissolved gases, and weak electrolyte acids (such as acetic acid $HC_2H_3O_2$ or oxalic acid $H_2C_2O_4$) will exist in solution as neutral molecules.

- Ionic compounds that are only slightly soluble are generally written in molecular form accompanied by a "solid" notation (e.g. $AgCl_{(s)}$)

- It is important to realize that many chemical reactions do not go to completion. They instead establish a dynamic equilibrium in solution phase, which can be influenced by adding or removing reagents or by changing physical conditions in accordance with Le Chatelier's principle. By applying this principle, the chemist can force precipitation to occur, cause some slightly soluble compound to dissolve, or create a complex ion that prevents interference with tests for other ions or that confirms the presence of a particular ion.

Acid-Base Reactions, Bronsted-Lowry

It is often necessary to control the acidity of a solution in order to effect separation of ions or, less frequently, perform a confirmation test. Formation of the hydronium ion H_3O^+, on addition of a Bronsted-Lowry acid, creates an acid medium (pH less than 7.0) via donation of a proton to water. A Bronsted-Lowry base such as ammonia (NH_3) accepts a proton from water to form OH^{-1} ions and a basic system. Careful control of solution pH is very important to the separation and confirmation procedures in our analysis procedure.

Hydrolysis

Many ions also react with water, resulting in the formation of either H_3O^+ or OH^- ions, thus affecting the pH of the solution. This type of reaction is commonly known as hydrolysis but is really the same proton donor or proton acceptor process described above. One example is the reaction of ammonium ion to form an acid solution and ammonia. Another is the reaction of the acetate ion to form a basic system and acetic acid:

$$NH_4^+{}_{(aq)} + H_2O_{(l)} \Leftrightarrow NH_3{}_{(aq)} + H_3O^+{}_{(aq)}$$

$$C_2H_3O_2^{-1}{}_{(aq)} + H_2O_{(l)} \Leftrightarrow HC_2H_3O_2{}_{(aq)} + OH^{-1}{}_{(aq)}$$

Under the Bronsted-Lowry definition, NH_4^+ ion is the conjugate acid of the base ammonia, while $C_2H_3O_2^{-1}$ is the conjugate base of the acid $HC_2H_3O_2$.

Precipitation Reactions

Addition of a reagent that forms an insoluble solid is extremely important to most qualitative analysis processes. In many cases the formation of solids by some of the ions in a mixture but not by others is what makes separation possible. In other cases the formation of a solid characteristic of only one ion is what allows us to confirm its presence in the system. The solubility of a very slightly soluble compound is expressed by its solubility product constant, its Ksp. Tables of Ksp values are available in your lecture textbook, but the information contained in the **solubility rules** is often more valuable to an understanding of qualitative analysis. For example, the fact that all ionic chloride compounds are soluble except those of silver(I), mercury(I), and lead(II) is what requires us to separate these ions as chloride compounds before dealing with others such as hydroxides or carbonates. The **solubility rules** are also summarized in your lecture textbook and will assist your understanding of the analysis process.

It is important to remember that the reverse of precipitation is also of extreme importance to qualitative analysis. Adding a reagent that causes a competing reaction that dissolves the solid, thus separating or confirming a particular ion, may alter the solubility of a particular species. For instance, silver(I) chloride (AgCl) is insoluble in distilled water but can be made to dissolve by adding aqueous ammonia:

$$AgCl_{(s)} \Leftrightarrow Ag^+{}_{(ag)} + Cl^{-1}{}_{(aq)} \qquad\qquad Ag^+{}_{(aq)} + 2\,NH_3{}_{(aq)} \Leftrightarrow Ag(NH_3)_2^+{}_{(aq)}$$

The competing NH_3 reaction consumes silver ion and causes the first reaction to proceed further toward product and thus forcing the solid AgCl to dissolve.

Decomposition Reactions

A decomposition reaction occurs when one chemical species spontaneously decomposes into one or more different products. The effervescence that results when acid is added to a carbonate is the result of decomposition of carbonic acid and the accompanying escape of carbon dioxide gas:

$$CO_3^{-2}{}_{(aq)} + 2\ H_3O^+{}_{(aq)} \Leftrightarrow H_2CO_{3(aq)} + 2\ H_2O_{(l)}$$

$$H_2CO_{3(aq)} \Leftrightarrow H_2O_{(l)} + CO_{2(g)}$$

The carbonate ion undergoes an acid-base (hydrolysis) reaction, producing carbonic acid. Carbonic acid is very unstable and spontaneously decomposes into water and carbon dioxide gas. Hydrogen peroxide (H_2O_2) also decomposes on heating to form water and oxygen gas. Both of these reactions are used in our analysis procedure to remove excess carbonate ion or excess hydrogen peroxide.

$$2\ H_2O_2{}_{(aq)} \Leftrightarrow 2\ H_2O_{(l)} + O_{2(g)}$$

Acid-Base Reactions, Lewis

Anions and many neutral molecules are able to donate a pair of electrons (a Lewis base is defined as an electron pair donor) to form a coordinate covalent bond. Metal cations, especially transition metal cations, are electron deficient and can thus accept electron pairs (a Lewis acid is defined as an electron pair acceptor) from the Lewis base. Water and ammonia (NH_3) are examples of neutral Lewis bases, while the anion Lewis bases include Cl^{-1}, Br^{-1}, I^{-1}, SCN^{-1}, and OH^{-1}. On the other hand, several of the metal cations in our analysis system, such as silver(I), iron(III), and aluminum(III), are Lewis acids. These accept electron pairs to form extremely stable aqueous solution complexes (co-ordination compounds), allowing both separation and/or confirmation of the cation.

For example, formation of a silver-ammonia complex ion dissolves silver(I) chloride thus permitting its separation from mercury(I) chloride. Formation of an aluminum–hydroxide complex ion separates it from other members of the "hydroxide group":

$$AgCl_{(s)} + 2\ NH_{3(aq)} \Leftrightarrow Ag(NH_3)_2^+{}_{(aq)} + Cl^{-1}{}_{(aq)}$$

$$Al(OH)_{3(s)} + OH^{-1} \Leftrightarrow Al(OH)_4^{-1}{}_{(aq)}$$

Other cations, such as iron(III), nickel(II), and copper(II), form highly colored co-ordination compounds in solution. The characteristic color serves to confirm the presence of the ion in our system.

$$Fe^{+3}{}_{(aq)} + SCN^{-1}{}_{(aq)} \Leftrightarrow FeSCN^{+2}{}_{(aq)} \quad \textbf{[RED]}$$

$$Cu^{+2}{}_{(aq)} + 4\ NH_{3(aq)} \Leftrightarrow Cu(NH_3)_4^{+2}{}_{(aq)} \quad \textbf{[BLUE]}$$

Oxidation–Reduction Reactions

A chemical process that results in a change in the oxidation state of an element is termed an oxidation-reduction reaction. An oxidation number cannot change, of course, unless electrons are gained or lost. Reduction is defined as a gain of electrons (reduction in <u>positive</u> oxidation state) and oxidation is defined as a loss of electrons (increase in <u>positive</u> oxidation state.) Both must occur in order to have an oxidation-reduction process. Zinc metal, for example, reacts with hydrochloric acid to produce hydrogen and zinc(II)chloride.

$$Zn_{(s)} + 2\,HCl_{(aq)} \rightarrow Zn\,Cl_{2(aq)} + H_{2(g)}$$

- Zinc <u>undergoes</u> oxidation (electron loss): $\quad Zn \rightarrow Zn+2 + 2\,e^-$

  While

- The hydrogen ion <u>undergoes</u> reduction (electron gain): $\quad 2\,H^+ + 2\,e^- \rightarrow H_{2(g)}$

- Hydrogen ion is the oxidizing AGENT -- it accepted the electrons that were "lost".

- Zinc is termed the reducing AGENT -- it provided the electrons that were "gained".

Oxidation–reduction reactions are used in qualitative analysis to affect a separation, confirm the presence of an ion, and sometimes to dissolve extremely insoluble compounds. The reactions can be accompanied by a color change that often provides a strong indication that a particular ion is present. However, the actual confirmation test may use a different reaction. If oxidation of a species is required, it is necessary to add an <u>oxidizing</u> agent. Nitric acid and hydrogen peroxide are oxidizing agents commonly used in qualitative analysis. Chromium, for instance, is separated from other ions by oxidation to chromate ion with hydrogen peroxide:

$$2\,Cr(OH)_{3(s)} + 3\,H_2O_{2(aq)} + 4\,OH^{-1}_{(aq)} \Leftrightarrow 2\,CrO_4^{-2}_{(aq)} + 8\,H_2O_{(l)}$$
$$\textbf{[GREEN]} \qquad\qquad\qquad\qquad \textbf{[YELLOW]}$$

The oxalate ($C_2O_4^{-2}$), tin(II), and iron(II) ions are examples of <u>reducing agents</u> utilized in our analysis system. Tin(II) ion is employed to reduce bismuth(III) to black elemental bismuth, thus confirming the presence of bismuth ion:

$$Bi(OH)_{3(s)} + Sn^{+2}_{(aq)} \rightarrow Bi_{(s)}\,\textbf{[BLACK]} + Sn^{+4}_{(aq)} + 3\,OH^{-1}_{(aq)}$$

Disproportionation is a special case of oxidation–reduction where a single compound undergoes both oxidation and reduction (it oxidizes and reduces itself.) The confirmation test for mercury(I), for example, is the disproportionation of the Hg_2^{+2} in Hg_2Cl_2 to form both black elemental mercury Hg and mercury(II) in the form of the white solid $HgNH_2Cl$:

$$Hg_2Cl_{2(s)} + 2\,NH_{3(aq)} \rightarrow Hg_{(l)} + HgNH_2Cl_{(s)} + NH_4^+_{(aq)} + Cl^{-1}_{(aq)}$$

We note that disproportionation actually requires PART of the compound to undergo oxidation and a different PART to undergo reduction. One of the Hg^+ in our Hg_2^{+2} ion was reduced to Hg, while the other Hg^+ was oxidized to Hg^{+2}.

As one proceeds through the scheme we have selected to demonstrate the concept of qualitative analysis, it will often be helpful to identify the TYPE of reaction involved in a step and WHAT the procedure step does (separation, or confirmation, or both.) Be aware, however, that sometimes more than one reaction type is important to the step. For instance, AgCl can not dissolve in ammonia if the solution is acid, and $Cr(OH)_3$ will not be oxidized to chromate ion unless the system is basic.

Qualitative Analysis of Aqueous Solutions

Demonstration of an Analysis Procedure for Cations

We have selected the following fourteen positive ions as the basis of our example of a qualitative analysis procedure:

NH_4^+ Ag^+ Hg_2^{+2} Pb^{+2} Bi^{+3} Al^{+3} Fe^{+3} Cr^{+3} Mn^{+2} Ba^{+2} Ca^{+2} Cu^{+2} Ni^{+2} Mg^{+2}

The analysis procedure must first separate these into smaller subgroups based on some chemical property of the ion. Each sub grouping of ions is then further separated until a reaction that produces a solid or solution characteristic of a particular ion can be carried out without interference from other ions. This reaction confirms the presence (or absence) of that ion in the solution. In short, qualitative analysis procedures must first accomplish SEPARATION of the ions and then conduct CONFIRMATION tests for each individual ion.

The ammonium ion NH_4^+ is not readily separated from other ions in aqueous solution. We therefore perform the confirmation test for the presence of this ion using a separate, small sample of the solution before beginning analysis of the others.

Silver(I), mercury(I), and lead(II) form insoluble compounds in the presence of chloride ion ($AgCl$ Hg_2Cl_2 $PbCl_2$) while the other ions do not. These are therefore the first ions separated by the addition of hydrochloric acid and are known as the **Chloride Group** ions.

The cations iron(III), bismuth(III), chromium(III), aluminum(III), and manganese(II) all form insoluble hydroxides in the presence of a weak electrolyte base, while the remaining ions on the list do not. Accordingly, this group of ions is separated next using aqueous ammonia as the precipitation reagent. Bi^{+3}, Al^{+3}, Fe^{+3}, Cr^{+3}, and Mn^{+2} are termed the **Hydroxide Group** ions. The group is then separated into two subgroups utilizing the fact that $Bi(OH)_3$, $Fe(OH)_3$, and MnO_2 remain insoluble in the strong base NaOH while one of the others dissolves as a complex hydroxide ion ($Al(OH)_4^{-1}$) and one ($Cr(OH)_3$) is oxidized to the yellow chromate ion CrO_4^{-2} in basic medium.

The remaining ions are in solution either as ions (+2) or as complex ions of ammonia ($Cu(NH_3)_4^{+2}$, $Ni(NH_3)_6^{+2}$). These are separated into two subgroups via formation of the insoluble carbonates $BaCO_3$ and $CaCO_3$. Collectively, Ba^{+2}, Ca^{+2}, Cu^{+2}, Ni^{+2}, and Mg^{+2} are classified as the **Alkaline Carbonate Group**.

General Procedures

The following is a brief summary of the experimental principles and techniques that one must follow in all of the qualitative analysis procedures specified in our demonstration scheme:

WASTE DISPOSAL	Discard all solutions and solids into a "waste beaker"(250mL) at your workstation. At the end of the lab period, transfer these to the waste container provided in the hood.
WATER	This symbol always means to use distilled or deionized water. Set up a labeled 50 mL beaker of water with a dedicated dropper at your work station.
STIRRING ROD	Set up a 400 mL beaker of water at your workstation to rinse your stirring rods after each use. Change the water once or twice during the lab period to keep contamination levels below detection limits.
TEST TUBE	This refers to 13 X 100 mm (small, centrifuge size) test tubes.
VOLUME AND MASS	One milliliter is approximately 20 drops. One gram is a solid volume approximately equal to one "pencil eraser" volume. Do not use a graduated cylinder or a balance; measure mass and volume by visual estimate or by drop count.
HEATING	Test tubes MUST always be heated in a WATER BATH. Never heat a test tube in a direct Bunsen flame!!! The water bath is a 250 mL beaker about two-thirds full of water. It is held on a wire gauze/iron ring supported by a ring stand. A second, larger ring is adjusted slightly below the top of the beaker as a guard against "tip over". Two students can share a bath.
CENTIFUGE	Place the centrifuge test tube containing the solid-solution mixture in the centrifuge; BALANCE it with another tube containing an identical amount of water or solution, and centrifuge at full speed. Fifteen seconds at full speed is sufficient for most separations. Allow the centrifuge to stop by itself when finished, do not attempt to stop the rotor with your hands.
TEST COMPLETE PRECIPITATION	Centrifuge and then add ONE ADDITIONAL DROP of the precipitating reagent. If no additional solid forms as a result, precipitation is complete. If solid forms add three or four additional drops, and repeat the test.
DECANT / WASH	Centrifuge and pour the liquid (supernatant solution) into a clean test tube. Do not allow the meniscus to disturb the solid even if some solution must be left in the tube. WASH THE SOLID: Add 25-30 drops of water to the solid, then stir, centrifuge, and decant the wash liquid. Combine the wash liquid with the original solution unless directed to discard it.
SEPARATION	<u>Includes:</u> **Centrifuging** the solution/solid mixture, **Testing** for (and completing if needed) complete **Precipitation**, **Decanting** the supernatant solution into another tube, and then **Washing** the solid. All steps are performed as described above.
SOLID TRANSFER	Solids must first be suspended in the solution (or in 20–30 drops of water) by stirring, and the suspension is then poured into the receiving container. Centrifuging and decanting separates the suspending liquid from the solid.

ADJUSTING ACIDITY	The acidity of a solution is determined by using a stirring rod to place a drop of the solution on LITMUS PAPER. (DO NOT insert the litmus paper into the solution.)
	
	    If ACIDIC – BLUE litmus paper will change to RED.
	
	    If BASIC – RED litmus paper will change to BLUE.
	
	• When adjusting a solution to ACID, the solution should begin basic. If it is not, add 6M NH_3 until it is basic. Then add the acid drop by drop until ONE DROP causes the change from blue to red.
	• When adjusting a solution to BASIC, the solution should begin acid. If it is not, add 6M HCl until it is acid. Then add the base drop by drop until ONE DROP causes the change from red to blue.
	• If the procedure requires EXCESS acid or base, the additional reagent is added after the one-drop color change has been achieved as above.

Laboratory Stock Solutions

All reagent solutions have been prepared in dispensing containers.

Qualitative Analysis reactants (solutions having concentration LESS THAN 3.0 M) are in dropper bottles on the <u>side</u> laboratory bench (or, on occasion, the <u>hood</u> area). Use these <u>at the side bench</u> (or in the <u>hood</u>). DO NOT move them to your workstation.

Acid and Base Stock solutions (solutions having concentrations of 3.0 M and 6.0 M) are in dropper bottles on the center shelf of the laboratory bench near your workstation. Use these <u>at your workstation</u>, returning them to the center shelf as soon as you have finished adding reactant to your test tube.

READ each label carefully before you open the bottle and withdraw the dropper. Add the solution a drop at a time into your test tube, but DO NOT INSERT the dropper into the test tube; the stock solution must not be contaminated with your test solution. If you believe accidental contamination may have occurred, notify your instructor – the reagent bottle will be replaced. Return the dropper to its' <u>original container</u> when finished. Return the bottle to its original location so that others may find it easily.

> **ALL analysis experiments are INDIVIDUAL. However, two (or three) students may share the WATER BATH, WASTE BEAKER, STIR ROD BEAKER and DISTILLED WATER.**

Conventions for the Preparation of Flow Diagrams

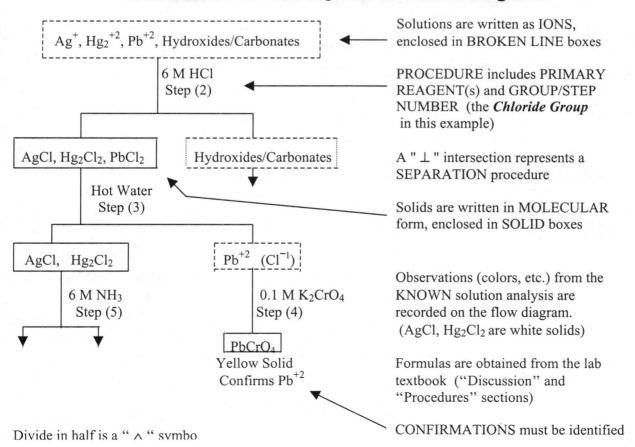

Solutions are written as IONS, enclosed in BROKEN LINE boxes

PROCEDURE includes PRIMARY REAGENT(s) and GROUP/STEP NUMBER (the ***Chloride Group*** in this example)

A " ⊥ " intersection represents a SEPARATION procedure

Solids are written in MOLECULAR form, enclosed in SOLID boxes

Observations (colors, etc.) from the KNOWN solution analysis are recorded on the flow diagram. (AgCl, Hg_2Cl_2 are white solids)

Formulas are obtained from the lab textbook ("Discussion" and "Procedures" sections)

CONFIRMATIONS must be identified

Divide in half is a " ∧ " symbo

229

Rewrite all flow diagrams (with observations) <u>after</u> completing the experiment. Diagrams must be LEGIBLE, and use the above format. Keep the corrected diagrams for reference, they will be required for future lab assignments and lab quizzes.

The "discussion" and the "procedures" sections of the *Chloride Group*, *Hydroxide Group*, and the *Alkaline Carbonate Group* experiments following this discussion contain the steps and the formulas necessary for preparing your flow diagrams. A brief summary of the GROUP separation is provided below.

Flow Diagram for the Group Separations

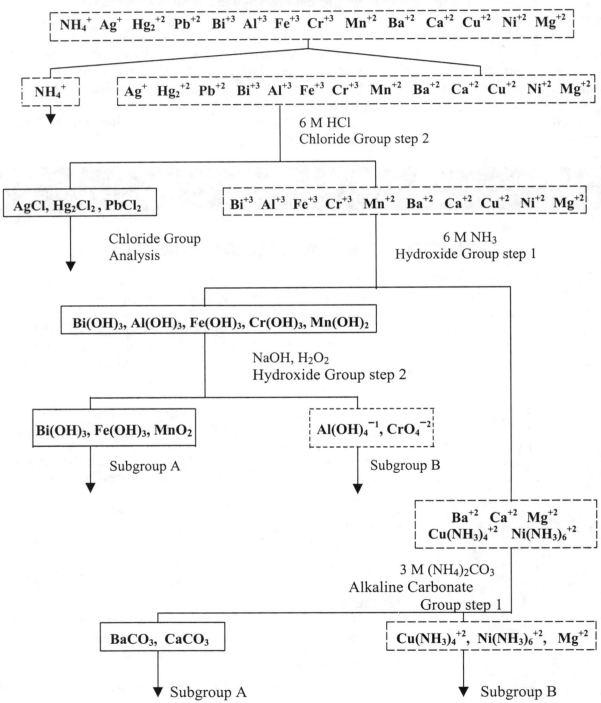

Disposal of Chemical Waste Materials

As you work through the procedures outlined in the qualitative analysis experiments, you will produce aqueous waste materials that contain some compounds that cannot be disposed of in the sink drain. Use care to minimize your waste quantity. If you have followed the procedure correctly, your total waste volume for each experiment will be less than 50 mL. Remember, excessive waste volumes will increase disposal costs.

As you perform your experiment, collect all of your waste materials in a 250 mL beaker at your workstation. DO NOT empty test tube contents into the sink.

When you have finished your experiment, take your beaker to the waste container provided in the hood area. STIR the beaker contents to thoroughly suspend the solids, and transfer the suspension into the waste container.

You may then rinse residual material from the beaker into the sink drain with flowing tap water.

QUALITATIVE ANALYSIS OF AQUEOUS SOLUTIONS I
The Chloride Group
Ag^{+1} Hg_2^{+2} Pb^{+2} NH_4^{+1}

Separation/Confirmation of NH_4^{+1}

Compounds of the ammonium ion are extremely soluble thus preventing its' separation by precipitation. The presence of ammonia must therefore be determined using a separate sample of the solution being analyzed prior to the addition of any other reagents.

In an acid medium, ammonia (NH_3) exists as ammonium ion, its Bronstead-Lowry conjugate acid. When the sample is made alkaline through the addition of the strong base sodium hydroxide, the NH_4^{+1} ion is converted back to ammonia gas. The $NH_{3(g)}$ is driven out of solution by heating the solution in a water bath thus separating it from other ions in the sample. The escaping gas then dissolves in the water on a piece of wet, red litmus paper, and reacts with the water as a Bronstead-Lowry base. The hydroxide ion thus formed turns red litmus to blue, indicating formation of a basic solution and confirming the presence of NH_4^{+1} in the original sample.

$$NH_4^{+1} \ + \ OH^{-1} \ \text{—heat→} \ H_2O \ + \ NH_{3(g)} \uparrow$$

$$NH_{3(g)} \ + \ H_2O \ (\text{RED Litmus}) \ \rightarrow \ NH_4^{+1} \ + \ OH^{-1} (\text{BLUE Litmus})$$

Separation of Ag^{+1}, Hg_2^{+2}, Pb^{+2}

The cations silver(I), mercury(I), and lead(II) all form insoluble chlorides in cold water. They can therefore be separated from other ions as a group by reaction with the strong electrolyte acid, HCl.

$$Ag^{+1} \ \& \ Hg_2^{+2} \ \& \ Pb^{+2} + Cl^{-1} \ \rightarrow \ AgCl_{(s)} \ \& \ Hg_2Cl_{2(s)} \ \& \ PbCl_{2(s)}$$

Some of these also form soluble complex ions with the chloride ion, necessitating the avoidance of excess hydrochloric acid during the precipitation process.

Separation/Confirmation of Pb^{+2}

Lead(II)chloride is reasonably soluble in hot water and therefore separates from the more insoluble chlorides of mercury and silver upon addition of hot water. Once the hot solution has been separated, the presence of lead ion in the solution is confirmed by addition of potassium chromate (K_2CrO_4). Formation of the bright yellow solid lead(II)chromate confirms the presence of lead.

$$PbCl_{2(s)} \quad \rightarrow HOT\ WATER \rightarrow \quad Pb^{+2} + 2\ Cl^{-1}$$

$$Pb^{+2} \quad + \quad CrO_4^{-2} \quad \rightarrow \quad PbCrO_{4(s)} \quad (\text{yellow solid})$$

Separation of Ag^{+1} and Hg_2^{+2} and Confirmation of Hg_2^{+2}

The remaining insoluble chlorides of silver and mercury are separated by reaction with aqueous ammonia. Silver(I) chloride dissolves in aqueous ammonia via the formation of the silver-ammonia complex $Ag(NH_3)_2^+$. Mercury(I) chloride simultaneously undergoes disproportionation (self oxidation-reduction) forming elemental mercury and mercury(II) as $HgNH_2Cl$.

$$AgCl_{(s)} \quad + \quad 2\ NH_{3(aq)} \quad \rightarrow \quad Ag(NH_3)_2^+ \quad + \quad Cl^-$$

$$Hg_2Cl_{2(s)} + 2\ NH_{3(aq)} \rightarrow \quad Hg_{(s)}\ (\text{black}) + HgNH_2Cl_{(s)}\ (\text{white}) + Cl^{-1} + NH_4^+$$

Formation of the gray to black colored mixture of Hg and $HgNH_2Cl$ confirms the presence of mercury, while the formation of the soluble $Ag(NH_3)_2^+$ complex permits separation of silver ion from mercury ion.

Confirmation of Ag^{+1}

Once the solution containing the silver-ammonia complex has been separated from the mercury solids, it is adjusted acid to litmus using the strong electrolyte acid HNO_3. Ammonia immediately accepts a proton to become an ammonium ion (NH_4^+). The Ag^{+1} ion thus released to the solution then reacts with the chloride ion that was originally present to form insoluble silver(I)chloride again.

$$Ag(NH_3)_2^+ \quad + \quad Cl^{-1} \quad + \quad 2\ H^+ \quad \rightarrow \quad AgCl_{(s)}\ (\text{white}) + \quad 2\ NH_4^+$$

The precipitation of white silver(I)chloride on acidification of the basic ammonia solution (without any additional source of chloride ion) confirms the presence of silver.

WEAR YOUR SAFETY GOGGLES/LAB COAT!
WASH YOUR HANDS WHEN FINISHED!

Experimental Procedure

DISPOSAL: Put all waste solutions in a 250 mL beaker at your work area. When you have finished ALL parts of the experiment, transfer these materials into the WASTE CONTAINER provided by your instructor.

Set up a water bath, stirring rod beaker and a waste beaker.
Transfer approximately 1–2 milliliters of solution to be analyzed into a test tube.

1. <u>Identification of the Ammonium ion</u>: Begin heating your water bath. It should be boiling before the ammonium ion test is started. Two pieces of RED LITMUS paper are also required. Moisten one with distilled water.

   Transfer 8-10 drops of your original solution into a separate test tube, saving the remainder for analysis below. Add 6 M sodium hydroxide (NaOH) drop by drop until the sample is basic to litmus (use the dry litmus paper). Place the test tube in the hot water bath, and use tongs to suspend the moist litmus paper above the test tube (the litmus paper must not touch the tube). If the ammonium ion is present, evolving ammonia gas will turn the moist red litmus paper blue, indicating the formation of ammonium hydroxide by reaction with the water on the test paper. This change from RED to BLUE confirms the presence of the NH_4^+ ion. Discard the test solution into your waste container when finished.

2. <u>Separation of the Chloride Group from Hydroxide and Alkaline Carbonate Groups ions</u>:
   Add two drops of 6 M hydrochloric acid (HCl) to the remainder of your original solution. Check for complete precipitation. Centrifuge and decant the solution into another test tube. (If Alkaline Carbonate Group or Hydroxide Group ions are present, label this tube and set it aside for later analysis. If only Chloride Group ions are possible, this solution may be discarded.) Save the white solid for Step 3.

3. <u>Separation of lead(II) ion</u>: Add 10-15 drops of water to the SOLID from Step 2, and heat in a boiling water bath for several minutes, stirring occasionally. Centrifuge and decant the HOT solution into another tube. Save the solid for silver and mercury analysis (Step 5 below).

4. <u>Confirmation of lead(II) ion</u>: To the SOLUTION from Step 3 above, add one drop of 1.0 M potassium chromate (K_2CrO_4) and centrifuge. The formation of the bright yellow solid $PbCrO_4$ confirms the presence of the lead(II) ion. Discard the solid/solution into your waste container when finished with this test.

235

5. <u>Separation of silver(I) and mercury(I); Confirmation of mercury(I)</u>: To the SOLID from step 3 above add about ten drops of 6 M ammonia (NH_3). The formation of a gray to black solid confirms the presence of the mercury(I) ion. (A white solid is left over lead chloride, not a test for mercury ion). Centrifuge and decant the solution into another test tube, then suspend any solid in water and discard into your waste container.

6. <u>Confirmation of silver(I) ion</u>: Add 6 M nitric acid (HNO_3) to the SOLUTION from Step 5 until acid to litmus. The formation of a cloudy white precipitate of silver chloride confirms the presence of silver(I) ion. (If you have a negative test for silver ion, check to be certain the solution is truly acid. If not, add nitric acid until it is.)

7. Repeat the Chloride Group analysis on a two-milliliter sample of your Chloride Group unknown. Report the ions present, ions absent, and the unknown identification number as your lab report.

8. When you have finished your experiment, take your waste beaker to the waste container provided in your hood area. <u>STIR the beaker contents to thoroughly suspend the solids</u>, and transfer the suspension into the waste container. You may then rinse residual material from the beaker into the sink drain with flowing tap water, and clean your glassware in preparation for the next experiment.

QUALITATIVE ANALYSIS OF AQUEOUS SOLUTIONS II
The Hydroxide Group
Bi^{+3} Fe^{+3} Cr^{+3} Al^{+3} Mn^{+2}

Separation of the Hydroxide Group ions from the Alkaline Carbonate Group

The ions of this group form insoluble hydroxides in slightly basic solution. They precipitate from solution in a small excess of aqueous ammonia, a weak electrolyte base.

$$El^{+3} + 3\, NH_{3(aq)} + 3\, H_2O \rightarrow El(OH)_{3(s)} + 3\, NH_4^{+1}$$

Where **El** represents the element: Bi^{+3} or Fe^{+3} or Cr^{+3} or Al^{+3}

$$Mn^{+2} + 2\, NH_{3(aq)} + 2\, H_2O \rightarrow Mn(OH)_{2(s)} + 2\, NH_4^{+1}$$

The *Alkaline Carbonate Group* remains in solution as ions or, in the case of copper(II) and nickel(II) as complex ions (of ammonia):

$$Cu^{+2},\ Ni^{+2},\ + NH_{3(aq)} \rightarrow Cu(NH_3)_4^{+2},\ Ni(NH_3)_6^{+2}$$

They are separated from the *Hydroxide Group* through centrifugation and decantation.

Separation of the Hydroxide Group into Subgroups A and B

The *Hydroxide Group* solids are separated into two subgroups by reaction with hydrogen peroxide (H_2O_2) or with the strong electrolyte base, sodium hydroxide. Bismuth and iron hydroxides do not react further, and the others are oxidized by the hydrogen peroxide or dissolve as complexes of the hydroxide ion.

$$Al(OH)_{3(s)} + OH^{-1} \rightarrow Al(OH)_4^{-1}$$

$$2\, Cr(OH)_{3(s)} + 3\, H_2O_{2(aq)} + 4\, OH^{-1} \rightarrow 2\, CrO_4^{-2} + 8\, H_2O_{(l)}$$

$$Mn(OH)_{2(s)} + H_2O_{2(aq)} \rightarrow MnO_{2(s)} + 2\, H_2O_{(l)}$$

The solids bismuth(III)hydroxide, iron(III)hydroxide and manganese(IV)oxide are referred to as *Subgroup A* in our procedure while $Al(OH)_4^{-1}$ and CrO_4^{-2} ions constitute *Subgroup B*.

Separation/Identification of Subgroup A: $Bi(OH)_3$ $Fe(OH)_3$ MnO_2

The *Subgroup A* solids are returned to solution phase by dissolving in the strong electrolyte acid HCl:

$$Bi(OH)_{3\,(s)} \,\&\, Fe(OH)_{3(s)} \,\&\, MnO_2 + H^+ \rightarrow Bi^{+3} \,\&\, Fe^{+3} \,\&\, Mn^{+4} + H_2O_{(l)}$$

Confirmation of each ion takes place without further separation:

- **Bismuth(III)** ion is converted to black elemental bismuth by reduction with tin(II) ion in basic solution:

$$Bi^{+3} + 3\,OH^{-1} \rightarrow Bi(OH)_{3(s)}$$

$$2\,Bi(OH)_{3(s)} + 3\,Sn^{+2} \rightarrow 2\,Bi_{(s)}\ \text{(black solid)} + 3\,Sn^{+4} + 6\,OH^{-1}$$

The formation of a black solid on addition of tin(II) confirms the presence of Bi^{+3} ion.

- **Iron(III)** forms an intense red complex with thiocyanate ion in aqueous solution:

$$Fe^{+3} + SCN^{-1} \rightarrow FeSCN^{+2}\ \text{(red solution)}$$

The formation of a dark red solution confirms the presence of the Fe^{+3} ion.

- **Manganese(IV)** is first reduced to manganese(II) with hydrogen peroxide, and then oxidized to the intensely purple MnO_4^{-1} (permanganate ion) with sodium bismuthate.

$$Mn^{+4} + H_2O_{2(aq)} \rightarrow Mn^{+2} + O_{2(aq)} + 2\,H^+$$

$$2\,Mn^{+2} + 5\,BiO_3^{-1} + 14\,H^+ \rightarrow 5\,Bi^{+3} + 7\,H_2O_{(l)} + 2\,MnO_4^{-1}\ \text{(purple)}$$

The appearance of a faint pink to purple color on addition
of $NaBiO_3$ confirms the presence of the manganese(II) ion.

Separation/Identification of Subgroup B: $Al(OH)_4^{-1}$ CrO_4^{-2}

The *Subgroup B* solution is heated to remove excess hydrogen peroxide and then divided into two equal samples. At this point chromium is present as the yellow CrO_4^{-2} and/or the orange $Cr_2O_7^{-2}$ ion and Aluminum is present as $Al(OH)_4^{-1}$.

Confirmation takes place without further separation:

- **Chromium(III):** A sample of the solution containing chromate/dichromate (and aluminum) is tested to verify it is basic (and adjusted to basic with NaOH if necessary) to ensure any dichromate ($Cr_2O_7^{-2}$) (orange) has been converted into the yellow chromate (CrO_4^{-2}) ion. The pale yellow solid barium chromate forms on addition of barium chloride:

$$CrO_4^{-2} \text{ (yellow solution)} \quad + \quad Ba^{+2} \quad \rightarrow \quad BaCrO_{4(s)} \text{ (pale yellow solid)}$$

The formation of the pale yellow solid <u>from</u> a <u>yellow</u> <u>solution</u> is confirmation of the presence of chromium as chromate ion.

- **Aluminum(III):** A sample of the solution containing the aluminum hydroxide complex ion $Al(OH)_4^{-1}$ (and chromate ion) is first adjusted acid to litmus with HCl to convert the complex ion back to Al^{+3}. The test for aluminum(III) ion involves adsorption of the red dye aluminon onto solid aluminum(III)hydroxide. The dye is added to the sample solution while it is acid (and aluminum is in solution as Al^{+3}), and the mixture is then adjusted basic to litmus with aqueous ammonia. The $Al(OH)_3$ that precipitates appears red because it was formed in the presence of the aluminon reagent.

$$Al^{+3} \; + \; 3\,NH_{3(aq)} \; + \; 3\,H_2O_{(l)} \; \xrightarrow{\text{ALUMINON}} \; Al(OH)_{3(s)} \text{ (red)} \; + \; 3\,NH_4^+$$

Formation of a red solid in the presence of aluminon reagent confirms aluminum(III) ion.

WEAR YOUR SAFETY GOGGLES/LAB COAT!
WASH YOUR HANDS WHEN FINISHED!

Experimental Procedure

DISPOSAL: Put all waste solutions in a 250 mL beaker at your work area. When you have finished ALL parts of the experiment, transfer these materials into the WASTE CONTAINER provided by your instructor.

If the solution to be analyzed contains ammonium, silver, mercury, or lead ions, it must first be treated to remove these according to Steps 1 and 2 of the preceding experiment, *"Chloride Group Analysis."* Failure to remove Chloride Group ions may interfere with identification of the Hydroxide Group.

Set up a stirring rod beaker and a waste beaker.
Set up and begin heating a water bath in preparation for the analysis.

Prepare a test tube containing twenty drops of 0.1 M $SnCl_4$ **prepared in** 3.0 M HCl. Add a small piece of aluminum wire, label the tube *tin(II) ion (Sn^{+2})*, and heat in a water bath until effervescence (bubbles) indicates the reaction has begun. Set this solution aside for later use in Step 4.

Clean a porcelain spot plate with tap water, rinse with distilled water and set aside.

Put three drops of <u>each</u> ion (Bi^{+3} Fe^{+3} Cr^{+3} Al^{+3} Mn^{+2}) in <u>separate</u> spot plate depressions, and <u>record</u> <u>the</u> <u>color</u> of each on your flow diagram. Add three or fours drops of 6 M NH_3 to <u>each</u>, and <u>record</u> <u>the</u> <u>color</u> of each <u>solid</u> <u>hydroxide</u> thus formed on your flow diagram. Discard the contents into your waste container and clean the spot plate.

Analysis of the Hydroxide Group

1. Separation of the Hydroxide Group from the Alkaline Carbonate Group ions: Transfer one to two milliliters of the solution to be analyzed into a clean test tube, and add 6 M ammonia until it is one drop basic to litmus. Then add three drops in excess. Check for complete precipitation, centrifuge, and decant the solution into another test tube. (If Alkaline Carbonate Group ions are present in this solution, label the test tube and set it aside for later analysis. If only Hydroxide Group ions are possible, this solution may be discarded into your waste container.)

2. Separation into subgroups: Wash the solid from Step 1 above twice with one milliliter of water, discarding the wash each time. Add about ten drops of 6 M sodium hydroxide and two drops of 3% hydrogen peroxide (H_2O_2) to the solid, stir, and allow to stand for about two minutes. Then, add ten drops of water and heat in the water bath for about five minutes to remove excess H_2O_2. Centrifuge, and decant the solution into a clean test tube. The solid is Subgroup A ($Bi(OH)_3$, $Fe(OH)_3$, MnO_2) and the solution contains Subgroup B (CrO_4^{-2}, $Al(OH)_4^{-1}$). Label both test tubes accordingly, and set the solution (Subgroup B) aside for later analysis. (The Subgroup B solution can be returned to the water bath in preparation for Step 7 below.)

3. Preparation of Subgroup A: Add one milliliter of water to the Subgroup A solid. Stirring occasionally, heat in a boiling water bath for five minutes to remove any excess hydrogen peroxide. Centrifuge and discard the solution, wash the solid with one milliliter of water, and discard the wash.

   Dissolve the solid in ten drops of 6 M hydrochloric acid, add ten drops of water, and heat for two or three minutes in the boiling water bath. If any solid remains, centrifuge and discard it, saving the SOLUTION for the Subgroup A analysis below.

SUBGROUP A

4. Confirmation of bismuth(III) ion: Put two drops of your Subgroup A solution in one of the spot plate depressions, add two drops of 6 M sodium hydroxide, and then add four to seven drops of the Sn^{+2} solution you prepared earlier in this procedure. The (often gradual) formation of a black solid (elemental bismuth) confirms its presence. *Black & grainy*

5. Confirmation of iron(III) ion: Place two or three drops of your Subgroup A solution in a CLEAN spot plate depression, and add one drop of 0.1 M potassium thiocyanate (KSCN) solution. The formation of a dark red solution ($FeSCN^{+2}$) confirms the presence of the iron(III) ion. *Blood Red liquid*

6. Confirmation of manganese(II) ion: Add two or three drops of 3% hydrogen peroxide (H_2O_2) to the remaining Subgroup A solution and heat for five minutes in a boiling water bath. While it's heating, prepare a DRY depression in your spot plate and a small, DRY stirring rod. Use the stirring rod to transfer a SMALL sample (2-4 grains) of sodium bismuthate ($NaBiO_3$) into the DRY spot plate depression. Cool the solution. Then transfer two or three drops into the spot plate depression. The formation of a pink color in the solution caused by a low concentration of the purple permanganate ion, MnO_4^{-1}, confirms the presence of manganese(II) ion. (Stir the solution with the rod containing residual sodium bismuthate if necessary. The pink color may fade rapidly.) *dark pink note: if hot will bubble*

245

SUBGROUP B

7. Preparation of _Subgroup B_: Heat the _Subgroup B_ solution prepared in Step 2 above in a boiling water bath to remove excess hydrogen peroxide. A yellow solution at this point indicates the presence of chromium as CrO_4^{-2} ion (orange indicates it is present as the dichromate ion and that the solution is too acid). Divide the solution into two equal samples and save for analysis in Steps 8 and 9 below.

8. Confirmation of chromium(III) ion: Verify that one of the solution samples is basic to litmus. (If not, add 6 M sodium hydroxide until the solution tests one drop basic to litmus.) A yellow solution at this point indicates the presence of chromium as chromate ion. Then add three drops of 1.0 M barium chloride ($BaCl_2$), stir, and centrifuge. The formation of a pale yellow solid ($BaCrO_4$) confirms the presence of chromium(III) ion. It is usually best to wash the solid with one milliliter of water (discard the wash) in order to be certain that the solid is indeed pale yellow. _almost chalky_

9. Confirmation of aluminum(III) ion: Add 6 M hydrochloric acid to the other half of the solution from Step 7 above until it tests one drop acid to litmus. Cool the test tube and add ten drops of ALUMINON REAGEANT. Then add 6 M ammonia until the solution is basic to litmus, add three drops in excess, and centrifuge. A red solid confirms the presence of the aluminum(III) ion. _Red like strawberry jelly_

10. Repeat the above _Hydroxide Group_ analysis on a two-milliliter sample of _your Hydroxide Group_ unknown. Report the ions present, ions absent, and the unknown identification number as your lab report.

11. When you have finished your experiment, take your waste baker to the waste container provided in the hood area. STIR the beaker contents to thoroughly suspend the solids, and transfer the suspension into the waste container. You may then rinse residual material from the beaker into the sink drain with flowing tap water, and clean your glassware in preparation for the next experiment.

QUALITATIVE ANALYSIS OF AQUEOUS SOLUTIONS III
The Alkaline Carbonate Group
Ba^{+2} Ca^{+2} $Cu(NH_3)_4^{+2}$ Mg^{+2} $Ni(NH_3)_6^{+2}$

The *Alkaline Carbonate Group* remains in the solution that was separated from the *Hydroxide Group* solids as ions or, in the case of copper(II) and nickel(II), as complex ions of ammonia. Two of these, Ba^{+2} and Ca^{+2}, precipitate as insoluble carbonates from a basic (ammoniacal) solution while the others remain unchanged.

$$Ba^{+2} \text{ \& } Ca^{+2} + CO_3^{-2} \rightarrow BaCO_{3(s)} \text{ \& } CaCO_{3(s)}$$

Addition of ammonium carbonate to the ammoniacal solution therefore divides the *Alkaline Carbonates* into **two subgroups**:

Subgroup A: barium and calcium as $BaCO_{3(s)}$ & $CaCO_{3(s)}$.

Subgroup B: magnesium as Mg^{+2} and copper(II) and nickel(II) as their ammonia complex ions.

Separation/Confirmation of Subgroup A

After separation from the *Subgroup B* solution, the solid barium and calcium carbonates are dissolved in acetic acid to form the positive ions again.

- **Barium(II):** Addition of potassium chromate (K_2CrO_4) to the acid solution separates and confirms barium(II) as the pale yellow solid, barium(II)chromate. Calcium ion does not form an insoluble chromate.

$$Ba^{+2} \text{ \& } Ca^{+2} + CrO_4^{-2} \rightarrow BaCrO_{4(s)} \text{ (pale yellow) \& } Ca^{+2}$$

- **Calcium(II):** The solution containing Ca^{+2} (now yellow because of the added chromate) is adjusted basic to litmus with aqueous ammonia followed by the addition of ammonium oxalate. The calcium ion forms an insoluble oxalate in basic solution:

$$Ca^{+2} + C_2O_4^{-2} \rightarrow CaC_2O_{4(s)} \text{ (white solid)}$$

Formation of the white solid CaC_2O_4 on addition of ammonium oxalate confirms the presence of calcium(II) ion. (The solid usually needs to be rinsed several times in order to remove residual chromate ion and verify the white color.)

Separation/Confirmation of Subgroup B

After separation from *Subgroup A* carbonates, the solution is adjusted acid to litmus with hydrochloric acid and heated to remove excess carbonate as CO_2 gas. Ammonia exists as the NH_4^+ ion in acid solution and thus converts copper and nickel back to their **+2** states.

- **Nickel(II):** A two drop sample of the acid solution is placed on a spot plate and made basic to litmus by the addition of aqueous ammonia. The dye dimethylglyoxime ($C_4H_8N_2O_2$) forms a red solid with nickel(II) in basic medium, confirming its presence in the sample.

$$Ni^{+2} + 2\ C_4H_8N_2O_{2(aq)} \rightarrow Ni(C_4H_7N_2O_2)_{2(s)}\ (red\ ) + 2\ H^+$$

- **Copper(II):.** A separate two drop sample of the acid solution is placed on a spot plate and made basic by the addition of excess aqueous ammonia. The formation of the intense blue copper ammonia complex [$Cu(NH_3)_4^{+2}$] in the presence of excess ammonia identifies the presence of copper in the solution.

$$Cu^{+2} + 4\ NH_{3(aq)} \rightarrow Cu(NH_3)_4^{+2}\ \textbf{(blue solution)}$$

Nickel(II) also forms a less intense and different shade of blue ammonia complex. It is therefore necessary to compare the color of the above copper test with "known" copper(II) and nickel(II) ammonia complex solutions to verify the test color as $Cu(NH_3)_4^{+2}$.

- **Magnesium(II):** A separate sample of the acid solution is adjusted to basic with ammonia and then treated with hydrogen phosphate ion (HPO_4^{-2} as Na_2HPO_4). Formation of the white solid magnesium ammonium phosphate ($MgNH_4PO_4$) confirms the presence of Mg^{+2} ion. Confirmation is verified by attempting to dissolve the solid in NaOH. If the solid does not dissolve in excess NaOH, it is $MgNH_4PO_4$ and magnesium has been confirmed.

$$Ni^{+2} + Cu^{+2} + Mg^{+2} + 11\ NH_{3(aq)} + HPO_4^{-2} \rightarrow$$

$$Cu(NH_3)_4^{+2} + Ni(NH_3)_6^{+2} + MgNH_4PO_{4(s)}\ \textbf{(white)}$$

WEAR YOUR SAFETY GOGGLES/LAB COAT!
WASH YOUR HANDS WHEN FINISHED!

Experimental Procedure

Acid Blue → Red
Base Red → Blue

DISPOSAL: Put all waste solutions in a 250 mL beaker at your work area. When you have finished ALL parts of the experiment, transfer these materials into the WASTE CONTAINER provided by your instructor.

If the solution to be analyzed contains Chloride Group and/or Hydroxide Group ions it must first be treated to remove these ions. Treatment according to Steps 1 and 2 of the preceding *"Chloride Group Analysis"* will identify the ammonium ion and separate silver, lead, and mercury ions as insoluble chloride compounds. Treatment of the resulting solution according to Step 1 of the preceding *"Hydroxide Group Analysis"* separates these ions as insoluble hydroxides or oxides. Chloride and Hydroxide Group ions that are not removed will interfere with identification of the Alkaline Carbonate Group ions.

Set up a stirring rod beaker and a waste beaker.
Set up and begin heating a water bath in preparation for the analysis.
(and/or the separation of Chloride and Hydroxide Group ions if necessary)

Prepare two <u>reference solutions</u> for use in identifying the copper and nickel ions:

a. Add five drops of 0.1 M Copper(II)nitrate to one milliliter of water in a separate test tube. LABEL this tube Cu^{+2} and set it aside for later use in the copper confirmation test. Record the color of Cu^{+2} solution on your flow diagram.

b. Prepare another, separate sample using five drops of 0.1 M nickel(II)nitrate in one milliliter of water. LABEL this tube Ni^{+2} and set it aside for later use in <u>Step 7</u>, the copper confirmation test. Record the color of Ni^{+2} solution on your flow diagram.

Clean a porcelain spot plate with tap water, rinse with distilled water, and set aside.

1. <u>Separation of the Alkaline Carbonate Group</u>: Transfer about one to two milliliters of the solution to be analyzed into a clean test tube. If the solution has not previously been treated with ammonia, add 6 M ammonia until it is basic to litmus and then add six drops in excess. Then add six <u>drops of 3 M ammonium carbonate</u> [$(NH_4)_2CO_3$] and heat. Test for complete precipitation, centrifuge and separate. LABEL the tube containing the <u>solid</u> as ***Subgroup A*** ($BaCO_3$ and $CaCO_3$) and LABEL the tube containing the <u>solution</u> as ***Subgroup B*** (Mg^{+2}, $Cu(NH_3)_4^{+2}$, $Ni(NH_3)_6^{+2}$). *Turn Dark blue*

2. <u>Preparation of **Subgroup A**: Confirmation of barium(II)ion</u>: Wash the SOLID from <u>Step 1</u> above TWICE with about one milliliter of water, discarding the wash each time. Add 6 M acetic acid ($HC_2H_3O_2$) to the solid one drop at a time, with stirring, until the solid has dissolved. Dilute this solution by adding one milliliter of water. Add one drop of 1.0 M

253

potassium chromate (K_2CrO_4), check for complete precipitation, centrifuge and separate. (Save the solution for calcium analysis below.) *bright yellow*

Formation of a pale yellow solid ($BaCrO_4$) on addition of potassium chromate confirms the presence of the barium(II) ion. It is usually best to wash this precipitate once or twice with one milliliter of water (discard the wash) in order to be certain that the solid is indeed pale yellow. *pale yellow solid*

3. Confirmation of calcium(II) ion: Add 6 M ammonia drop by drop until it tests basic to litmus to the solution from Step 2 above, and then add three drops in excess. Add ten drops of 0.5 M ammonium oxalate $(NH_4)_2C_2O_4$. The formation of the white solid calcium oxalate (CaC_2O_4) confirms the presence of calcium(II). It is usually best to separate the solid and wash it two or three times with water in order to be certain the solid is white.

4. Preparation of **Subgroup B**: Add 6 M hydrochloric acid to the *Subgroup B* solution from Step 1 above until it is acid to litmus. Heat this solution in a boiling water bath, with occasional stirring, for five minutes to remove excess carbonate ion as carbon dioxide gas. Divide the solution in half, saving each portion for analysis below.

5. Confirmation of magnesium(II) ion: Add 6 M ammonia to one of the solution samples from Step 4 above until basic to litmus and then add five drops in excess. Add ten drops of 1 M Na_2HPO_4 (sodium hydrogen phosphate), and warm for three to five minutes in the water bath. The formation of white magnesium ammonium phosphate ($MgNH_4PO_4$) confirms the presence of magnesium(II) ion. Centrifuge and discard the solution. Wash the solid if necessary to verify that it is indeed white. Add five drops of 6 M sodium hydroxide to the solid and allow it to stand about five minutes. If the solid dissolves, it was not $MgNH_4PO_4$ and magnesium is not present. If the solid does not dissolve, $MgNH_4PO_4$, and the presence of magnesium(II) ion, has been verified (the magnesium compound is not soluble in strong base). *white*

6. Confirmation of nickel(II) ion: Put two drops of the other solution sample saved from Step 4 in a clean spot plate depression. To this add three drops of 6 M ammonia and one drop of DIMETHYLGLYOXIME test solution. Formation of a red solid confirms the presence of nickel(II) ion. *reddish violet*

7. Confirmation of copper(II) ion: Put two drops of the other solution sample saved from Step 4 in a clean spot plate depression. Also put two drops of the nickel(II) and the copper(II) reference solutions (prepared before beginning this procedure) into separate, clean, spot plate depressions. Add three drops of 6 M ammonia to the sample and to both reference solutions. Formation of the blue $Cu(NH_3)_4^{+2}$ solution in the sample confirms the presence of copper(II) ion. Compare this color with that of the copper and the nickel reference test colors to verify the sample color is $Cu(NH_3)_4^{+2}$ and not $Ni(NH_3)_6^{+2}$, which is a less intense and distinctly different shade of blue. *more like blue*

Record the color of the copper and nickel reference tests on your flow diagram.

8. Repeat this analysis on a two-milliliter sample of your unknown.

9. When you have finished your experiment, take your waste baker to the waste container provided in the hood area. STIR the beaker contents to thoroughly suspend the solids, and transfer the suspension into the waste container. You may then rinse residual material from the beaker into the sink drain with flowing tap water, and clean your glassware in preparation for the next experiment.

QUALITATIVE ANALYSIS OF NEGATIVE IONS
Tests for Anions
SCN^{-1} CO_3^{-2} SO_4^{-2} PO_4^{-3} Cl^{-1} I^{-1} NO_3^{-1}

IMPORTANT

READ each section completely before starting the test procedure.
CLEAN your work area and your hands when finished.
NOTE that each test is performed on a separate, fresh sample of unknown.

WEAR YOUR SAFETY GLASSES/LAB COAT!

WASH YOUR HANDS WHEN FINISHED!

Experimental Procedure

DISPOSAL: Put all test solids and solutions in a 250 mL beaker at your work area. When you have finished ALL parts of the experiment, transfer these materials into the WASTE CONTAINER provided by your instructor.

Set up a stirring rod beaker and a waste beaker.
Set up and begin heating a water bath in preparation for the anion analysis procedure.

1. **THIOCYANATE ION**: This ion forms a deep red ("blood red") solution of the iron thiocyanate ion ($FeSCN^{+2}$) on addition of iron(III)chloride. This intense red color confirms the presence of the thiocyanate ion. If iodide ion is also present, however, it is oxidized to iodine by the iron(III) ion, forming a brown solution. A brown solution therefore must <u>not</u> be interpreted as confirmation for thiocyanate ion.

   (1) $SCN^{-1} + Fe^{+3} \rightarrow FeSCN^{+2}$ (Red Solution)

   (2) $2\,I^{-1} + 2\,Fe^{+3} \rightarrow 2\,Fe^{+2} + I_{2(aq)}$ (Brown Solution)

KNOWN: 1.0 mL water and 0.5 mL of 0.1 M potassium thiocyanate (KSCN) solution.

PROCEDURE: Add 6 M hydrochloric acid dropwise until the sample is acid to litmus. Then, add five drops of 0.1 M iron(III)chloride ($FeCl_3$) solution and stir. The formation of a "blood red" solution confirms the presence of the thiocyanate ion. ($FeCl_3$ is also called ferric chloride.)

REPEAT this procedure on a one mL sample of your unknown. Do not add water to the unknown.

2. **CARBONATE ION**: The carbonate ion is separated from other ions by conversion to carbon dioxide gas. Carbonic acid forms upon acidification of the carbonate solution. It then decomposes on heating to form water and carbon dioxide gas:

   (1) $CO_3^{-2} + 2 H^+ \rightarrow H_2CO_{3(aq)} + heat \rightarrow H_2O + CO_{2(gas)}$

The evolved gas is then bubbled into a calcium hydroxide [$Ca(OH)_2$] solution, where it is converted back to carbonic acid and then to carbonate ion:

   (2) $CO_{2(g)} + H_2O \rightarrow H_2CO_{3(aq)}$

   (3) $H_2CO_{3(aq)} + 2 OH^- \rightarrow 2 H_2O + CO_3^{-2}$

The formation of a cloudy white precipitate of calcium carbonate by reaction with the Ca^{+2} ion confirms the presence of the carbonate ion:

   (4) $CO_3^{-2} + Ca^{+2} \rightarrow CaCO_{3\,(s)}$

KNOWN: 1.0 mL water and 2.0 mL 0.1 M sodium carbonate, Na_2CO_3.

PROCEDURE: Fill a small (13×100 mm) test tube approximately half way with saturated calcium hydroxide solution. If the calcium hydroxide solution contains any solid, centrifuge and transfer the solution to another small test tube. Place the sample in a large (16×100mm) test tube and add 6 M hydrochloric acid until acid to litmus and then add six drops in excess. Insert the stoppered end of the delivery tube apparatus (provided on the laboratory cart), and place the test tube in a water bath. Immerse the other end of the delivery tube in the 13×100 mm test tube containing the calcium hydroxide solution, and heat the water bath. The formation of a cloudy white precipitate (in the small test tube) as the evolving carbon dioxide bubbles through the calcium hydroxide solution confirms the presence of carbonate.

REPEAT this procedure on a two mL sample of your unknown. Do not add water to the unknown.

3. **SULFATE AND PHOSPHATE IONS**: Both ions form insoluble barium(II) compounds in slightly basic solution. Barium phosphate will dissolve in nitric acid, but barium sulfate does not. The sulfate ion is therefore separated by first adding barium chloride to precipitate $BaSO_4$ and $Ba_3(PO_4)_2$. Nitric acid is then added to the solids, dissolving the phosphate of barium, but leaving barium sulfate as an insoluble residue. The presence of this insoluble solid in the acidic solution confirms sulfate ion.

(1) $SO_4^{-2} + PO_4^{-3} + Ba^{+2} \rightarrow BaSO_{4(s)} + Ba_3(PO_4)_{2(s)}$

(2) $Ba_3(PO_4)_{2(s)} + H^+ \rightarrow Ba^{+2} + H_3PO_{4(aq)}$

After centrifuging and separating solid barium sulfate, the solution is analyzed for phosphate ion.

The solution is tested for the presence of phosphate through the addition of ammonium molybdate $[(NH_4)_2MoO_4]$, which reacts to precipitate yellow solid ammonium molybdophosphate $[(NH_4)_3P(Mo_3O_{10})_4]$. The appearance of this yellow solid confirms the presence of phosphate ion.

KNOWN: Mix 0.5 mL each of 0.1 M sodium sulfate (Na_2SO_4) and 0.1 M sodium phosphate (Na_3PO_4) into 1.0 mL of water.

PROCEDURE: Add 6 M ammonia to the sample drop by drop until basic to litmus and then add three drops of 1.0 M barium chloride ($BaCl_2$). The formation of a white solid indicates the presence of carbonate, sulfate, and/or phosphate ions. Check for complete precipitation, centrifuge, and discard the solution. Add fifteen drops of 6 M nitric acid to the solid, stir, and heat in the water bath (evolution of a colorless gas indicates the presence of carbonate ion.) A white precipitate that remains insoluble in nitric acid confirms sulfate ion. Centrifuge and transfer the solution to a clean test tube.

Add 6M NH_3 to the solution until basic to litmus. Then add five drops of saturated ammonium molybdate $[(NH_4)_2MoO_4]$. Heat the mixture in the water bath for about five minutes. Formation of a yellow solid confirms the presence of phosphate ion.

REPEAT this procedure on a one mL sample of your unknown. Do not add water to the unknown.

4. **CHLORIDE AND IODIDE IONS**: Both chloride and iodide ions form insoluble compounds with silver ion, but only silver chloride dissolves in aqueous ammonia. The ions can therefore be separated by first adding silver nitrate to precipitate both silver(I)chloride and silver(I)iodide and then adding aqueous ammonia to the solids. Silver chloride dissolves in aqueous NH_3 but silver iodide does not.

   (1) $Cl^- + I^- + 2Ag^+ \rightarrow AgCl_{(s)}$ (white solid) $+ AgI_{(s)}$ (yellow solid)

   (2) $AgCl_{(s)} + AgI_{(s)} + 2NH_{3(aq)} \rightarrow Ag(NH_3)_2^+ + Cl^- + AgI_{(s)}$

After centrifuging and separating, the solution is acidified with nitric acid. The reprecipitation of white silver chloride from the clear solution is confirmation of the chloride ion.

   (3) $Ag(NH_3)^{2+} + Cl^- + 2H^+ \rightarrow 2NH_4^+ + AgCl_{(s)}$

The pale yellow solid that remains after treatment with ammonia is silver iodide. The appearance of this yellow solid confirms the presence of iodide ion.

Acid Blue→Red
Base Red→Blue

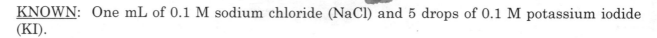

<u>KNOWN</u>: One mL of 0.1 M sodium chloride (NaCl) and 5 drops of 0.1 M potassium iodide (KI).

<u>PROCEDURE</u>: Add 6 M nitric acid to the sample until acid to litmus and then add three drops of 0.1 M silver(I)nitrate ($AgNO_3$). Centrifuge, and discard the solution. Add 15 drops of 6 M NH_3 and ten drops of water to the <u>solid</u>. Mix to completely dissolve the silver chloride, centrifuge, and separate. The presence of a yellow solid at this point confirms iodide ion.

Add 6 M nitric acid to the <u>solution</u> until acid to litmus and then add six drops in excess. The formation of a cloudy white solid confirms the presence of chloride ion. (If the chloride test is negative, verify that the solution is truly acid. If not, add HNO_3 until it is.)

<u>REPEAT</u> this procedure on a one mL sample of your unknown. Do not add water to the unknown.

5. **NITRATE ION**: The iodide and thiocyanate ions interfere with this test. Analyze the unknown for these ions before beginning the nitrate test. The treatment of nitrate ion with concentrated sulfuric acid (H_2SO_4) results in the formation of nitric acid. The addition of iron(II)sulfate ($FeSO_4$) causes reduction of the nitric acid to nitrogen oxide (NO). The nitrogen oxide then reacts with excess iron(II)sulfate to form a brown solution of $FeSO_4 \bullet$ NO. This appears as a "brown ring" at the interface between the concentrated sulfuric acid layer and the solution thus confirming the presence of the nitrate ion. (Iron(II)sulfate is also called ferrous sulfate.)

The reactions, both in aqueous solution, are as follows:

(1) $2\ HNO_3\ +\ 6\ FeSO_4\ +\ 3\ H_2SO_4\ \rightarrow\ 3\ Fe_2(SO4)_3\ +\ 2\ NO\ +\ 4\ H_2O$

(2) $FeSO_4\ +\ NO\ \rightarrow\ FeSO_4 \bullet NO$ (brown "ring")

<u>KNOWN</u>: 1.0 mL of water and 1.0 mL of 0.1 M potassium nitrate (KNO_3).

<u>PROCEDURE</u>: The iodide ion and thiocyanate ion will interfere with this test. If both are <u>absent</u>, omit procedure **A** below.

A. The iodide, and thiocyanate ions are removed by adding 20 drops of saturated silver(I)acetate ($AgC_2H_3O_2$) to the solution and heating for about four minutes. Centrifuge, <u>check</u> for <u>complete precipitation</u>, and separate. The solid may be discarded, while the solution is saved for the nitrate ion test in Section **C** below.

The reactions are:

(1) $I^-\ +\ Ag^+\ \rightarrow\ AgI_{(s)}$ (yellow solid)

(2) $SCN^-\ +\ Ag^+\ \rightarrow\ AgSCN_{(s)}$ (white solid)

B. Prepare fresh iron(II)sulfate (also called ferrous sulfate) solution by adding solid iron(II)sulfate to a centrifuge test tube to a depth of approximately one half centimeter. Fill the tube two thirds full with water, and stir to saturate the solution. Centrifuge and discard the excess solid. Save the solution for Section **C** below.

C. Add <u>dilute</u> (3 M) sulfuric acid to your sample until acid to litmus, then add 3 drops in excess. Then add 20 drops of the fresh iron(II)sulfate solution (from Section **B**), incline the sample tube, and add 20 drops of <u>concentrated</u> (18 M) sulfuric acid slowly so that it runs down the side of the tube and forms a layer at the bottom. A "brown ring" at the interface between the concentrated acid (bottom layer) and the solution (top layer) confirms the presence of nitrate ion. Allow several minutes for the color to form.

<u>REPEAT</u> with a one mL sample of your unknown. Do not add water to the unknown.

A violet or purple color at the acid–solution interface indicates interference from the iodide ion. An orange or yellow color in the solution (top) layer indicates interference from the thiocyanate ion.

6. When you have finished your experiment, take your waste baker to the waste container provided in the hood area. <u>STIR the beaker contents to thoroughly suspend the solids</u>, and transfer the suspension into the waste container. You may then rinse residual material from the beaker into the sink drain with flowing tap water, and clean your glassware in preparation for the next experiment.

GENERAL UNKNOWN INSTRUCTIONS
Flow Diagram Assignment

Your instructor will assign a list of ions that specifies nine of the fourteen possible cations in the qualitative analysis procedure for the *Chloride Group, Hydroxide Group,* and *Alkaline Carbonate Group.* They are the only ions that can be present in YOUR General Unknown.

Prepare a FLOW DIAGRAM for the analysis of a sample that can contain ONLY these ions:

1. Include <u>only</u> the steps and reagents that apply to the ions on YOUR list.

2. <u>Omit</u> those steps and reagents that do <u>not</u> apply to the ions on YOUR list.

3. Include the page and step numbers from the laboratory manual that reference the instructions for these procedures.

OR:

Include the complete written procedure that must be followed to carry out each step in the analysis of the ions contained in YOUR list/diagram.

4. Use the same diagram conventions (solid line boxes, etc.) that you used in previous flow diagram assignments.

5. Make your diagram neat and easy to read. You will have to follow this procedure in order to analyze your General Unknown.

6. You MUST complete this diagram BEFORE you begin laboratory analysis of your unknown. Your unknown solution will contain some, but not all, of the ions on your list.

YOU MUST ANALYZE THE UNKNOWN SAMPLE

THAT HAS THE SAME IDENTIFICATION NUMBER AS YOUR LIST.

ACID – BASE EQUILIBRIUM AND pH

According to the Bronsted-Lowry concept, an ACID is a substance which donates a proton (H^+ ion) and a BASE accepts a proton. In the case of weak electrolyte acids or bases the reaction occurs only to a small extent and the relative strength is indicated by the value of the acid or base ionization constant (**Ka** or **Kb**). Depending on what it is reacting with, water is a substance which can behave either as an acid or a base:

Acid: $HF_{(aq)}$ + H_2O $\Leftrightarrow$ $H_3O^+_{(aq)}$ + $F^{-1}_{(aq)}$ **Ka** = $[H_3O^+][F^{-1}] / [HF]$
Acid   Conjugate base

Base: $NH_{3(aq)}$ + H_2O $\Leftrightarrow$ $NH_4^+{}_{(aq)}$ + $OH^{-1}_{(aq)}$ **Kb** = $[NH_4^+][OH^{-1}] / [NH_3]$
Base   Conjugate acid

Water, of course, also undergoes an acid-base reaction:

$$H_2O + H_2O \Leftrightarrow H_3O^+_{(aq)} + OH^{-1}_{(aq)} \qquad \textbf{Kw} = 1.0 \times 10^{-14} = [H_3O^+][OH^{-1}]$$

A BUFFER is a solution prepared by mixing a weak electrolyte acid and its conjugate base or a weak base and its conjugate acid (e.g. HF and NaF or NH_3 and NH_4Cl).

If the concentration of the weak acid or weak base is known (or, in the case of a buffer the concentrations of the acid-base pairs), experimental determination of the H_3O^+ concentration (or through that the OH^{-1} concentration) provides the information required to calculate a value for the ionization constant. The acidity of a solution is usually expressed as **pH** (pH= $-$ log $[H_3O^+]$), and can be measured using an electrochemical device calibrated in pH units, a *pH meter*.

In this experiment we will measure the pH of a weak electrolyte acid at three different concentrations and the pH of its corresponding buffer solution. A value of Ka for this acid will then be calculated based on the concentration and pH values for each solution. We will also add a strong acid to observe the impact of a buffer system on attempts to change the pH.

NEUTRALIZATION refers to the reaction between an acid and a base, producing water and their conjugates (often termed a "salt"). For instance, the weak electrolyte acid HF reacts with the strong base NaOH, forming fluoride ion, the conjugate base of HF:

$$HF_{(aq)} + OH^{-1}_{(aq)} \rightarrow H_2O + F^{-1}_{(aq)}$$

If the sodium hydroxide solution is added under controlled conditions, the process is termed "TITRATION", and the solution being added (NaOH) becomes the "TITRANT". As long as acid is present during the titration the solution remains acid. At the point where the base exactly consumes the acid (the "equivalence point" of the titration) only the conjugate base fluoride ion is present, and the solution quickly becomes basic. Continued addition of NaOH causes the solution to become progressively more basic, of course.

One should also note that as soon as the titration has begun some HF has been converted to the conjugate base (F^{-1}), and the solution is therefore a BUFFER. At the halfway point of a titration the concentration of the acid equals the concentration of the conjugate base, making the [H$_3$O$^+$] identical in value to the Ka of the acid (or the [OH^{-1}] identical to the Kb of a base). If one measures the pH of the solution at the halfway point, **Ka** is then equal to the antilog of (– pH).

A titration curve is a graph of pH values for the acid (or base) solution against the volume of base (or acid) added throughout the titration (Figure 1). The graph clearly identifies the point (volume) at which equivalence was achieved and from that the "halfway point" volume and pH value. The equivalence point is approximately at the middle of the steepest (most vertical) portion of the titration curve. The following procedure, sometimes termed the "bisector method," is often employed to identify the equivalence point volume.

The pH of the solution is measured as a function of the volume of titrant added. At least six pH–Volume points before and after the equivalence point are required. A graph of pH (vertical axis) against volume of titrant added (horizontal axis) is then constructed (Figure 1.)

A straight line is drawn through the LINEAR POINTS on the graph before the equivalence point, and again through the linear points after the equivalence point. Vertical lines (parallel to the pH axis) are then drawn through these to the left and the right of the equivalence point (Figures 2 and 3). One then measures to locate the midpoint of each vertical line. A line is drawn joining the midpoints (the "bisector"). The intersection of the bisector with the titration curve identifies the equivalence point volume (Figure 4). The halfway point volume and pH can then be determined from the graph.

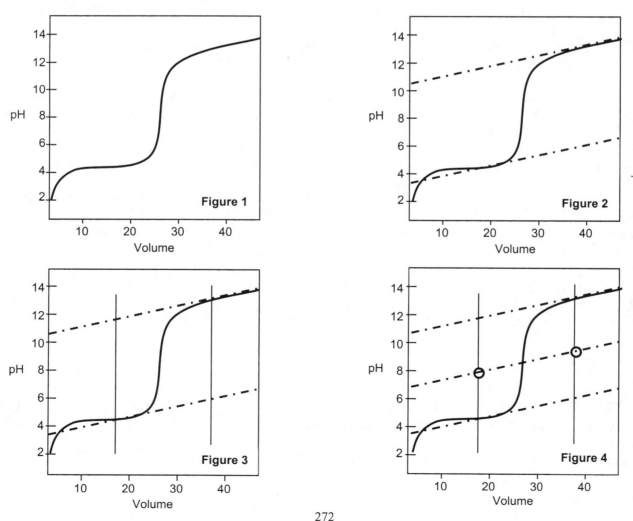

WEAR YOUR SAFETY GLASSES/LAB COAT!
WASH YOUR HANDS WHEN FINISHED!

Experimental Procedure

YOU MAY WORK IN PAIRS DURING THIS EXPERIMENT.

PART A: Solution Preparation

Prepare the following solutions from the sodium hydroxide and acetic acid stock solutions provided on the laboratory cart. Use a 10.0 mL volumetric pipet to transfer samples into their receiving containers. Refer to *Appendix: Use of a Volumetric Pipet* for instructions on the use of a pipet and pipet pump. DO NOT pipet by mouth suction.

USE SMALL (50, 100 or 150 mL) CALIBRATED beakers as receiving containers, and LABEL each container with both the solute (NaOH or $HC_2H_3O_2$) <u>and</u> its concentration. Set up a 400 mL "waste beaker" at your station. Put ALL solution waste into this container and hold for **PART D** of the procedure.

You and your laboratory partner will share the pH Meter / Calibration Buffers and a Magnetic Stirrer / Stirring Bar.

1. **Sodium Hydroxide, 0.10 M:** Measure 15-18 mL of 0.50 M NaOH (the stock solution) into a 50 mL graduated cylinder. Rinse a 10.0 mL volumetric pipet with a small sample (3-4 mL) of the 0.50 M NaOH, and discard the rinse into a waste beaker at your workstation. Then use this pipet to transfer 10.0 mL of 0.50 M NaOH into a 100 or 150.0 mL calibrated beaker. Carefully dilute this to the 50.0 mL mark on the beaker, and <u>label</u> the container as 0.10 M NaOH

   Rinse the pipet twice with distilled water. Discard excess 0.50 M NaOH into your waste beaker. Thoroughly rinse the 50 mL graduated cylinder.

2. **Acetic Acid, 0.60 M:** Measure 15-18 mL of 3.0 M acetic acid ($HC_2H_3O_2$) (the stock solution) into a 50 mL graduated cylinder. Rinse a 10.0 mL volumetric pipet with a small sample (3-4 mL) of the 3.0 M acetic acid, and discard the rinse in the waste beaker at your workstation. Then use this pipet to transfer 10.0 mL of 3.0 M $HC_2H_3O_2$ into a 100.0 or 150.0 mL calibrated beaker. Carefully dilute this to the 50.0 mL mark on the beaker, and <u>label</u> the container as 0.60 M $HC_2H_3O_2$.

   Rinse the pipet twice with distilled water. Discard the excess 3.0 M acid into your waste beaker.

3. **Acetic Acid, 0.20 M:** Rinse a 10.0 mL volumetric pipet with a small sample (3-4 mL) of the 0.60 M acetic acid solution prepared in <u>Step 2</u> above, and discard the rinse into the waste beaker at your workstation. Then use this pipet to transfer 10.0 mL of the 0.60 M $HC_2H_3O_2$ into a 50.0 mL calibrated beaker. Carefully dilute this to the 30.0 mL mark on the beaker, and <u>label</u> the container as 0.20 M $HC_2H_3O_2$. **Do Not** rinse the pipet with distilled water.

4. **Acetic Acid, 0.10 M:** Use your 10.0 mL pipet to transfer 10.0 mL of the 0.60 M $HC_2H_3O_2$ solution prepared in Step 2 above into a 100.0 or 150.0 mL calibrated beaker. Carefully dilute this to the 60.0 mL mark on the beaker and mix. **Set about 10 mL of this solution aside** for later use in **PART C.** Label both containers as 0.10 M $HC_2H_3O_2$. **Do Not** rinse the pipet with distilled water.

5. **Acetic Acid–Sodium Acetate Buffer:** Use your 10.0 mL pipet to transfer 10.0 mL of the 0.60 M $HC_2H_3O_2$ solution prepared in Step 2 above into a 50.0 mL calibrated beaker. Carefully dilute this to the 40.0 mL mark on the beaker by **USING the 0.10 M NaOH solution** prepared in Step 1 above (10.0 mL of 0.60 M acetic acid + 30.0 mL 0.10 M sodium hydroxide = 40.0 mL buffer solution). Label the container as "Buffer." Rinse the pipet several times with distilled water. Return it to the laboratory cart.

PART B: Determination of Solution pH

1. **pH Meter Calibration:** With the meter selector on "STANDBY", rinse the electrode with distilled water and then place it in the **pH 7.00** standard buffer solution. Set the TEMPERATURE control to room temperature and the SLOPE control to 100 %. Set the selector switch to "pH," allow the meter to stabilize, and then adjust the reading to 7.00 using the **CALIBRATE** control.

   Return the selector switch to STANDBY, remove the electrode from the pH 7.00 solution, and rinse the electrode with distilled water.

   Place the electrode in a **pH 4.00** standard buffer solution, and set the selector switch to "pH". Allow the meter to stabilize and then adjust the pH reading to 4.00 by **USING THE "SLOPE" CONTROL.**

   Return the selector switch to STANDBY, remove the electrode from the pH 4.00 solution, and place the electrode in distilled water in readiness for the solution pH measurements below.

   > **DO NOT DISCARD the pH 7.00 and the pH 4.00 Standard Buffer solutions.**

2. **pH Determination:**

   > **REMEMBER: Set the selector switch to STANDBY whenever you change solutions or rinse the electrode. RINSE the electrode with distilled water after each measurement, and store it in distilled water between measurements if necessary. Do NOT change the TEMPERATURE, CALIBRATE, or SLOPE control settings. Do NOT measure the pH of the 0.10 M NaOH (Solution 1).**

   a. Transfer your remaining 0.60 M acetic acid into a 50 mL beaker. Measure and record the pH of your 0.60 M acetic acid (Solution **2**). Return the selector switch to STANDBY, and rinse the electrode with distilled water. Discard the 0.60 M acetic acid into the waste beaker at your workstation.

   b. Place the electrode in your 0.20 M acetic acid (Solution **3**). Measure and record the pH of this solution. Return the selector switch to STANDBY, and rinse the electrode with distilled water. Discard the 0.20 M acetic acid into the waste beaker at your workstation.

c. Put a small magnetic stirring bar in the larger sample of your 0.10 M acetic acid (solution **4**), place the beaker on the magnetic stirrer, and begin the stirring process. Then measure and record the pH of the solution.

While the electrode is still in the 0.10 M solution, add 5 drops of 6.0 M hydrochloric acid (HCl). Wait for the reading to stabilize and measure/record the pH. Return the selector to STANDBY, and immerse the electrode in distilled water. Remove the stirring bar and discard the mixture into the waste beaker at your workstation. Calculate the pH CHANGE (Δ**pH**) caused by the addition of HCl.

d. Put a small magnetic stirrer in your acetic acid–sodium acetate buffer solution (Solution **5**) and begin the stirring process. Measure and record the pH of the buffer solution.

While the electrode is still in the buffer solution, add 5 drops of 6.0 M hydrochloric acid HCl. Mix the solution, wait for the reading to stabilize and measure/record the pH. Return the selector to STANDBY, and return the electrode to distilled water. Remove the stirring bar and discard the mixture into the waste beaker at your workstation. Calculate the pH CHANGE (Δ**pH**) caused by addition of HCl.

PART C: Titration Curve and Determination of Ka

1. Rinse a dropper with distilled water and then with a small amount of the 10 mL sample of your 0.10 M acetic acid solution (Solution **4**) <u>saved</u> <u>from</u> **PART A Step 4**. Use this dropper to transfer 15 drops of 0.10 M acetic acid solution into a 50 mL calibrated beaker. Use distilled water to dilute this to the 20 mL mark. Add two drops of phenolphthalein indicator. Put a small magnetic stirring bar in the beaker, place the beaker on the magnetic stirrer, and begin the stirring process.

2. Rinse the acetic acid out of your dropper with distilled water, and then rinse the dropper with a small amount of your 0.10 M NaOH solution (Solution **1**.) Rinse the pH meter electrode with distilled water and insert it into the acid beaker. Be sure the sensor tip of the electrode is immersed and the stirring bar is not in contact with the electrode body. Turn the selector switch to "pH," allow the meter to stabilize, and record the pH. (The pH at 0.0 drops NaOH added.)

3. Add 0.10 M NaOH drop by drop. Allow the meter to stabilize, and record the pH after <u>each</u> addition. You may add NaOH two drops at a time until the pH change exceeds 0.2 units, then <u>one</u> <u>drop</u> at a time until the endpoint has been passed (phenolphthalein turns pink, the pH changes rapidly from acid to basic, and then "levels off" at a change rate of 0.2 units or less). You may then add the NaOH two drops at a time to complete the titration curve data (usually about 10 drops past the endpoint, a total of approximately 26-34 drops).

Return the selector to STANDBY, and return the electrode to distilled water. Discard the solution into the waste beaker at your workstation.

Rinse and <u>RETURN</u> <u>THE</u> <u>STIRRING</u> <u>BAR</u>.

PART D: Neutralization

ADD all remaining solutions into the waste beaker at your workstation.

DO NOT DISCARD the **pH 7.00** and the **pH 4.00** standard solutions that you used to calibrate the pH meter.

ADD three drops of PHENOLPHTHALEIN indicator to the WASTE beaker.

ADD 6 M NaOH into the beaker slowly until the solution develops a faint pink color. DO NOT add excess NaOH.

ADD 1 M HCl drop by drop, with stirring, until the pink color fades to clear.

DISPOSE of this neutralized solution in the laboratory sink with flowing tap water.

PART E: Calculations

- Calculate the acid ionization constant **Ka** of acetic acid based on the measured pH values for Solution **2**, Solution **3**, and then for Solution **4**. Determine the **percent ionization** of acetic acid for each solution. (Refer to Advance Problem 1)

- Calculate the molarity of acetic acid and acetate ion in the acetic acid–sodium acetate buffer solution (Solution **5**). Determine the acid ionization constant **Ka** of acetic acid based on the measured pH of this solution. Determine the **percent ionization** of acetic acid in the buffer solution. (Refer to Advance Problem 2)

- What **concentration–percent ionization** relationship can you establish based on your results for solutions **2, 3** and **4** (if any)? Was the percent ionization for your **buffer solution** consistent with this relationship? If not, why?

- What was the pH change of the 0.10 M acetic acid upon addition of HCl? What was the pH change of the buffer solution upon addition of HCl? Which was smaller, and why?

Each laboratory partner is to prepare a graph of pH (vertical axis) vs. drops of NaOH added (horizontal axis). Use the "bisector method" to determine the endpoint volume and the "halfway point" volume. (Refer to Advance Problem 3.) Refer to *Appendix: The Graph – A Data Analysis Tool.*

- Use the graph to obtain pH at the halfway point of the titration.

- Calculate the acid ionization constant **Ka** from the halfway point pH.

- Compare this value to the **Ka** obtained for the buffer solution (Solution **5**).

REPORT your measured pH values and calculation results on the attached CALCULATION SUMMARY PAGE. Include your titration curve graph.

SOLUBILITY PRODUCT EQUILIBRIUM:
The Solubility Product Constant of PbI$_{2(s)}$

Prerequisite: Chemical Analysis by Spectrophotometric Methods
Background: Solution Concentration Calculations: Dilution
Law of Chemical Equilibrium

When an ionic solid dissolves in water it usually forms its' composite ions. These ions, moving at random throughout the solution, may collide and precipitate out of solution to form the ionic solid again. As the solution process continues, the rate at which the solid dissolves becomes identical to the rate at which it forms, and a state of dynamic equilibrium between the solid and its ions in solution is established. At this point the solution contains the maximum possible amount of solute and is said to be *SATURATED*. The amount of solute in solution, expressed as moles of solid per liter of solution, is the *MOLAR SOLUBILITY* of the solid.

In the case of our sample compound lead(II) iodide, this equilibrium is represented as:

$$(1) \quad PbI_{2(s)} \quad \Leftrightarrow \quad Pb^{+2}_{(aq)} + 2\,I^-_{(aq)} \quad Ksp = [Pb^{+2}][I^-]^2$$

Since the value of the constant represents the *SOLUBILITY* of the solid and the expression consists of only the product concentrations, the equilibria between slightly soluble solids and their ions in solution are called *SOLUBILITY PRODUCT EQUILIBRIA*. The equilibrium constant is therefore termed a *SOLUBILITY PRODUCT CONSTANT Ksp*. The concept of solubility product equilibrium is usually applied only to very slightly soluble ionic solids (i.e.: the Ksp values are very small).

The equilibrium can be established by mixing solutions containing the ions, which then react to form the ionic solid. Or, a sample of pure solid can be dissolved to form the ions in solution. Once the system has achieved equilibrium, the solution is analyzed to determine the concentration of one of the ions. The molarity of the other ion, and the Ksp value, can then be calculated.

In this experiment, two trials will prepare the PbI$_2$ equilibrium system by mixing solutions of lead(II)nitrate and potassium iodide to form solid lead(II) iodide.
[*Reaction* (1) *above proceeds LEFT.*]

In trial three we will prepare a sample of pure solid and then allow it to dissolve forming lead and iodide ions. [*Reaction* (1) *above proceeds RIGHT.*]

All of the solutions will be prepared in a 0.20 M potassium NITRATE solution. The potassium and nitrate ions do not react, but their relatively high concentrations will keep the ionic strength of each trial essentially constant.

The iodide ion molarity will be determined via colorimetric analysis in a manner similar to previous experiments. The solid lead(II) iodide will be removed, and the colorless iodide ion (I^-) in the solution will then be converted to iodine (I_2) by reaction with potassium NITRITE in acid solution.

Iodine forms an aqueous solution that is brown in color, absorbing light in the vicinity of 525 nm. The absorbance of each solution is measured at 525 nm and the iodide ion molarity taken from the Beer's Law calibration graph of molarity vs. absorbance. The equilibrium lead ion molarity and the solubility product constant for PbI_2 are then calculated for each trial.

Refer to the experiment: *Chemical analysis by Spectrophotometric Methods*

CAUTION

Be certain you are using the correct solution when preparing a trial. In particular, note the distinction between KNO_3 (potassium nitrATE) and KNO_2 (potassium nitrITE).

Remember to consider the equation stoichiometry (equation coefficients) in your advanced problem and lab report calculations. The amount of lead ion that is formed or consumed to establish equilibrium is one-half the amount of iodide ion formed or consumed!

WEAR YOUR SAFETY GOGGLES/LAB COAT!

WASH YOUR HANDS WHEN FINISHED!

DISPOSAL of reaction products: Put all waste solutions and solids in a 250 mL beaker at your work area. When you have finished ALL parts of the experiment, stir to suspend the solids and transfer the suspension into the WASTE CONTAINER provided by your instructor.

Experimental Procedure

Work in PAIRS so that all the trials will be ready for the shaking (equilibrium) process (Part C) at approximately the same time.

A. One student is to prepare trials ONE and TWO according to *Table 1* below. Solution volumes must be measured accurately using burets or pipets provided. Use LARGE test tubes and LABEL each solution for identification! Label and save the solution/solid mixtures for Part C below.

Table 1	*TEST TUBE*	*0.012 M Pb(NO$_3$)$_2$*	*0.030 M KI*	*0.20 M KNO$_3$*
Partner A	1	5.0 mL	3.0 mL	2.0 mL
	2	5.0 mL	5.0 mL	0.0 mL
Partner B	3	approx. 10 mL	approx. 10 mL	0.0 mL

B. At the same time the OTHER STUDENT is to prepare trial THREE. The solution volumes (10mL) need only be approximate. Use a LARGE test tube to mix the solutions and SMALL (13 x 100 mm) tubes for the centrifuge. Remember that the centrifuge MUST be BALANCED! *Do not use your cuvettes for the centrifuge.*

Mix the 10 mL of Pb(NO$_3$)$_2$ and 10 mL of KI in a large test tube for about one minute, and then let the solid settle to the bottom of the tube. About two thirds of the solution above the solid is then decanted into the waste beaker. Mix the remaining solution and the solid, and transfer into a centrifuge test tube. Centrifuge for approximately thirty seconds, and discard the solution (SAVE THE SOLID). Add about 3 mL of 0.20 M KNO$_3$ to the solid, mix, and centrifuge again. Discard the liquid.

You now have an essentially pure sample of solid PbI_2 in the centrifuge test tube. Add 0.20 M KNO_3 until the tube is about half full, stir to suspend the solid in the liquid, and pour the mixture into a LARGER test tube. Add approximately 10 mL more of KNO_3 to the test tube.

Label and save this solution/solid mixture for Part C below.

DO NOT BEGIN Part C until Parts A and B are both completed.

C. Both partners should now stopper and shake all three solid/solution mixtures at 2-3 minute intervals for about twenty minutes to establish the solubility product equilibrium in each. (All three tubes are shaken at approximately the same time, NOT in succession.) When the twenty-minute shaking process has been completed, allow each tube to stand for three or four minutes so that the solid will settle to the bottom of the tubes.

FROM THIS POINT ON, each of the three samples is to be treated independently according to Part D and Part E below. The solutions from each of the tubes are NEVER mixed or combined in any way!

D. Decant the solution from tube 1 into a small (centrifuge), DRY test tube until it is full. Centrifuge this sample to settle any remaining solid. If solid particles remain in the meniscus, use a DRY stirring rod to "push" them into the liquid. (Particles sticking to the stirring rod may be wiped off with paper towel and discarded.) Centrifuge again. Transfer the clean solution into another DRY test tube and SAVE for Part E. Suspend the solids in a little water, and discard into the waste container.

REPEAT this procedure on each of the remaining samples.

USE CARE in transferring liquids -- you will need 4.0+ mL of solid-free solution from each trial for the remaining steps.

NOTE: You should have a set of five cuvettes (optically matched 13 x 100 mm test tubes) from a previous experiment. If not, one partner is to prepare a set of cuvettes while the other partner begins PART E below. Consult your instructor if you do not know how to prepare matched cuvettes.

E. The following procedure develops color in the solutions via reaction with potassium NITRITE (in acid) to produce iodine:

For **SOLUTION Number One** saved from Part D above:

a.) PIPET 3.0 mL of the solution into a LARGE, dry test tube.
b.) Use the same pipet to add 3.0 mL of 0.02 M KNO_2 (Potassium NITRITE).
c.) Use the same pipet to add 3.0 mL of 0.2 M KNO_3 (Potassium NITRATE).
d.) Add 3 drops of 6.0 M HCl from the dropper bottle. (This must be the last step!) Mix the solution.

e.) Rinse the pipet with approximately 1.5 mL of 0.2 M Potassium Nitrate in preparation of the next solution. *Discard the rinse into the waste container.*

f.) Repeat steps a) through e) on each of the remaining solutions (#2 and #3)

g.) Use a paper towel to dry a cuvette, and fill the cuvette at least half way with solution **1**. Set the cuvette/solution aside for use later in Step i.

h.) Repeat step (g) on the remaining solutions. Use a different, matched cuvette for each.

i.) Measure and record the ABSORBANCE of all three solutions on a colorimeter (Spectronic-20) with its wavelength set at 525 nanometers. (NOTE the identification number of the colorimeter.)

Refer to the experiment: *Chemical Analysis by Spectrophotometric Methods*

F. When you have finished your experiment, take your waste baker to the waste container provided in the hood area. <u>Stir the beaker contents to thoroughly suspend the solids</u>, and transfer the suspension into the waste container. You may then rinse residual material from the beaker into the sink drain with flowing tap water, and clean your glassware in preparation for your next experiemnt.

G. Prepare the Beer-Lambert calibration curve for <u>YOUR</u> colorimeter from the concentration-absorbance data provided in *Table 2* below. Be sure to use the absorbance values that correspond to YOUR colorimeter identification number.

Refer to Appendix: *The Graph – A Data Analysis Tool*

Table 2				IODIDE ION CONCENTRATION vs ABSORBANCE								
	ABSORBANCE											
COLORIMETER #	1	2	3	4	5	6	7	8	9	10	11	12
I⁻ MOLARITY												
3.0×10^{-3}	.25	26	.26	.26	.25	.22	.23	.36	.25	.23	.23	.26
6.0×10^{-3}	.40	.40	.41	.40	.37	.35	.37	.48	.38	.38	.37	.40
9.0×10^{-3}	.56	.54	.55	.53	.50	.49	.51	.57	.53	.52	.51	.53
12.0×10^{-3}	.71	.68	.70	.67	.63	.62	.65	.68	.67	.67	.65	.67
NOTE: The graph Does NOT pass through the origin.												

G. Use this graph to determine the EQUILIBRIUM iodide concentration for each of the above solutions from their measured absorbances. Then, for <u>each</u> trial calculate the EQUILIBRIUM lead ion concentrations, and then calculate the K_{sp} values.

The calculation of equilibrium concentrations and equilibrium constants is similar to the prior experiment: *Equilibrium Constant Determination*

Summarize your results on the data page provided.

CHECK-OUT PROCEDURE

1. Unlock your equipment drawer and remove it from the bench enclosure.

2. Remove the contents of your equipment drawer placing them on the laboratory bench.

3. Clean the equipment drawer.

4. Reline the equipment drawer with new, fresh paper towels.

5. Clean all drawer contents thoroughly.

6. Use the check-in/check-out sheet to determine what is to be returned to the drawer.

7. Place any extra equipment on the glassware cart.

8. Return the equipment to the drawer.

9. Ask your instructor to inspect your drawer.

10. Return the locker to the opening in the bench enclosure.

11. Lock the drawer.

12. Return the check-in/ch_____ _____ to ___ instructor.

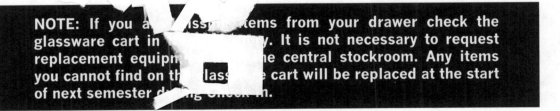

NOTE: If you a__ ___ss___ items from your drawer check the glassware cart in _____. It is not necessary to request replacement equip_____ ___ ___ central stockroom. Any items you cannot find on th_ _lass____ cart will be replaced at the start of next semester d____ _____.

295

The VOLUMETRIC PIPET is a calibrated volume-measuring device that is designed to deliver a specific volume into a receiving container. The pipet is filled using suction to draw liquid into the device. The suction must be created using a rubber pipet bulb or a pump. NEVER PIPET BY MOUTH suction.

3-WAY BULB

A three-way pipet bulb is used to draw a liquid into any type of pipet. A three-way bulb is sometimes selected because it reduces the possibility of contact with the liquid, and any liquid drawn into a pipet can easily be held in the pipet until delivery. The three valves: air valve, suction valve and empty valve provide additional comfort and ease of use. Your instructor will demonstrate the proper use of this device prior to use during experimentation. You should familiarize yourself with the function of each valve and practice using the three-way bulb before starting an experiment that is dependent on your pipetting technique.

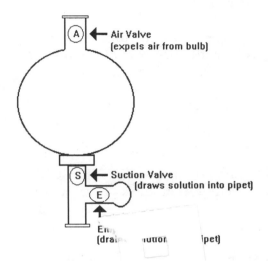

Air Valve
(expels air from bulb)

Suction Valve
(draws solution into pipet)

Empty
(drains solution from pipet)

USING THE 3-WAY BULB or THE PIPETTE PUMP™

Hold the pipet near the top and insert the top end of the pipet into the bulb or pump with a slight pressure and twist. Insert the end about one-quarter inch.

WARNING—Extreme care should be taken when inserting disposable glass pipettes because of the possibility of shattering. To loosen the pipette, hold it near the chuck, twist slightly and pull.

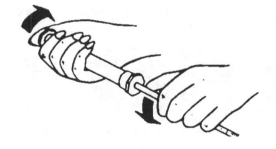

Draw a small amount of rinse water into the stem of the pipet, and pause long enough to verify that the level remains constant and the bulb/pump is not leaking. Draw in a little more water, and roll the liquid around inside the pipet to insure that the inner surface is washed. Discard the rinse into a WASTE CONTAINER.

Rinse the pipet with several small portions of tap water and then with distilled water.

Transfer the solution or liquid you intend to pipet into a small beaker, never insert the pipet directly into the reagent bottle. Transfer enough extra liquid to insure the tip of the pipet can remain below the surface of the liquid in the beaker when the pipet is full.

Draw a small volume of the liquid into the pipet as a rinse. Roll the liquid around inside the pipet to insure that the inner surface is washed. Discard the rinse into a WASTE CONTAINER

To fill the pipet, rest the tip on the bottom of the beaker and use the bulb or pump to draw liquid into the pipet until the level is 2 or 3 cm above the calibration mark. Check to be certain there are no air bubbles in the tip.

Carefully lift the pipet (with the pump still attached) from the beaker and slowly drain excess liquid into a WASTE CONTAINER until the bottom of the meniscus is aligned with the calibration mark. Touch the tip of the pipet to the side of the waste container to remove excess liquid fron the outside of the pipet. Failure to "touch off" excess liquid results in a volume transfer that is larger than the rated pipet volume.

Put the tip of the pipet inside your receiving container (a beaker or a flask), REMOVE the pipet from the bulb/pump, and allow the liquid to drain naturally into your receiving container.

DO NOT use the bulb or pump to "blow out" the small amount of liquid that remains in the tip. The pipet contains slightly more than the rated volume but is designed to DELIVER only the calibrated volume.

Touch the tip of the pipet to the inside of the receiving container to add any liquid that remains outside the pipet. Failure to "touch off" a remaining droplet results in a volume transfer that is smaller than the rated pipet volume.

After use, the pipet must be rinsed several times with tap water before it is returned to the laboratory cart.

APPENDIX: Properties of Water

Table 1: Density and Vapor Pressures at Selected Temperatures

Temperature, $^\circ C$	Vapor Pressure, torr	Density, $g.cm^{-3}$
0.0	4.6	0.9998395
4.0	6.1	0.999972
15.0	12.8	0.9990996
16.0	13.6	0.998943
17.0	14.5	0.9987749
18.0	15.5	0.9985956
19.0	16.5	0.9984052
20.0	17.5	0.9982041
21.0	18.7	0.9979925
22.0	19.8	0.9977705
23.0	21.1	0.9975385
24.0	22.4	0.9972965
25.0	23.8	0.9970449
26.0	25.2	0.9967837
27.0	26.7	0.9965132
28.0	28.3	0.9962335
29.0	30.0	0.9959448
30.0	31.8	0.9956473
31.0	33.7	0.995341
32.0	35.7	0.9950262
33.0	37.7	0.994703
34.0	39.9	0.9943715
35.0	42.2	0.9940319

Table 2: Boiling Point of Water at Selected Vapor Pressures

Pressure, torr	Boiling Temperature, $^\circ C$
735	99.0
740	99.2
745	99.4
750	99.6
755	99.8
760	100.0
765	100.2
770	100.4
775	100.5
780	100.7
785	100.9
790	101.0

APPENDIX: Stock Laboratory Acids and Bases

COMMON LABORATORY ACIDS AND BASES

NAME	FORMULA	CONCENTRATED	DILUTE	BOTTLE TOP	HAZARD	HAZARD COLOR
Hydrochloric Acid	HCl	12M	6M	BLUE	CORROSIVE	WHITE
Nitric Acid	HNO_3	15M	6M	RED	CORROSIVE	WHITE
Sulfuric Acid	H_2SO_4	18M	3M	YELLOW	CORROSIVE	WHITE
Acetic Acid	$HC_2H_3O_2$	GLACIAL	6M	WHITE	CORROSIVE	RED
Sodium Hydroxide	$NaOH$	X	6M	ORANGE	CORROSIVE	WHITE S
Ammonium Hydroxide	NH_4OH	15M	6M	GREEN	CORROSIVE	WHITE S
Ammonia (aqueous)	NH_3 (aq)	Ammonium Hydroxide and aqueous ammonia are the same solution.				

DO NOT INSERT DROPPERS IN STOCK BOTTLES. TRANSFER A SMALL SAMPLE OF THE ACID OR BASE TO A SMALL BEAKER, THEN USE DROPPER TO ADD THE REAGENT TO YOUR SAMPLE.

APPENDIX: Appendix: The Graph, A Data Analysis Tool

Graphs are commonly used in chemistry to visually represent information from related data tables. They generally are the best way to demonstrate relationships and trends between properties (or substances) within a system. Many times, it is necessary to plot your data to see what relationship or trend exists. A well-constructed graph will often reveal a relationship that was not obvious from a numerical set of experimental measurements. On the other hand, a poorly constructed graph is generally a waste of paper and generally ineffective for imparting informative results. Therefore the graph is an important tool for the analysis of experimental data if constructed properly.

The most common type of graph is an **x–y graph** that uses a set of horizontal and vertical coordinates to show the relationship of two variables. The lined pattern on which the graph is drawn is called the **grid**. The vertical (**y**) axis is called the **ordinate**, and the horizontal (**x**) axis is termed the **abscissa**. The axes intersect at the **origin**. **Coordinates** (x, y) represent a point on the graph identified by its corresponding data value pair. Each axis has a **scale**. This is a set of numbers equally distributed along the axes that represent the range of values from the data. Scale numbers increase from bottom to top along the vertical (**y**) axis and left to right on the horizontal (**x**) axis.

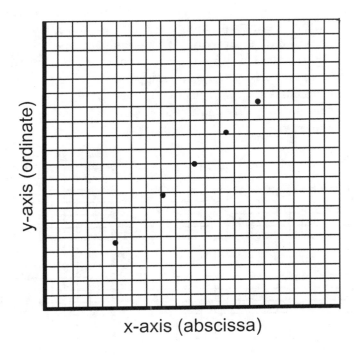

Preparing a graph according to the following guidelines should ensure that the resulting graphical display illustrates a meaningful relationship.

- Use **graph paper** with a line grid of at least 10 lines per centimeter.

- A graph should have a **title** that clearly identifies the properties being compared or the relationship one is attempting to demonstrate (e.g.: Absorbance vs. Wavelength or the title "Absorption Spectrum".) One must also **label each axis**, including dimensions (e.g.: Wavelength, nm or Volume, mL.)

305

- Determine if a zero point is required on the **x**-axis, the **y**-axis, or both (the **origin 0,0.**)

  Not all graphs require zero axis values. If a zero or origin (0,0) is not required, the axis numbers can begin a little below the lowest value and end a little above the highest value of the property you are graphing.

- Examine the range of your x and y values and assign "calibration numbers" to each axis accordingly. The range of values should yield approximately the same overall length for each axis, and allow the graph to occupy as much of the page as possible. If the numbers you are attempting to graph contain powers of ten, it is easier to multiply by a power of ten, and then scale the axis. For instance, 3×10^{-3}, 6×10^{-3}, 9×10^{-3}, 1.2×10^{-2} can be multiplied by 10^{+3}, and graphed as 3, 6, 9, and 12. The **label** for this axis would then include a specification: $\times \mathbf{10^{-3}}$.

- The value of each line on the grid should have a simple "counting relationship" to whole number values (i.e.: values of 1.0, 2.0, 3.0 or 0.10, or 0.20, or 0.50 will be easier to interpret than values like 0.33 or 0.15.) If you cannot easily determine a value <u>between</u> the calibration numbers you have assigned, a different assignment for each line is probably necessary.

- If the relationship that you develop is linear, the graph is the "best straight line" through the data points. If the relationship is non-linear, the graph must be a smooth curve from data point to data point, not a "connect the dots" diagram. While it is true that not all relationships are either linear or a smooth nonlinear curve, those you evaluate using this laboratory textbook will fall under one of these situations. If your data points are too scattered to establish either a linear or a smooth curve pattern, examine your axis calibrations for any errors in numerical assignment. If there are no assignment errors, your experimental measurements are flawed. Repeating the measurements for the most suspicious data points is probably required.

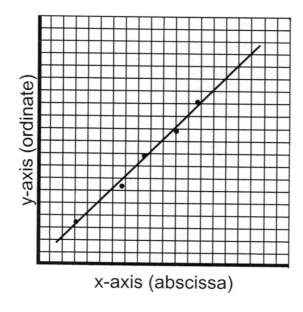

x-axis (abscissa)

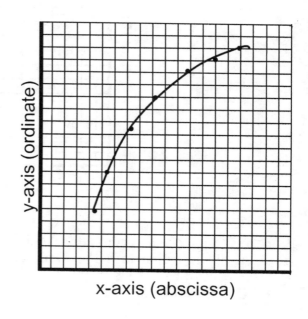

x-axis (abscissa)

306

APPENDIX: Spectrophotometer Operating Instructions

The Spectronic 20™ is used to measure the absorbance (transmittance) of solutions. A Spectronic 20™ is capable of measuring % transmittance and absorbance over a wavelength range of 340 to 950 nm. Data collected with a spectrophotometer can be used to perform both qualitative and quantitative analyses.

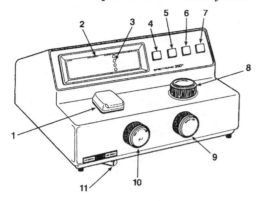

```
KEY
1.   Sample compartment
2.   Digital readout
3.   Mode indicators
4.   Mode selection
5.   Decrease
6.   Increase
7.   Print
8.   Wavelength control
9.   Transmittance/Absorbance Control
10.  Power switch/Zero Control
11.  Filter lever
```

1. **POWER ON** — Turn the POWER SWITCH/ZER0 CONTROL clockwise to turn on the instrument. The digital readout will light up. Allow five minutes warm-up time.

2. **WAVELENGTH** — Turn the WAVELENGTH CONTROL to the desired setting. The wavelength setting appears in the left side of the DIGITAL READOUT panel.

3. **ZERO ADJUST** — Use the MODE button to select TRANSMITTANCE mode as indicated on the right side of the DIGITAL READOUT panel. Adjust the POWER SWITCH/ZERO CONTROL until a reading of 0.0 % transmittance appears in the center of the DIGITAL READOUT panel. (The SAMPLE COMPARTMENT must be empty and closed.)

4. **ADJUST LIGHT CONTROL** — Fill a cuvette (matched 13mm × 100mm test tube) half full with water, wipe off drops and fingerprints, and insert the cuvette in the SAMPLE COMPARTMENT. The reference marks should be aligned and the compartment closed.

   While still in TRANSMITTANCE mode, use the TRANSMITTANCE/ABSORBANCE CONTROL to set the center digital readout at 100.0 % transmittance. (The 100% mark must be reset whenever the wavelength is changed.) Remove the water-filled cuvette.

5. **ABSORBANCE MEASUREMENT** — Fill other cuvettes with your sample solutions to the approximate half way point. Use a different cuvette for each sample.

   Depress the MODE switch until ABSORBANCE is selected (right side of the digital panel). A reading of 1.999 appears while the sample compartment is empty. Insert a sample in the SAMPLE COMPARTMENT, align the reference marks, close the compartment, and record the ABSORBANCE reading. Obtain and record the values for the other samples as rapidly as possible.

   The 100.0% and 0.0% Transmittance calibrations should be rechecked (and adjusted) every five to seven minutes. DO NOT CHANGE THE WAVELENGTH WITHOUT PRIOR APPROVAL FRON YOUR INSTRUCTOR.

   FLUCTUATIONS OF UP TO FIVE UNITS IN THE LAST SIGNIFICANT FIGURE OF ANY READING WILL NOT AFFECT YOUR RESULTS AND CAN BE IGNORED.

6. DO NOT use the CONCENTRATION mode, the FACTOR mode, or the DECREASE and INCREASE switches without specific directions from your instructor.

APPENDIX: The pH Meter

Introduction

The Fisher Model AR10 Accumet digital pH meter is a general laboratory instrument that incorporates up-to-date electronics and state-of-the-art control features.

The meter contains all the necessary controls and connections to compensate manually or automatically for the effects of solution temperature, electrode response, and standardization with a buffer. The 4-digit display is direct reading for pH from 0 to 14 and voltage potential from 0 to ± 1999 mV.

Operating Controls

Before operating the meter, locate and become familiar with the MODE of the controls and the readout display.

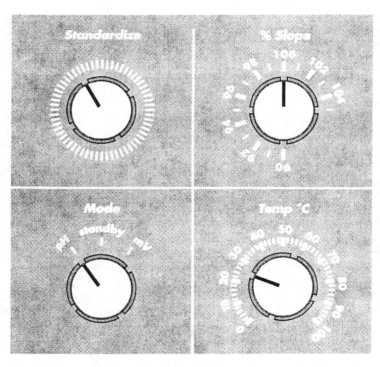

MODE: A switch that places the instrument on STANDBY when measurements are not being taken and selects the operating mode: pH for pH determination and MV for millivolt measurements.

% SLOPE: A potentiometer used in the pH mode to compensate for electrodes that exhibit less than 100% efficiency response.

TEMP °C: A potentiometer used for manual temperature compensation in the pH-measuring mode. During operation, it is set initially to the temperature of the standardizing buffer then to that of each sample.

STANDARDIZE: A potentiometer used in pH determinations to set the meter to the pH value of a buffer solution, thereby compensating for the difference in the zero potential of electrode systems.

Recorder INPUT Jack. Connects an external strip chart recorder.

FET INPUT Jack. Connects a field effect transistor (FET) indicator electrode for measuring the hydrogen ion concentration.

AUTO-TEMP COMP Jack. Receives the male connector of the automatic temperature compensator and disconnects the manual TEMPERATURE control.

Ref INPUT Jack. A standard reference jack to connect a reference indicator electrode.

BNC INPUT Jack. A standard BNC jack that accepts the BNC plug of an indicator electrode or combination electrode.

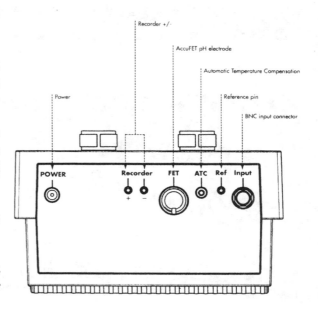

Operation

Prior to making pH or millivolt determinations, the meter must be connected to a suitable power source and the appropriate electrode system properly installed. The following procedures should be performed with the unit located on a flat, clean and dry surface near the power source.

Basic operating modes for the meter are covered separately below. Included are procedures for pH measurement with subsections covering the use of manual temperature compensation and SLOPE control adjustments.

pH Measurement

Prior to making one or a series of pH measurements, the meter must be standardized to compensate for the difference in the zero potential of the electrode(s). Immersing the electrode(s) into a buffer solution of known pH and adjusting the meter reading to the specified value of the buffer will accomplish this requirement. This single-point standardization is appropriate for samples having a pH value within two units of the buffer pH.

In meter standardization, as well as in pH measurement, attention also must be given to the temperature of both the buffer and the sample solutions. The pH of a solution changes with temperature (buffer pH at a specified temperature is usually indicated on the manufacturer's label), and temperature affects the voltage output of the electrode(s). During operation, temperature compensation is accomplished by manually adjusting the TEMPERATURE control – first to the temperature of the buffer, then to that of the sample. However, the instrument can be equipped with a probe that provides automatic temperature compensation in the pH-measuring mode.

NOTE: Proper electrode care is fundamental to obtaining reliable pH measurements. Improper care of electrodes may cause the meter reading to drift, respond slowly, or produce erroneous readings. For this reason the electrode should always be conditioned and used according to manufacturer's instructions.

310

One Point Standardization with Manual Temperature Compensation

1. Set MODE selector to STANDBY position.

2. Set SLOPE control to 100%.

3. Select a buffer that has a pH value within 1 or 2 units of the solution to be measured.

4. Immerse electrode(s) and a thermometer into the buffer solution.

5. Wait until electrode(s) and buffer solution reach thermal equilibrium (about two minutes), then adjust the TEMPERATURE control to agree with the buffer temperature.

6. Determine the exact pH of the buffer solution from a table of buffer pH versus temperature. Set the MODE selector to the pH position and adjust the STANDARDIZE control until the digital display indicates the pH of the buffer solution.

NOTE: The display will read to two decimal places (i.e., 0.00 to 14.00 pH).

7. Set MODE selector to STANDBY.

8. Remove electrode(s) and thermometer from the buffer solution.

9. To avoid contamination, rinse the electrode(s) and thermometer with distilled water before proceeding with any measurements of pH for other solutions.

10. Immerse electrode(s) and thermometer into the sample solution.

11. Wait until electrode(s) and sample solutions reach thermal equilibrium. Then adjust TEMPERATURE control to agree with the sample temperature.

12. Set MODE selector to pH.

13. Read and record the sample pH from the digital display. Set the MODE selector to STANDBY.

14. Remove electrode(s) and thermometer the solution.

15. Rinse the electrode(s) and the thermometer with distilled water before proceeding with the next measurement.

16. Repeat steps 10 through 15 for any remaining samples that fall within the pH and temperature ranges of the buffer.

17. Following the last measurement set the MODE selector to STANDBY.

The instrument must be restandardized via steps 3 through 9 if the sample pH is 2 or more units different than the buffer pH.

Slope Control, 2-Point Standardization

To measure the pH values of samples that vary over a range wider than 2 pH units, a two-point standardization method is required to compensate for less than 100% electrode efficiency. The STANDARDIZE control is used to set the first point, and the SLOPE control sets the second.

At pH 7, the SLOPE control has no effect on the reading. But as readings increasingly differ from pH 7, the control's effect becomes more pronounced. For this reason, a buffer very close to 7 should always be used as the first standard.

1. Set MODE selector to STANDBY and SLOPE control to 100%.

2. Obtain two buffer solutions with values that bracket the desired measuring range (e.g., pH 7.00 and pH 10.00 for samples that fall between pH 7 and 10).

NOTE: For best results, both solutions should be at the same temperatures.

3. Place a beaker, containing the buffer nearest in value to pH 7, in position and immerse electrode(s) and thermometer into the solution.

4. Allow about two minutes for the thermometer to equilibrate, and then set the TEMPERATURE control to the buffer solution temperature.

5. Set MODE selector to pH.

6. Adjust STANDARDIZE control until the digital display indicates the pH value of the buffer at the temperature of the experiment.

7. Set MODE selector to STANDBY.

8. Remove electrode(s) and thermometer from the buffer, and rinse both with distilled water.

9. Place a beaker containing the second buffer in position, and immerse electrode(s) into the solution.

NOTE: With buffer and sample solutions maintained at the same temperature, there should be no need to readjust the TEMPERATURE control.

10. Set MODE selector to pH.

11. Adjust SLOPE control until the digital display indicates the pH of the buffer at the temperature of the experiment.

12. Set MODE selector to STANDBY.

13. Remove electrode(s) from the buffer and rinse with distilled water.

14. Being careful not to change the STANDARDIZE or the SLOPE controls, measure the pH of samples as previously described.

NOTE: The manual TEMPERATURE control must be adjusted to the sample temperature.

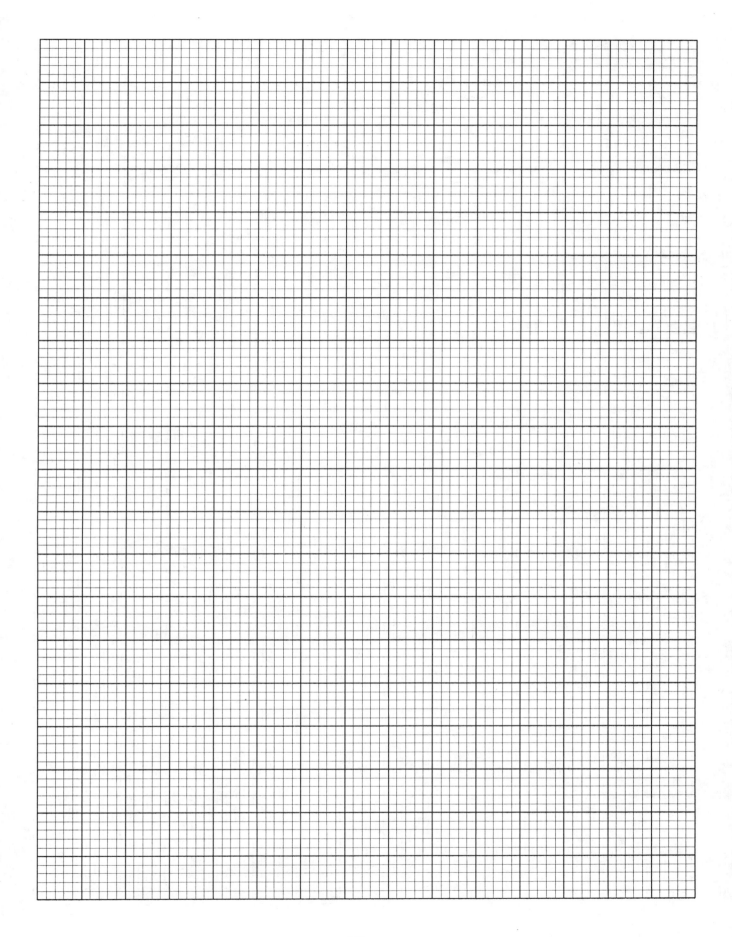

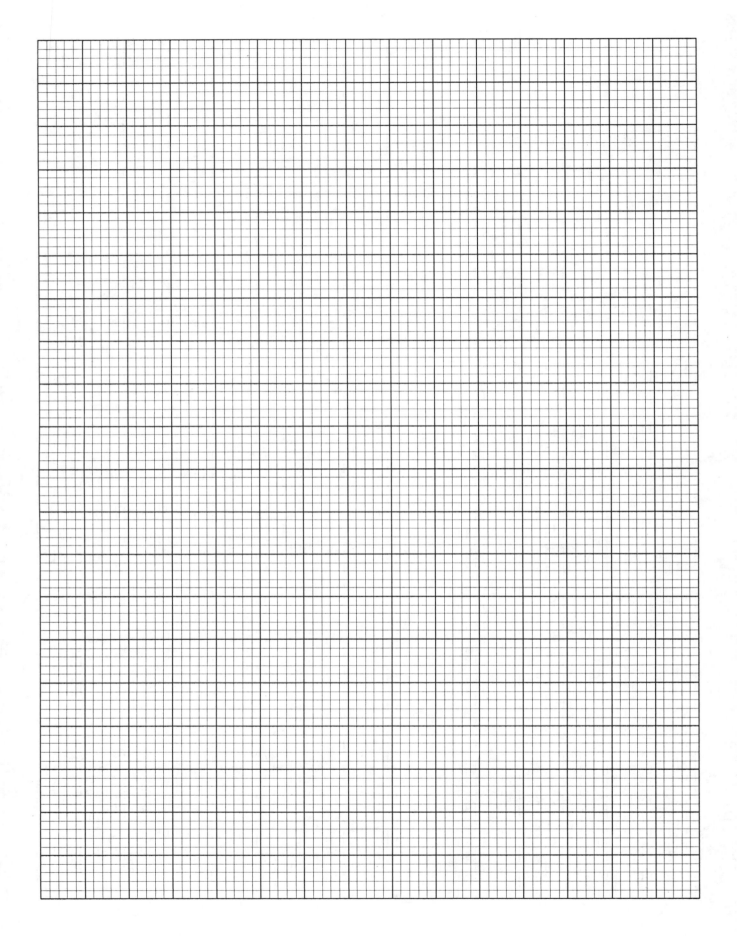

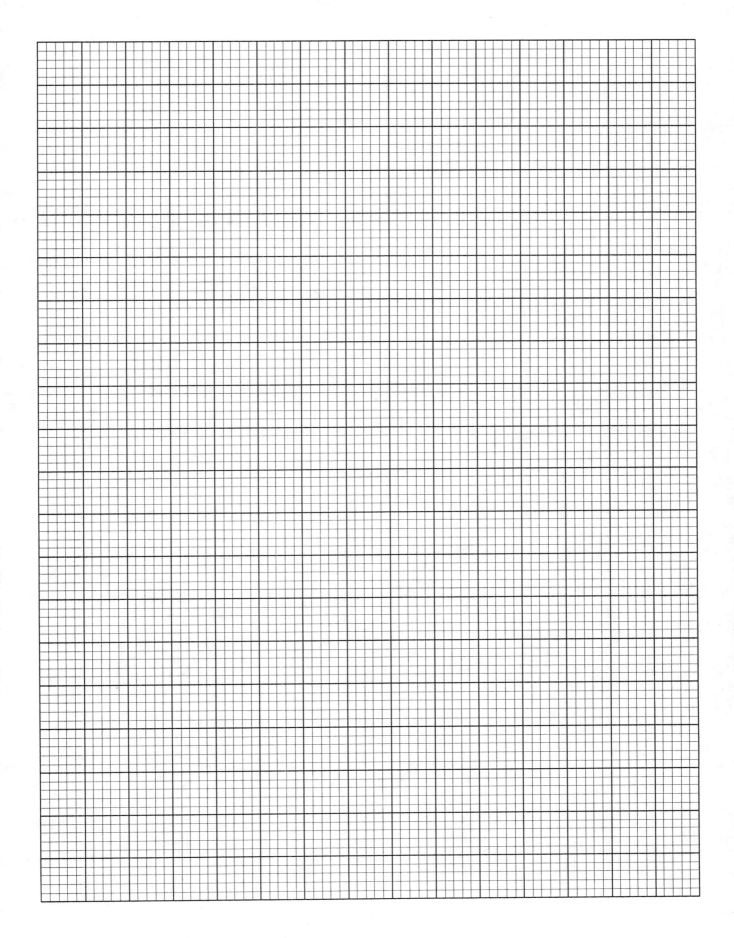

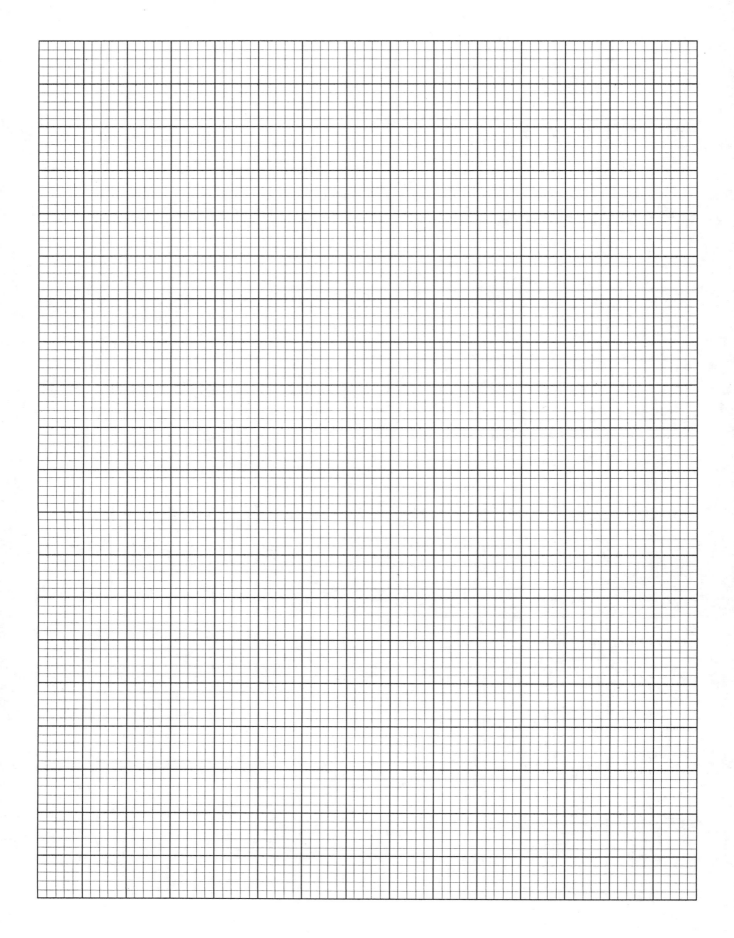

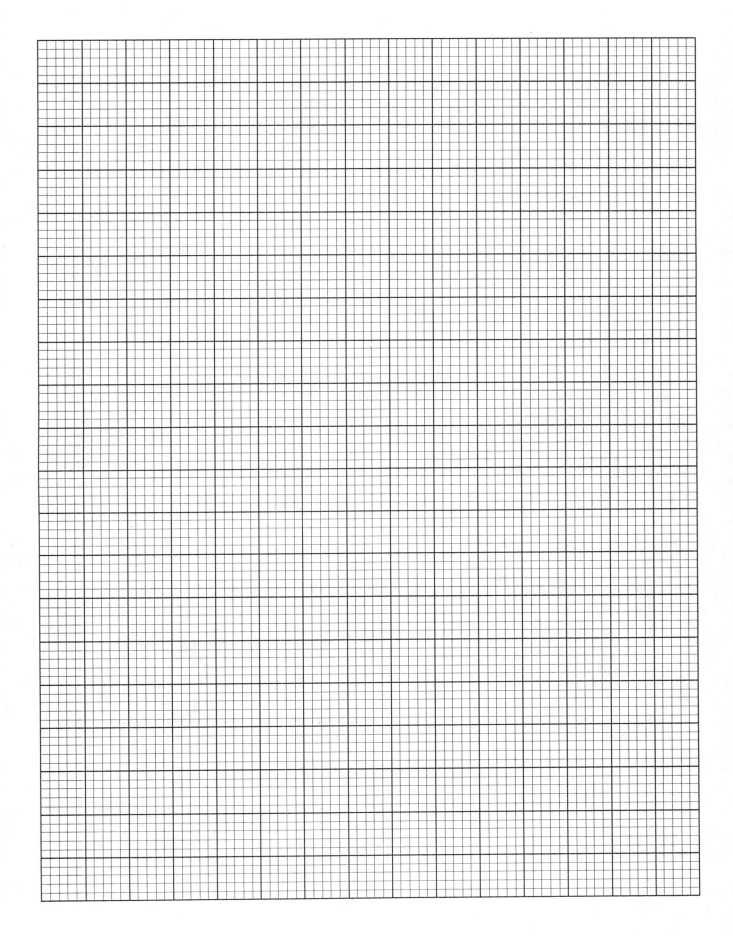

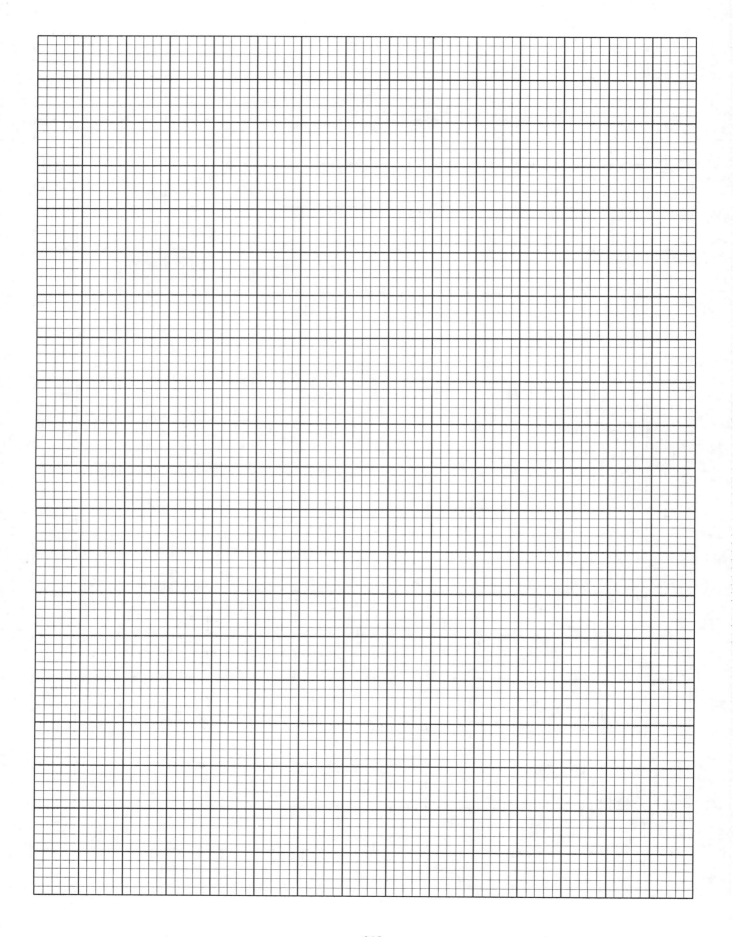

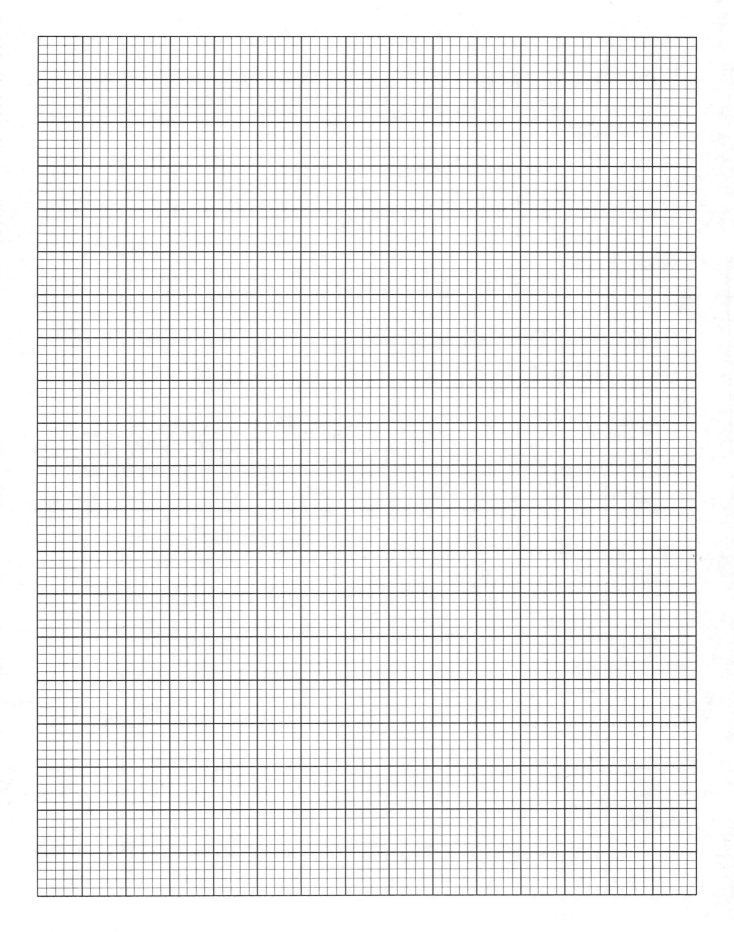

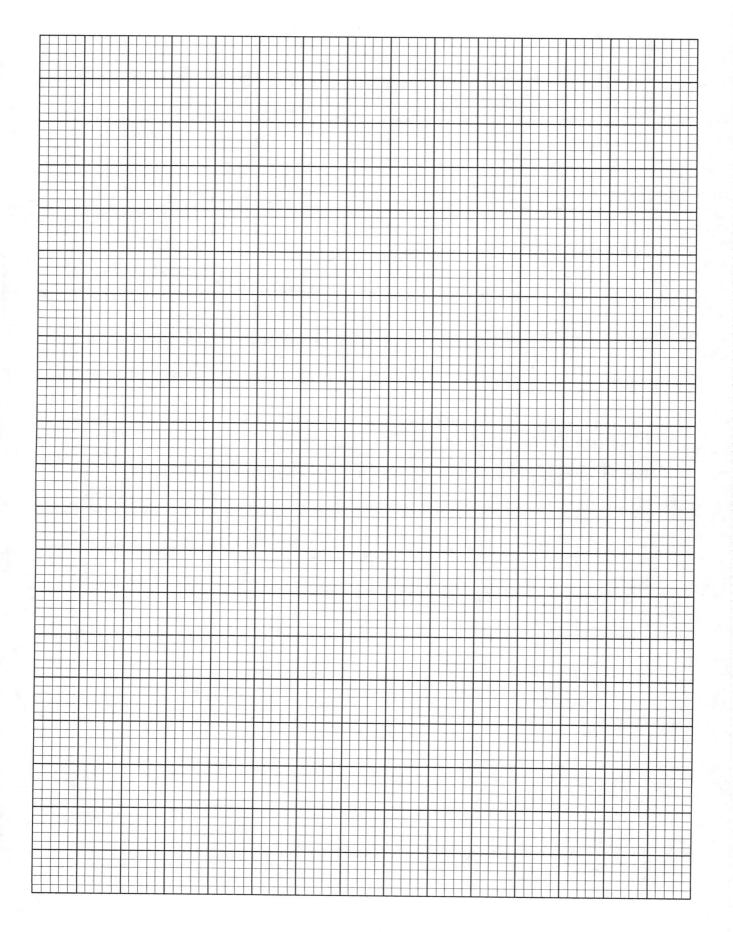